QC343.U

MW00575008

2/21/90

SOUND PROPAGATION IN THE SEA

ROBERT J. URICK

PENINSULA PUBLISHING

P.O. Box 867 • Los Altos, CA 94023 USA • (415) 948-2511

SOUND PROPAGATION IN THE SEA

Revised and edited by Peninsula Publishing.

Library of Congress Catalog Card Number 82-081923
ISBN 0-932146-08-2

PREFACE TO THE REVISED EDITION

Sound Propagation in the Sea was originally published by the Advanced Research Projects Agency of the Department of Defense, and was based on lecture notes for a short course on the subject given over a period of several years. They have been revised, expanded, updated and are adorned with references to enable the interested reader to follow up on a particular topic. A chapter on the subject of propagation modeling by Paul Etter has been added.

The specialized subject of sound propagation in the ocean has a surprisingly vast literature and comprises the most active research aspect of sonar and underwater sound. It includes a wide variety of phenomena and effects. No summary of it could said to be complete and comprehensive. The present summary, like all summaries, reflects the interests and knowledge of its author, perhaps to an inordinate degree. Yet it is hoped that this summary will be useful as a point of departure to those getting started in, or already working on, this multi-facetted subject.

The author is indebted to Dr. Frank Andrews of Catholic University and to Captains Henry Cox and V.P. Simmons, U.S. Navy for their many efforts in seeing the manuscript through to publication.

Robert J. Urick

January, 1982

TABLE OF CONTENTS

CHAPTER 5   ATTENUTATION AND ABSORPTION (*Continued*)

CHAPTER 6   THE SURFACE DUCT

CHAPTER 7   THE DEEP SOUND CHANNEL

CHAPTER 8   CAUSTICS AND CONVERGENCE ZONES

CHAPTER 9   SHALLOW WATER DUCTS

CHAPTER 10   REFLECTION AND SCATTERING BY THE SEA SURFACE

CHAPTER 11   REFLECTION AND SCATTERING BY THE SEA BOTTOM

CHAPTER 12   TEMPORAL COHERENCE (FLUCTUATION)

CHAPTER 12   TEMPORAL COHERENCE (FLUCTUATION)   *(Continued)*

CHAPTER 13   SPATIAL COHERENCE (CORRELATION)

CHAPTER 14   MULTIPATHS IN THE SEA

CHAPTER I

HISTORICAL REVIEW
AND METHODS OF INVESTIGATION

HISTORICAL REVIEW

Early Achievements

The earliest quantitative studies in underwater sound were concerned with the speed of sound in natural bodies of water. In 1827, Colladon and Sturm (1) measured the speed of sound in Lake Geneva, and obtained results surprisingly close to modern values. Many years later, in response to the needs of radioacoustic ranging and depth sounding, the speed of sound was determined more accurately at sea. In 1923, Stephenson (2) timed the transmission of a bomb explosion between two hydrophones a known distance apart in Long Island Sound, while at about this same time, Heck and Service (3) measured the travel time of pulses reflected from the sea bottom and determined the velocity from depth obtained by wire sounding. These measurements established the velocity of sound in sea water for many years thereafter.

Concerning propagation generally, the first theoretical and field investigations were done by German scientists during World War I. In a paper published in 1919, entitled (English translation) "On the Influence of Horizontal Temperature Layers in Seawater on the Range of Underwater Sound Signals" (4), the effects on sound velocity of temperature, salinity and pressure were deduced from existing static measurements on water, and the equations of sound rays in the presence of gradients of their quantities were obtained. Shorter ranges in summer than in winter were said to be expectable due to downward refraction in summer and upward refraction in winter; this expectation was borne out by measurements made before the war in six widely scattered shallow water areas over a one-year period. This paper was far ahead of its time, and is an indication of the highly advanced state of German physics in the early years of this century.

In the militarily lean years of the 1920's following World War I, no attention was given to propagation, other than to sound velocity in sea water for application to depth sounding as just mentioned. Rather, the work during these years in the U.S. and the U.K. was necessarily directed to hardware — most importantly to the development of sound projectors and receivers for echo ranging. However, by the early 1930's, enough sea-going experience had accumulated to prove that the ranges being obtained with the newly-developed equipment were extremely variable, both from area to area and even, in a single area, at different times of day. It was soon clear that this erratic variability could not be blamed on the equipment or the observers, but must somehow be due to the ocean itself. To determine the cause, and to obtain basic data for design and prediction, a continuing measurement program was initiated in 1934 by a small group of scientists and engineers at the Naval Research Laboratory, using the destroyer SEMMES as the echo-ranging vessel and the submarine S-20 as the target. From transmission runs, the "absorption" coefficient* at frequencies from 17 to 30 kHz was measured off Long Island, Guantamamo, Cuba, and in the Atlantic and Pacific approaches to the Panama Canal, and order-of-magnitude values of the "reflection coefficient"** of the submarine was obtained. Several reports by E. B. Stephenson were published in the years 1935-1939 (5-7).

A mysterious vagary of propagation that received much attention during this time was the regular reduction of echo ranges observed during the afternoons of calm sunny days. This phenomenon was soon dignified by the term "Afternoon Effect." At first, a biological cause involving the generation of gas bubbles by photosynthesis or an after-lunch lethargy of sonar operators (!) was suspected, since the then-crude temperature data indicated no change in the temperature structure of the upper ocean. By 1937, the use of sensitive thermometers placed at close intervals along a wire showed that warmer water, which developed near the surface during sunny days, was sufficient to cause downward ray bending and to carry the sound from a shallow source downward, away from a shallow target. An example of some early observations by R. L. Steinberger (8) of the Afternoon Effect, showing the correlation between a negative temperature gradient and poor transmission, is given in *Figure 1*. The finding that small shallow temperature gradients were important led to the development of the mechanical bathythermograph — a non-electronic device (*Fig 2*) giving a trace of temperature against depth on a smoked glass slide — which, by the start of World War II in 1941 was installed on all U.S. destroyers and patrol craft in order to give them their own capability to determine the temperature conditions in the upper few hundred feet of the water column at the time and place where they were needed.

---

*This coefficient was poorly named. It was the slope of the line fitted to the transmission data after allowing for spherical spreading, and included the effects of refraction as well as absorption.

**Equivalent, in modern terminology, to "target strength".

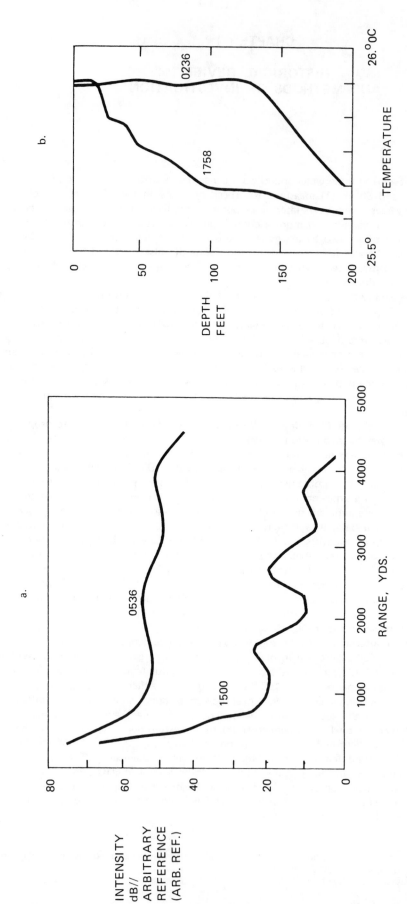

Fig. 1. The once-mysterious Afternoon Effect, as observed by Steinberger in 1937 (4). (a) Intensity vs. range of a 24 kHz CW signal in the morning (0536) and in the afternoon (1500); (b) Temperature profiles observed in the morning (0236) and afternoon (1758). These observations clearly established refraction caused by a shallow temperature gradient to be the cause of the Afternoon Effect.

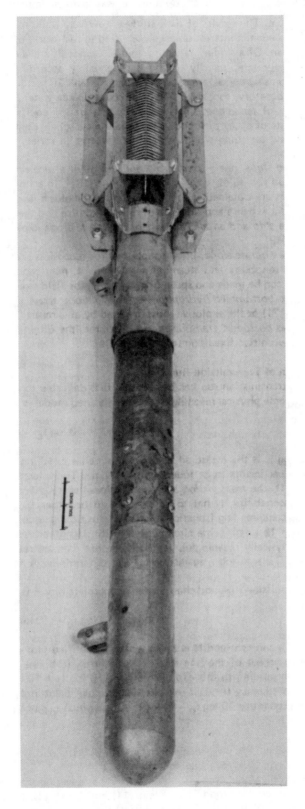

Fig. 2   The mechanical bathythermograph. The instrument was lowered to a depth from a moving surface ship and then retreived. It gave a trace of temperature vs. depth on a small glass slide. The coil at the tail is a Bourdon tube filled with xylene for indicating temperature, while a spring-bellows arrangement (not visible) indicates depth or pressure.

World War II Achievements

The establishment of the National Defense Research Committee was a major impetus for a great influx of physicists and acousticians into underwater sound early in World War II. Much attention was given to propagation phenomena, and much of our present understanding and quantitative data stems from the work of Division 6 of the NDRC. At the end of the War, this work was summarized by the various Divisions in a Summary Technical Report. The report of Division 6, under the subject of Subsea Warfare, was issued in 23 volumes. One of them, entitled *Physics of Sound in the Sea,* is a fine summary of propagation as it was known and understood at the time (9). It contains chapters on deep-water transmission, shallow-water transmission, intensity fluctuations, and explosions as sources of underwater sound, each written by an eminent acoustician. This wartime work remains today a valuable source of information on propagation at the high frequencies (15-30 kHz) and out to comparatively short ranges (to about 6000 yds) of interest to the wartime sonars.

Post-War Achievements

The years since the War have seen a great expansion of knowledge of propagation, in response to the persistent trend in sonar over the years to lower frequencies and longer ranges. Of the many noteworthy accomplishments in propagation made during the last 30 years, the following ten may be cited:

(1) The discovery of the cause of the excess attenuation of sound in sea water at frequencies in the range 5-100 kHz.

(2) Measurements of bottom loss in many deep-water areas for application to bottom-bounce sonars in those areas.

(3) An elucidation of the propagation characteristics and losses in the Deep Sound Channel and in the surface duct.

(4) An understanding of the nature of propagation in the Arctic (i.e., under an ice cover).

(5) Measurements of wavefront coherence and stability.

(6) The discovery of an excess attenuation at frequencies below 1 kHz, and its explanation in terms of a minor constituent of sea water.

(7) The discovery and understanding of the occurrence of convergence zones in deep water.

(8) The easy production of ray diagrams and wave theory predictions through the use of digital computers.

(9) Measurements of extremely accurate values for the velocity of sound in sea water, making possible accurate range prediction for fire control purposes.

(10) Generally speaking, an improvement of our prediction capability for propagation in deep water, out to longer ranges and to frequencies not previously considered.

As mentioned in the Preface, propagation research continues at an ever-increasing rate. As evidence of this, *Figure 3* is a plot of the number of papers in the subject category entitled "Propagation of Sound in Water. Attenuation. Fluctuation" appearing in the Journal of the Acoustical Society of America since its founding in 1929. Evidently, the number of papers in this category doubles about every five years, with half the total number so far having appeared in the years 1972-1977. It appears that of all the many ramifications of underwater sound and sonar, propagation has been, and continues to be, the most popular from a research standpoint, thus indicating that the ocean, like the human ear, is still a fascinating subject for acoustic study.

Some Remaining Major Problems in Propagation

In spite of its long history and the high level of current research activity, a number of problem areas still remain in the general subject of sound propagation in the sea. Five of these are the following:

(1) An extension of the frequency range of present knowledge to higher frequencies (beyond 60 kHz) and to lower frequencies (below 20 Hz).

(2) A prediction capability for shallow water transmission, especially at low frequencies and the long ranges of interest for passive sonars.

(3) A better understanding and more measurements of second-order effects, such as fluctuations and wavefront coherence, and their exploitation in system design and prediction.

(4) Statistical validation, compared to the real ocean, of the many elaborate mathematical techniques, supported by digital-computer computations, now available for solving propagation problems. This means making quantitative statistical comparisons with the body of field data, using the available input parameters for each sgement of that data.

(5) More and better quantitative values for the propagation parameters, obtained from at-sea measurements, for use as primary working data by the sonar design engineer and predictor.

For the acoustic historians, some excellent historical summaries of sonar covering the era prior to and during World War II are available. These are papers by Wood (10), Klein (11) and Lasky (12-14) which authoritatively deal with this interesting, formative period of the subject. No historical summary of sonar in the post-War period has yet appeared in an unclassified publication.

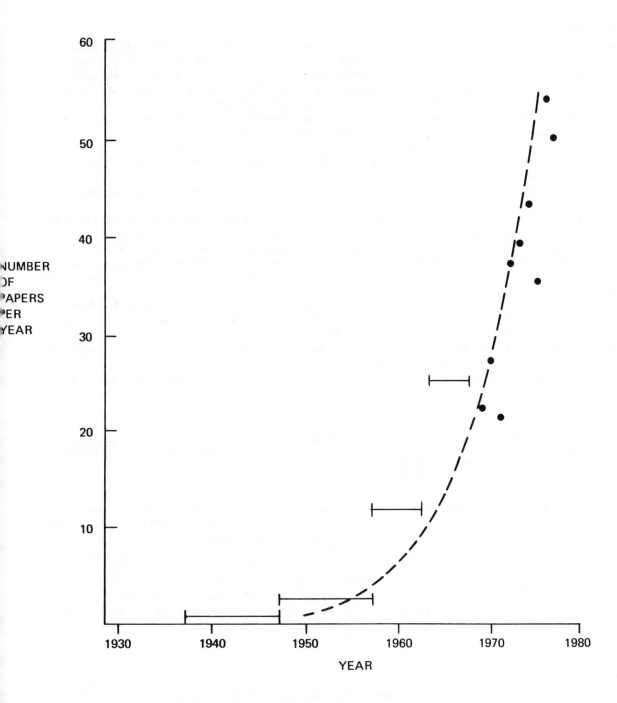

Fig. 3. Number of papers and letters to the editor per year in JASA 1977 on the subject "Propagation of Sound in Water. Attenuation. Fluctuation", as obtained from the Cumulative Indices to 1968 and individual Journal volumes beyond. The curve illustrates an exponential increase of published papers beyond 1950.

Methods of Research

A wide variety of techniques are available, and have been used, in propagation studies. Most widely used at the present time is *computer modelling,* wherein a mathematical model of the ocean is set up and exercised by a computer program. The results of such studies, however, while relatively inexpensive to carry out, are often of hardly more than academic interest unless closely tied to real-world data, because of the difficulty of realistically modelling the real ocean. Of a similar nature to computer models are *analog models,* wherein the ocean is physically modelled in a laboratory tank, usually scaling the frequency according to the size of the tank. An example is the work of Wood (15) on shallow water propagation using a tank 20 feet long, 5 feet wide and 8 inches deep.

In the laboratory, too, the velocity of sound in sea water has been measured to an exquisite degree of precision by a variety of techniques (16), while the attenuation coefficient has been determined in the laboratory by measuring the rate of decay of sound in a resonant glass sphere containing sea water (17).

Concerning sea-going studies and measurements, a variety of different measurement platforms have been used. These include

(1) *Two ships,* one a source ship and the other a receiving ship, changing the range between them and making a *transmission run* so as to yield level vs. range (18)[*]. In echo-ranging studies, one ship is the target submarine from which echoes are obtained and recorded. This is the oldest, and now classic, technique, but it is now almost obsolete because of the expense and slowness of using two ships and the availability of other sources, receivers and platforms.

(2) *One ship and an aircraft,* where the latter drops explosive sound signals while flying toward or away from the former (19).

(3) *One aircraft alone,* using sonobuoys for reception and recording on board the aircraft (20). A surface ship, launching a sonobuoy and steaming away from it, may replace the aircraft, though at a sacrifice of the range to which a run can be made and speed of conducting the field exercise.

(4) *One bottommed hydrophone or hydrophone array,* cable-connected to shore, receiving signals transmitted from a ship (21) or the explosive shots dropped by an aircraft (22).

(5) *Two bottomed transducers,* one a source, the other a receiver, in studies of the fluctuation of sound transmission between two fixed points in the sea (24).

Rectification of Transmission Run Data

When a transmission run has been made, it is desirable to fit the data to some simple rational model that gives the results some physical meaning. The data can be said to be "rectified" if the model is a linear relationship between intensity and range. A commonly used model is

$$10 \log I_r = 10 \log I_0 - (N \log r + Ar)$$

where $10 \log I_r$ is the measured signal level at range r, $10 \log I_0$ is the source level of the source of sound, and N and A are coefficients to be found from the data. The $N \log r$ term is the spreading loss; the Ar term, called, during World War II, the *transmission anomaly,* includes every other source of loss (assumed proportional to range). For physical reasonability, N has to be assumed to be either 10, 20 or 30, corresponding to cylindrical, spherical, or hyperspherical spreading (spherical spreading plus time stretching). In shallow water, there is theoretical justification to take N = 15 under some circumstances (25). No other values of N, while they may fit the data better statistically, are physically meaningful. Transmission run data are readily fitted to this model, after selecting a value for N by plotting TL – N log r against range and determining A from the slope of a straight line through the plotted points.

For transmission in sound channels, an appropriate model is

$$10 \log I_r = 10 \log I_0 - (10 \log r_0 + 10 \log r + Ar)$$

where r_0 is a constant and N is taken as 10. A rectified plot of measured data fitted to this model yields $10 \log r_0$ from the intercept of the line at r = 1 yd and A from the slope as before. *Fig. 4* is an example of field data "rectified" according to this expression. Here $10 \log I_r + 10 \log r$ is plotted against r; the slope of the fitted line, in any octave frequency band, is the attenuation coefficient in that band. The intercept of the line at 0 miles (actually 1 yd.) is the quantity $10 \log I_0 - 10 \log r_0$, from which r_0 can be found if the source level $10 \log I_0$ is known.

---

[*]The references in this section are to examples reported in literature, where some experimental details can be found.

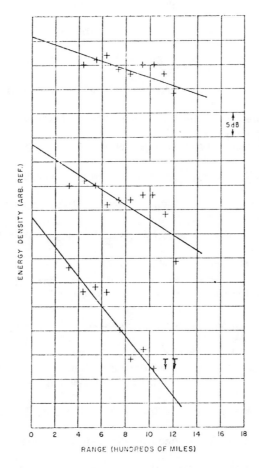

Fig. 4.   Energy density levels plus 10 log r in 3 frequency bands for a series of explosive shots dropped across the Atlantic Ocean eastward from Bermuda. The levels, when corrected for the source level in each band, give the quantity 10 log r_0. The slope of the straight lines fitted by eye to the points is the attenuation coefficient, (24).

REFERENCES*

1. A. B. Wood, *A Textbook of Sound,* Macmillan Co., New York, 1941, p. 261.
2. E. B. Stephenson, Velocity of Sound in Sea Water, Phys. Rev. 21, 181, 1923.
3. N. H. Heck and J. H. Service, Velocity of Sound in Sea Water, U.S. Coast and Geodetic Survey Special Publ. 108, 1924.
4. H. Lichte, Uber den Einfluss Horizontaler Temperaturschichtung des Seewassers auf die Reichweite von Unterwasserschallsignalen, Phys. Zeits. *17,* 385, 1919. English translation, by A. F. Wittenborn, TRACOR, Inc., 1977.
5. E. B. Stephenson, Transmission of Sound in Sea Water: Absorption and Reflection Coefficients, Naval Research Lab. Report S-1204, 1935.
6. E. B. Stephenson, Absorption Coefficients of Sound in Sea Water, Naval Research Lab. Report S-1466, 1938; also S-1549, 1939.
7. E. B. Stephenson, The Effect of Water Conditions on the Propagation of Supersonic Underwater Sound, Naval Research Lab. Report S-1670, 1940.
8. R. L. Steinberger, Underwater Sound Investigation of Water Conditions — Guantanamo Bay Area, Sound Laboratory, Navy Yard, Washington, D.C., 1937.
9. Physics of Sound in the Sea, National Defense Research Committee (NDRC), Division 6, Vol. 8, Part I, Transmission, 1947.
10. A. B. Wood, From the Board of Invention and Research to the Royal Naval Scientific Service, Journal Royal Navy Sci. Serv. *20,* 185, 1965.
11. E. Klein, Underwater Sound Research and Applications Before 1939, JASA *43,* 931, 1968.
12. M. Lasky, Review of World War I Acoustic Technology, J. Underwater Acous. *24,* 363, 1973.
13. M. Lasky, A Historical Review of Underwater Acoustic Technology 1916-1939, J. Underwater Acous. *24,* 597, 1974.
14. M. Lasky, Review of Undersea Acoustics to 1950, JASA *61,* 283, 1977.
15. A. B. Wood, Model Experiments on Sound Propagation in Shallow Seas, JASA *31,* 1213, 1959.
16. W. D. Wilson, Speed of Sound in Distilled Water as a Function of Temperature and Pressure, JASA *31,* 1067, 1959.
17. O. B. Wilson and R. W. Leonard, Measurements of Sound Absorption in Aqueous Salt Solutions by a Resonator Method, JASA *26,* 223, 1954.
18. *Physics of Sound in the Sea,* NDRC Div. 6, Vol. 8, 1947, Chapter 4.
19. R. J. Urick and G. R. Lund, Coherence of Convergence Zone Sound, JASA *43,* 723, 1968.
20. R. J. Urick, A Method of Airborne Bottom Reflection Surveying, Naval Ordnance Lab. Tech. Rep. TR65-90, 1965.
21. D. J. Ramsdale, Acoustic Sidebands from CW Sources Towed at Long Ranges in the Deep Ocean, JASA *63,* 391, 1978.
22. C. Levenson and R. Doblar, Long Range Acoustic Propagation Through the Gulf Stream, JASA *59,* 1134, 1976.
23. T. Ewart, Acoustic Fluctuations in the **Open** Ocean — A Measurement Using a Fixed Refracted Path, JASA *60,* 46, 1976.
24. R. J. Urick, Low Frequency Sound Attenuation in the Deep Ocean, JASA *35,* 1413, 1963.
25. L. N. Brekhovskikh, *Waves in Layered Media,* Academic Press, New York, 1960, pp. 417-421.

---

*Throughout this book, the abbreviation JASA is used to denote the Journal of the Acoustical Society of America.

CHAPTER 2

SOME BASIC THEORY

Introduction

This chapter presents a bare-bones rudimentary introduction to the theory of sound propagation in the ocean, with the aim of showing how the physical properties of the ocean medium determine the propagation in terms of the wave equation and how the latter is solved in the most simple of cases.

Our approach will be to show how the wave equation is derived from some simple equations of physics and then go on to the *wave acoustic* solution and the *ray acoustic* solution. One or the other of these solutions are encountered in all theoretical descriptions of propagation. We will end with a statement of the strong and weak points of these two theoretical formulations, and give a brief description of some of the extant computer models based on the theory.

A vast literature is available to the reader interested in pursuing the theory further. Excellent starting points are two chapters in *Physics of Sound in the Sea* (1) written at the end of World War II by some of the eminent acousticians of the time. A number of books (2-5) are available. Current theoretical developments can be found in almost any issue of the monthly Journal of the Acoustical Society of America (JASA).

The Basic Equations Of Physics

We will restrict ourselves to the classical, simple case of low amplitudes in a non-viscous perfect fluid. We will ignore the effects of high amplitudes, with their interesting non-linear effects, viscosity (no absorption) and rigidity (no shear waves).

For this most simple case, there are four equations of physics that underlie the propagation of sound:

(a) *Equation of Continuity.* No mass of fluid is created or destroyed: any difference in the amount of fluid entering or leaving a given volume must be accompanied by changes in density. That is, there are no sound sources or sinks anywhere in the medium. For small changes in density, this leads to the equation

$$\frac{\partial s}{\partial t} = -\left(\frac{\partial u_x}{\partial x} + \frac{\partial u_y}{\partial y} + \frac{\partial u_z}{\partial z} \right) \qquad 1)$$

where s is the "condensation" $= \frac{\rho - \rho_o}{\rho_o}$, ρ is the instantaneous density, ρ_o is the ambient density, and u_x, u_y, u_z are the three components of the particle velocity of the fluid.

(b) *Equations of Motion.* The force components per unit volume of fluid can be written

$$f_x = \rho_o \frac{\partial u_x}{\partial t}$$

$$f_y = \rho_o \frac{\partial u_y}{\partial t} \qquad 2)$$

$$f_z = \rho_o \frac{\partial u_z}{\partial t}$$

provided no shear forces (viscosity) are involved and provided all velocities and accelerations are small (i.e. higher order terms neglected). These equations are essentially nothing more than Newton's Second Law: force equals mass times acceleration.

(c) *Equation of State.* This is a relation between the pressure P, temperature T, and density ρ, which may be written

$$P = f(\rho, T)$$

For small changes in density and pressure, and for adiabatic (i.e., rapid) changes, meaning that there is no conduction of heat, this relationship becomes

$$p = Ks \qquad \text{3)}$$

where p is the incremental pressure, or the difference between the instantaneous pressure and the ambient pressure. K is a proportionality factor relating p to s and is called the *bulk modulus* of the fluid.

(d) *Equations of Force.* The three components of force per unit volume of a non-viscous fluid are related to the pressure acting on a unit volume according to

$$f_x = -\frac{\partial p}{\partial x}$$

$$f_y = -\frac{\partial p}{\partial y} \qquad \text{4)}$$

$$f_z = -\frac{\partial p}{\partial z}$$

These equations say merely that the force in a given direction is the negative of the rate of change of pressure in that direction.

Derivation of the Wave Equation

The wave equation is a partial differential equation that combines the above four sets of equations. The synthesis is accomplished as follows:

(a) Eliminate f_x, f_y, f_z from 4) and 2).
(b) Differentiate 3) with respect to x, y and z and substitute in a).
(c) Differentiate again and add.
(d) Substitute 1), and obtain a partial differential equation in terms of the condensation s.
(e) Use 3) again to eliminate s and obtain an equation in terms of p.

The result is

$$\frac{\partial^2 p}{\partial t^2} = \frac{K}{\rho_0}\left(\frac{\partial^2 p}{\partial x^2} + \frac{\partial^2 p}{\partial y^2} + \frac{\partial^2 p}{\partial y^2}\right)$$

The quantity $\frac{K}{\rho_0}$ can be shown to have the dimensions of the square of a velocity and may be replaced by c^2. Our final result is a relationship between the temporal and spatial changes of pressure in a sound wave, called the *wave equation*:

$$\frac{\partial^2 p}{\partial t^2} = c^2\left(\frac{\partial^2 p}{\partial x^2} + \frac{\partial^2 p}{\partial y^2} + \frac{\partial^2 p}{\partial z^2}\right)$$

Solutions

For a particular problem, the wave equation we have just obtained must be solved for the *boundary* and *initial* conditions that apply in that problem. *Boundary* conditions are the known pressures and particle velocities existing at the boundaries of the medium. In underwater sound, one ubiquitous boundary condition is that the pressure p is zero along the plane (or wavy) sea surface. *Initial* conditions are those of the source of sound, whose location is usually taken to be at the origin; p(o,o,o,t) ordinarily is a known function that describes the manner is which the source varies with time. The initial (source) conditions play no part in *ray acoustics,* in which the sound field is described by *rays. Both* boundary and initial conditions are needed for a *wave theory* solution; such a solution is therefore complete, at least to the extent that the model of the real world that it assumes is accurate. The wave theory solution is difficult or impossible to obtain whenever the real surface and sea bottom have to be realistically approximated.

Wave Theory

In one dimension the wave equation is

$$\frac{\partial^2 p}{\partial t^2} = c^2 \frac{\partial^2 p}{\partial x^2}$$

This was known to the mathematicians of the 18th century to be satisfied by an (arbitrary) function of $(t-x/c)$ or $(t+x/c)$. This may be seen by differentiating $f(t\pm x/c)$ twice and noting that the wave equation is satisfied regardless of what the function f may be. Moreover, it can be shown that $p=f(t\pm x/c)$ is *necessary* as well as *sufficient*; that is, any function not of this form cannot satisfy the wave equation.

If the pressure $p=f(t-x/c)$ at an arbitrary point x_1 and an arbitrary time t_1 happens to be same as that at points x_2 at time t_2, then we must have $t_1 - x_1/c = t_2 - x_2/c$, from which it follows that $c = (x_1-x_2)/(t_1-t_2)$. The quantity c may therefore be interpreted as the *velocity of propagation* along the line from x_2 to x_1. Similarly, from $p=f(t+x/c)$, c may be seen to be the propagation velocity from x_1 to x_2. Therefore, *functions with arguments $(t-x/c)$ represent waves travelling in the $+x$ direction; those having arguments $(t+x/c)$ represent waves going in the $-x$ direction.*

If the 3-dimensional wave equation is transformed to spherical coordinates, it will be found that functions of the form

$$p = \frac{1}{r} f(t \pm \frac{r}{c})$$

will be solutions. These represent spherical waves radiating to or from the origin. Commonly selected functions are the cosine, sine and exponential functions which are added to satisfy the source and boundary conditions.

Returning to one dimension, we try solutions of the form

$$p = \psi(x)\, e^{i\omega(t-\varphi)}$$

where $\psi(x)$ is any function of the space coordinate x. On substituting, we find $\psi(x)$ has to satisfy the relationship

$$\psi(x) + \frac{c^2}{\omega^2} \frac{d^2 \psi}{dx^2} = 0$$

which has the solution

$$\psi(x) = A \sin kx + B \cos kx$$

where $k = \omega/c$ and $\omega = 2\pi f$.

Let us now apply this to waves travelling vertically between a plane pressure-release sea surface where $p=0$ and a plane rigid bottom, where p is a maximum. Take the x coordinate to be in the vertical, and let the surface be at $x=0$ and the bottom at $x=H$. The upper boundary condition requires that $p(0)=0$, from which it follows that $B=0$. Our solution is now

$$p = A \sin kx \cdot e^{i\omega(t-\varphi)}$$

To satisfy the lower boundary condition, we return to the basic equations and eliminate f_x from 2) and 4), and obtain

$$\frac{\partial u}{\partial t} = -\frac{1}{p} \frac{\partial p}{\partial x}$$

Since the particle velocity $u=0$ at $x=H$, $\partial u/\partial t$ must be zero there also, or

$$\left. \frac{\partial p}{\partial x} \right|_{x=H} = 0$$

Hence we must have

Hence we must have

$$Ak \cos kH = 0$$

so that

$$k_n H = (n + \frac{1}{2})\pi; \quad n = 0, 1, 2 \ldots$$

These values of k are called *eigenvalues* or *characteristic values,* one for each value of n, i.e.

$$k_n = \frac{(n + \frac{1}{2})\pi}{H}$$

For a single frequency source of plane waves, we then have as a solution of the wave equation

$$p = A_n \sin k_n y \cdot e^{i\omega_n(t - \varphi)}$$

The A_n and ϕ can be inserted to take care of the characteristics of the source. Only frequencies $\omega_n = ck_n$ can propagate between the surface and bottom. The sum of an arbitrary number of such terms will also be a solution of the wave equation. Thus, for a multi-frequency source, we would have

$$p = \sum_n A_n \sin k_n y \cdot e^{i\omega_n(t - \varphi_n)}$$

for each term of which the eigenvalues k_n are defined by $k_n = (n+1/2)\pi/H$. The various terms of this sum are called *normal modes.* With a broad-band source, the medium permits only certain discrete frequencies (determined by this relationship) to propagate.

The case of horizontal propagation in a layer of water between the surface and the bottom is much more interesting than this trivial case of vertical propagation, and some aspects of it will be considered when discussing propagation in shallow water.

Ray Theory

In the expression for a plane wave travelling in the +x direction, p=f(t−x/c), let the argument (t−x/c) be designated by φ. φ designates those parts of the wave having the same pressure amplitude p. Note that x=c(t−φ), so that φ may be regarded as a kind of phase angle. With increasing time φ determines the distance x at which p is a constant. Such distances are, in three dimensions, surfaces of constant phase, called *wave-fronts.*

The defining equation of the wave-fronts is

$$W(x,y,z) = c(t - \varphi)$$

and it can be shown (1, p. 44) that the partial differential equation of these surfaces is

$$\frac{\partial^2 W}{\partial x^2} + \frac{\partial^2 W}{\partial y^2} + \frac{\partial^2 W}{\partial z^2} = n^2 (x,y,z)$$

where $n^2(x,y,z)$ is the square of the *index of refraction* and the (x,y,z) indicates that n is a function of the coordinates. In terms of sound velocity,

$$n = c_0/c(x,y,z)$$

where c_o is a constant. The above relationship is called the *eikonal equation,* so-called from the Greek word "eikon", for image.

Successive normals to the wave fronts W are called *rays* and are the paths of energy flow away from the source. Within any bundle of adjacent rays, called a *pencil,* the acoustic energy flux is a constant; that is, the energy contained within the bounding rays of a pencil of rays is everywhere constant. In ray theory, there is no "leakage" of energy out of the pencil, and the interesting effects of diffraction and scattering have no place in ray theory.

What good is the eikonal equation vis-a-vis the wave equation? There are two important advantages to it:

1) It has no time dependence and the propagation it describes is independent of frequency

2) It leads to a set of ordinary differential equations that describe the paths of individual rays. These equations are

$$\frac{d(n\alpha)}{ds} = \frac{\partial n}{\partial x}$$

$$\frac{d(n\beta)}{ds} = \frac{\partial n}{\partial y}$$

$$\frac{d(n\gamma)}{ds} = \frac{\partial n}{\partial z}$$

where α, β, γ are the direction cosines of a ray at any point (x,y,z) viz: $dx/ds=\alpha$; $dy/ds=\beta$; $dz/ds=\gamma$.

To see what these mean, take the two-dimensional case in x and y and let n be a function of y only. That is, we put $\partial n/\partial x = o$ and ignore the third equation in z. Then, in terms of the angle θ of the ray with the x direction, we can write

$$\alpha = \cos\theta$$
$$\beta = \sin\theta$$

and we have

$$\frac{d(n\cos\theta)}{ds} = 0; \quad \frac{d(n\sin\theta)}{ds} = \frac{dn}{dy}$$

where the total derivitive dn/dy can replace $\partial n/\partial y$, since n depends on y only. The first of these two equations says that, along any individual ray, $(n\cos\theta)$ is a constant:

$$n\cos\theta = \frac{c_o}{c(y)}\cos\theta = \text{a constant} = \cos\theta_o$$

giving

$$\frac{c_o}{\cos\theta_o} = \frac{c(y)}{\cos\theta}$$

This is *Snells' Law,* a relation that is a always used, in one form or another, in drawing ray diagrams. The second equation leads to expression for the *radius of curvature* of a ray at any point. It can be shown (1, p. 47) that

$$\frac{1}{R} \equiv \frac{d\theta}{ds} = -\frac{d\,c(y)}{dy}\frac{\cos\theta_o}{c_o}$$

since $d\theta/ds$ is the reciprocal of the radius of curvature R. For a linear velocity gradient, $c=c_0+gy$; this gives

$$\frac{1}{R} = \frac{-g\cos\theta_0}{c_0}$$

This is a constant for any one ray, which therefore is an arc of a circle. With positive g, the velocity increases in the +y direction; the minus sign means that the center of curvature is in the negative or –y direction. *Fig. 1* illustrates the above result for a ray starting upward with a velocity increasing in the upward (+y) direction.

Comparison of Wave and Ray Theories

A comparison between the two theories may be made by the following statements:

(1) *wave theory* gives a formally complete solution, applicable under all conditions; *ray theory* does *not* handle problems involving diffraction and scattering, such as sound in a shadow zone.

(2) *wave theory* is valid for all gradient conditions; *ray theory* is said (2) to hold only when $(\Delta c/c)/\Delta y \ll 1/\lambda$. Practically, this is equivalent to saying that the velocity gradient (in $\sec^{-1}$) must everywhere be less than the frequency. Another statement is that the fractional change in velocity $\Delta c/c$, in a distance of one wave-length $(\Delta y=\lambda)$ must be less than unity.

(3) *wave theory* gives a mathematical solution that is difficult to interpret; *ray theory* gives a *ray diagram* showing visually, *and so*metimes dramatically, where the source energy is going.

(4) *wave theory* cannot handle real boundary conditions existing in the sea, but requires simplified modeling thereof; *ray theory* handles many realistic boundary conditions easily.

(5) in contrast, *wave theory* accounts for any arbitrary source function; *ray theory* gives a result that does not involve the nature of the source.

(6) before the advent of digital computers, practical *wave theory* solutions could be obtained only for *long* ranges, where only a few trapped modes were important; *ray theory* was limited to *short* ranges where only a few rays were necessary to describe the sound field. Nowadays, this distinction has vanished.

(7) practically speaking, *wave theory* is used at low frequencies whenever the validity of ray theory is questionable; *ray theory* is used at high frequencies when the fundamental requirement of ray theory — that the sound energy radiated by the source into a pencil of rays remains within that pencil — is felt to be valid.

Computer Models

Before the advent of the digital computer, considerable mathematical ingenuity was required to get an answer from either theory. Nowadays, the problem is one of mathematical programming, in either the ray or mode solutions, to incorporate the most nearly realistic conditions into the problem and to do so in the most economical manner of computer time.

A great variety of computer "models" are available. The FACT model (6) is the Navy Interim Standard Propagation Model for ocean environments that may be reasonably treated by assuming a flat bottom and a range-independent sound-speed profile. The FACT model computes propagation loss from source to receiver as a function of range and frequency. The model is based on classical ray theory, but has been augmented with higher order asymptotic corrections in the vicinity of caustics.*This has been done in order to yield a more complete model of diffraction effects. Three model approaches to combining energy arriving via different ray paths are available to the FACT model user. These approaches include the coherent summation of all ray paths, an rms summation of ray paths, and a combination of coherent and rms summations referred to as the "semi-coherent" option. A coherent summation of all ray paths will produce rapid oscillations in the computer propagation loss as a function of range. These rapid oscillations are smoothed out by an rms summation, but so are significant long-term interference effects. The semi-coherent option attempts to overcome these problems by using an rms summation of all ray paths except for those selected paths which experience significant, but predictable, coherence effects. These paths are coherently combined.

Many other models, using either ray-trace or normal mode computational techniques, are available. Among these are TRIMAIN (7) and GRASS (8) of the Naval Research Laboratory and CONGRATS (9) and FFP (10) (Fast Field Program) of the Naval Underwater Systems Center. Other Navy laboratories and contractors have their own programs, many of which are modifications of others to suit particular programming and output requirements (11). All require as input data a velocity profile, the bottom profile along the direction of propagation, and bottom loss as a function of angle. In many, these can vary with range, so as to be different in different range segments.

---

*A "caustic" is the envelope of the intersections of adjacent rays in a ray diagram.

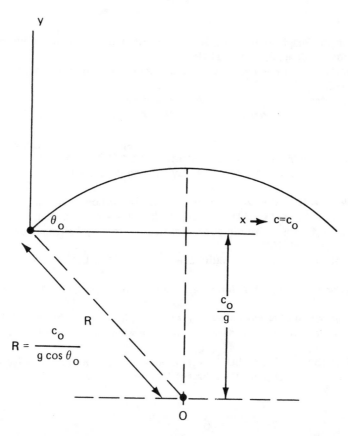

Fig. 1. In a linear velocity gradient, such that $c(y) = c_0 + gy$, where g is the gradient, a ray leaving the origin at angle θ_0 is a circle of radius $c_0/g \cos \theta_0$. All the rays from the origin have their centers along the horizontal line through O a distance of c_0/g below $x=o$. For a proof of the circularity of rays in a linear gradient see Chap. 3.

Ray theory programs can handle horizontal variations in the velocity profile or water depth relatively easily. Wave theory solutions, however, have difficulty accommodating problems where the sound velocity, c, is a function of range as well as depth. A theoretical method to overcome this difficulty is the *parabolic approximation technique* (12), in which the two-dimensional wave equation containing two second-order partial derivatives (an elliptic equation) is converted into an equation containing a first and a second order partial derivative (a parabolic equation), for which solutions can be obtained. The parabolic method is limited to conditions such that the fractional changes in sound velocity over one wavelength are small (the condition of validity of ray theory), and to small angles of the propagation direction with the horizontal. These restrictions are not severe, however, for prediction problems in long-range propagation in the ocean, for which the method has particular value.

The question arises, given these various propagation models, which one is the best for predicting the actual transmission loss measured at sea. This question has not yet been answered. A number of workshops have been held wherein different models have been compared with each other — as to results, cost, computer memory requirements, etc. (13, 14). But no extensive statistical comparisons have been made against field data. Here everything depends on the validity of the input data; if the comparison is poor, it is likely that the input parameters are incorrect, or vary incorrectly with range. With uncertain input data, an elaborate computer program is useless (the GIGO (Garbage In, Garbage Out) principle of computer programming).

REFERENCES

1. Physics of Sound in the Sea, National Defense Research Committee Division 6 Summary Tech. Rept. 8, 1946; Chap. 2, Wave Acoustics, Chap. 3, Ray Acoustics.
2. C. B. Officer, *Introduction to the Theory of Sound Transmission, with Applications to the Ocean,* McGraw-Hill, New York, 1958.
3. L. N. Brekhovskikh, *Waves in Layered Media,* Academic Press, New York, 1960.
4. I. Tolstoy and C. S. Clay, *Ocean Acoustics: Theory and Experiment in Underwater Sound,* McGraw-Hill, New York, 1966.
5. W.M. Ewing, W. S. Jardetsky and F. Press, *Elastic Waves in Layered Media,* McGraw-Hill, New York, 1957.
6. C. W. Spofford, The FACT Model, USN Maury Center Report 109, 1974.
7. B. G. Roberts, Horizontal Gradient Acoustical Ray Tracing Program TRIMAIN, Naval Research Lab. Report 7621, 1973.
8. J. J. Cornyn, GRASS, A Digital Ray-Tracing and Transmission Loss Prediction System, I: Description, Naval Research Lab. Report 7621, 1973; II: User's Manual, Naval Research Lab. Report 7642, 1973.
9. J. S. Cohen and L. J. Einstein, Continuous Gradient Ray Tracing System (CONGRATS), USN Underwater Systems Center Report 1069, 1970.
10. F. R. diNapoli, Fast Field Program for Multi-layered Media, USN Underwater Systems Center Report 4103, 1971.
11. F. R. diNapoli, Computer Models for Underwater Sound Propagation, USN Underwater Systems Center Tech. Rep. 5267, 1975.
12. S. T. McDaniel, Propagation of Normal Modes in the Parabolic Approximation, JASA *57,* 307, 1975.
13. P. R. Tatro and C. W. Spofford, Underwater Acoustic Models, Ocean 73 IEEE International Conference Proceedings, 1973.
14. C. W. Spofford, A Synopsis of the AESD Workshop on Acoustic Propagation by Non-Ray-Tracing Techniques, USN Acoustic Environmental Support Detachment Technical Note 73-05, 1973.

CHAPTER 3

UNDERWATER ACOUSTIC MODELING TECHNIQUES*

Introduction

This chapter presents a state-of-the-art literature review of underwater acoustic models developed by the Navy sonar modeling community. Three types of acoustic models are addressed: propagation loss, noise, and active sonar/ reverberation models. The basic features of each type of model and areas of application are discussed. Problems associated with model evaluation and validation are described.

The field of underwater acoustics has been extensively developed over the last four decades in response to practical needs originating within the sonar and seismic communities (1). Since 1960 considerable emphasis has been placed on the development of mathematical models to analyze data collected during field experiments. These models have historically been used to predict acoustic conditions for application to various problems including the planning of improved at-sea experiments and the designing of optimized sonar systems. However, although the underlying theories have been well developed for some time, the transition from theory to operational computer models has not progressed as rapidly. This lag can be attributed to a number of factors; these include limitations in existing computer capabilities, a lack of adequate mathematical methods, and insufficient environmental-acoustic data of suitable resolution for proper support of model validation.

The emphasis in this chapter will be directed at those underwater acoustic models developed by the Navy sonar modeling community over the past several years. Although reviews of acoustic models are not new (2-4), the scope of this chapter is apparently unique in that it embraces three broad types of models comprising propagation loss, noise, and active sonar/reverbation models. The breadth of this review precludes detailed discussions of any particular model type. Rather, the intent is to acquaint the reader with the availability of the state-of-the-art acoustic models.

A more fundamental category of models, not fully described here, is environmental models. This category includes empirically-derived models that are frequently used as integral parts of acoustic models to generate input parameters or predict intermediate quantities. Examples of such models currently in use include sound speed (5-9), absorption coefficients (10-12), surface reflection losses (13), bottom reflection losses (14), surface backscattering strengths (15, 16), bottom backscattering strengths (17, 18), volume scattering strengths (19), ambient noise (20), and surface duct propagation loss (13).

The acoustic models discussed here are generally restricted to those mathematical models of acoustic theory that have been converted to computer codes for application to well-defined sonar-related problems. The scope of this review necessarily precludes citations of that literature which, protected by national security provisions, lies outside the public domain. Thus, it can be assumed that certain areas of acoustic modeling will be advanced beyond the level of sophistication depicted here.

Irrespective of acoustic model type, the intended applications will fall into one of two basic categories: research or operational. The research-oriented modeling techniques are developed for investigative studies in laboratory environments where accuracy is important, computer time is not a critical factor, and facilities are supportive of the modeling efforts. Operational-oriented models are those that support field activities, including Fleet operations, and must be executed rapidly, often under demanding conditions. In this latter situation, model accuracy may be subordinate to processing speed.

The three types of acoustic models will be described. The first type of model, propagation loss, is a fundamental building block for ambient noise and active sonar/reverberation models. Furthermore, propagation loss models, together with noise models, reverberation models, and environmental models are components of the active sonar models.

Propagation Loss Models

This section describes those stand-alone acoustic propagation loss models that are applicable to passive sonar systems.

Formulations of acoustic propagation loss models generally begin with the three-dimensional, time-dependent wave equation. However, the wave equation is derived from the general equations of continuity, state, and motion.

---

*By Paul C. Etter, Senior Engineer, MAR Incorporated, 1335 Rockville Pike, Rockville, Maryland 20852.

Consequently, depending on the governing assumptions and intended applications, the exact form of the wave equation can vary considerably (21, 22). For most applications, however, a simplified linear, hyperbolic, second-order partial differential equation is used:

$$\nabla^2 \phi = \frac{1}{c^2} \frac{\partial^2 \phi}{\partial t^2}$$

where

∇^2 =   Laplacian operator

ϕ =   field variable

c =   speed of sound

t =   time

Subsequent simplifications frequently incorporate a harmonic solution in order to obtain the time-independent Helmholtz (or elliptic reduced) wave equation. Without such simplifications, general solutions to the wave equation with non-trivial boundary conditions are usually limited to iterative finite difference techniques (23).

Various theoretical approaches are applicable to the Helmholtz equation. The approach used depends on the specific geometrical assumptions made for the propagation and the type of solution chosen for ϕ.

Although acoustic propagation loss models can be classified according to the theoretical approach employed, the cross-connections that exist among the various approaches complicate a strict classification, or taxonomic, scheme. Consequently, the more detailed the scheme, the more incestuous the approaches appear (3). A generalized classification scheme has been constructed on the basis of five theoretical approaches (2, 3). The approaches can be reduced to two major categories: ray models and wave models.

The breakdown of model approaches into these two basic categories affords a simplistic but useful classification mechanism. Specifically, ray models are generally fast-running, simply-executed programs that are valid over a broad range of frequencies. The wave models, on the other hand, are generally more accurate than the ray models but require longer running times and more operator intervention; in addition, the wave models are usually limited to acoustic frequencies below about 300 Hz. It is not surprising, therefore, that the ray models are most closely associated with operational applications, and the wave models are most frequently applied to research problems. This particular classification scheme has been used in earlier work (24).

Within the categories of ray and wave models, a further subdivision can be made into range-independent and range-dependent types. Range-independence means that the model assumes cylindrical symmetry for the environment (i.e., a horizontally stratified ocean). Range-dependence indicates that some properties of the ocean medium are allowed to vary as a function of range from the receiver. Such range-varying properties commonly include sound speed and bathymetry.

The five theoretical approaches mentioned earlier are grouped according to ray or wave models as follows:

Ray Models

- ray theory with corrections
- multipath expansion techniques

Wave Models

- normal mode solutions
- fast field theory
- parabolic approximation

Ray Models

Ray models calculate propagation loss principally on the basis of ray-tracing. As a result much attention has been devoted to the manner in which the sound-speed profile is approximated and the method by which earth-curvature corrections are applied to the profile.

Ray theory with corrections starts with the Helmholtz equation. The solution is then separated into amplitude and phase components under the assumption that the amplitude varies more slowly with position than does the phase (geometrical acoustics approximation). This assumption limits the method to the high frequency domain. However, with appropriate frequency-dependent corrections and proper evaluation of caustics, the theory can be extended to lower frequencies (25-32). Extensions to range-dependence can be accomplished in several ways: by mapping rays over discrete range intervals in which the environment remains constant (33-36), by dividing the range-depth plane into triangular regions (37-40), or by allowing the environment to vary smoothly as a function of range (41, 42).

Multipath expansion techniques expand the acoustic field integral representation of the wave equation in terms of an infinite set of integrals, each of which is associated with a particular ray path. This method has also been referred to in the literature as the WKB method because a generalized WKB technique is used to solve the depth-dependent equation derived from the normal mode solution. Each normal mode can then be represented by corresponding rays (43). To date, this technique has not been extended to range-dependent environments.

Models categorized as ray models are summarized in Table 1 (a) together with references to available documentation.

TABLE 1
Summary of Propagation Loss Models

(a) Ray Models

Range-Independent	Range-Dependent
FACT (30, 31)	FACTEX (33)
FLIRT (25)	Four Segment Ray Tracing Model with Range Dependency (34, 35)
Moving Source Simulation (26-29)	GRASS (41, 42)
PLRAY (32)	MPP (37)
RAYMODE X (43)	RAYWAVE II (38, 39)
	SHALFACT (36)
	TRIMAIN (40)

(b) Wave Models

Range-Independent	Range-Dependent
FFP (56, 57)	ASERT (48)
Kutschale FFP (58)	ASTRAL (49, 50)
NLNM (44)	Kanabis Shallow Water (46, 47)
NORMOD 3 (45)	MOATL (51-53)
	PAREQ (59)
	PE (60)
	Corrected PE (61)
	SNAP (154)
	Three Dimensional Ocean Acoustics Model (55)

Wave Models

Wave models either expand the acoustic field integral in terms of a discrete set of normal modes or numerically integrate the wave equation.

Normal mode solutions assume that the solution to the Helmholtz equation is the product of a depth-dependent Green's function and a range-dependent Bessel function. The depth-dependent function is composed of trapped modes and continuous modes. Using Cauchy's residue theory, the trapped (or discrete) modes correspond to a sum of residues; the continuous mode spectrum is associated with a branch cut integral (44, 45). Extensions to range dependence are accomplished either by mode coupling (46, 47), which considers the energy scattered from a given mode into other modes, or by invoking the adiabatic assumption (48-55), which assumes that all energy in a given mode transfers to the corresponding mode in the new environment, provided that the environmental variations in range are gradual. One model (55) allows for cross-track variations as well.

Fast field theory separates the wave equation parameters according to the normal mode approach by a Hankel transform of the Helmholtz equation with respect to range. The resulting transform is then numerically evaluated using a Fast Fourier Transform (FFT) algorithm (56-58). This method requires that the sound speed vary exponentially with depth within each layer of the model. Models based on fast field theory do not allow for environmental range dependence.

The parabolic approximation method replaces the elliptic reduced wave equation with a parabolic equation under the assumption that the ray paths are almost horizontal. Solutions to the parabolic equation are commonly generated using the split-step algorithm (59-61). Some methods partially correct for the parabolic approximation (61). The computational advantage of the parabolic approximation lies in the fact that a parabolic differential equation can be marched in the range dimension; on the other hand, the elliptic reduced wave equation must be numerically solved in the entire range-depth region simultaneously (62). However, the implementation of the approximation is complicated by the fact that the solution at the starting range must be calculated by another method. All models reviewed here using the parabolic approximation allow for environmental range dependence. Models categorized as wave models are summarized in Table 1(b) together with references to available documentation.

One of the more pressing problems in the area of propagation loss modeling is the proper accounting of bottom interaction phenomena. Current approaches are leaning toward geophysical representations of the sea floor for the modeling of bottom reflection and refraction of sound.

Noise Models

For purposes of the present discussion, noise models can be segregated into separate but closely-related types: ambient noise models and beam-noise statistics models. Ambient noise models predict the mean levels sensed by an acoustical receiver when the noise sources include surface weather, biologics, and such commercial activities as shipping and oil drilling (63-67). Beam-noise statistics models predict the properties of low-frequency shipping noise. The latter models use either analytic (deductive) or simulation (inductive) techniques to arrive at statistical descriptions of the beam-noise. In this context, beam-noise is the convolution of the receiver beam pattern with the sum of the intensities from the various noise sources (4). The analytic models (68-73) calculate statistical properties directly from the components (e.g., source level, propagation loss); the simulation models (74, 75) use Monte Carlo or related techniques.

Noise models can be further differentiated by their treatment of the noise sources, the propagation loss, and the receiver response, as discussed below. Noise sources can be treated as either variable densities or as discrete sources.

Propagation loss can be computed internal to the noise model or input externally from other model predictions or from field data. Furthermore, the propagation loss must be specified either as range-averaged or as point-to-point to be consistent with the specification of the noise sources.

Receiver response determines the noise field directionality information required for application to either vertically or horizontally oriented receiver arrays. Models categorized as noise models are summarized in Table 2 together with references to available documentation.

TABLE 2

Summary of Noise Models

Ambient Noise	Beam-Noise Statistics
DANES (63, 64)	BBN Shipping Noise Model (68-71)
FANM I (65)	DSBN (74, 75)
Normal Mode Ambient Noise Model (66)	USI Array Noise Model (72)
RANDI (67)	Wagner Associates Noise Model (73)

Active Sonar/Reverberation Models

Reverberation models and active sonar models have been grouped together because it is extremely difficult to separate reverberation models from specific active sonar system applications. As mentioned earlier, active sonar models are composed of smaller modules: environmental models, propagation loss models, noise models, and reverberation models. In addition, active sonar models incorporate echo level models and signal processing models (76-88).

Reverberation models generally predict three different types of reverberation depending on the location of the scatterers (i.e., volume, surface, or bottom). The volume scattering can be treated as a layered function of depth or as an integrated column strength. The principal cause of volume reverberation in the ocean is the existence of migrating biological scatterers (19). Consequently, measurements of volume scattering strengths as a layered function of depth are not considered stable enough for many sonar applications; therefore, the integrated column strength formulation is generally used (83).

The reverberation models can be differentiated by their treatment of source/receiver geometries, back-scattering formulations, the method of computing reverberation ray paths (e.g., straight line or refracted), the number of reverberation ray paths examined, the manner in which the ensonified volume is divided (e.g., on the basis of time or range), Doppler gain, and computation of power spectra.

All active sonar/reverberation models reviewed here use specialized ray models to predict propagation loss. The multipath expansion technique is used in one case (79); all other models employ ray theory with corrections. One model (81) is based on a generic approach using a modular design to incorporate several candidates for each type of model. Models categorized as active sonar/reverberation models are summarized in Table 3 together with references to available documentation.

TABLE 3

Summary of Active Sonar/Reverberation Models

CONGRATS I, II, III, V [76-79]
DOP [80]
Generic Sonar Model [81]
LIRA [82]
LORA [83]
NISSM II [84]
RAIBAC [85]
REVGEN [86]
SONAR [87, 88]

In an effort to promote standardization, the Navy has recently established the Acoustic Model Evaluation Committee (AMEC). The specific charter of AMEC is to establish a management structure and administrative procedures for the evaluation of acoustic models of propagation loss, noise, and reverberation (90). Specific evaluation factors to be considered include model accuracy, running time, core storage, complexity of program execution, ease of implementation, ease of effecting slight program alterations, and available ancillary information (89).

Descriptions of other models not reviewed here, together with summaries of data available for model development and operation are reported in reference (93).

Supporting Data

A list of data banks to support acoustic models was compiled in reference (24). It was generated from the proceedings of the NORDA Environmental/Acoustic Data Bank Symposium held in Bay St. Louis, Missouri, U.S.A. 18-21 January 1977. The data are divided into three banks or collections.

a. *Primary Data Bank* categorized as Primary owing to their uniqueness in volume of data and/or types of data contained. Table 4 lists eleven Primary data banks and summarizes the data base parameters.

b. *Modified Data Banks,* listed in Table 5, are built on Primary data banks but the Primary data have been smoothed or interpolated to satisfy requirements for compactness and ease of handling.

c. *Data Collections.* The Environmental Data Base Directory (EDBD) of the National Oceanic and Atmospheric Administration (NOAA), Oceanographic Data Center (NODC) of the National Oceanic and Atmospheric Administration (NOAA) as a computerized inventory of environmental data bases located at federal, state and local government agencies, educational and research institutions and private industry in the U.S. and Canada. An interactive search of this inventory identified forty files describing marine acoustic data.

Model Evaluation and Validation

The large number of available acoustic models complicates the selection of the model most appropriate for specific user needs. The topic of acoustic model evaluation, therefore, is important in any review of acoustic modeling techniques (89, 90).

A severe limitation on the degree to which models can be evaluated and validated is the lack of environmental-acoustic data of sufficient spatial and temporal resolution with which to generate and compare model outputs, particularly the range-dependent versions. In the past this situation has encouraged the proliferation of model-to-model comparisons.

A methodology for comparing models against measured data developed by the Panel on Sonar System Models, or POSSM (91, 92), was applied to numerous propagation loss models. Among the many observations made by POSSM was the lack of documentation standards for acoustic models (89).

TABLE 4

Summary of Primary Data Banks

DATA BANK & CUSTODIAN	DATA BASE PARAMETERS		
National Oceanographic Data Center (NODC) Data Files NOAA, NODC	• Temperature • Marine Chemical Parameters	• Salinity • Marine Meteorological Parameters	• Surface Currents
National Geophysical & Solar-Terrestrial Data Center (NGSDC) Marine Geology and Geophysics Data Files NOAA, NGSC	• Airborne Magnetic Survey (Elements D,I,F) • Digital Hydrographic Survey • Seismic Profiles	• Marine Magnetic Survey (Total Intensity F Only) • Marine Gravity • Marine Bathymetry	• Megascopic Core Description, Marine Geological Sample Index, Grain-size Analysis
National Climatic Center (NCC) Marine Climatic Data Files NOAA, NCC	• Wind • Air Temperature • Total Clouds • Low Clouds	• Visibility • Dew Point Temperature • Waves	• Pressure • Sea Surface Temperature • Present Weather
Naval Oceanographic Office Data Files NAVOCEANO	• Temperature, Salinity Sound Velocity • Bathymetric Precise • Seismic Profile • Geomagnetics • Core Samples • Ambient Noise	• Surface Currents • Wave Climatology • Random Bathymetry (12 KHz) • Gravity • Bottom Loss, Propagation Loss	• Subsurface Currents • Sea Ice • Random Bathymetry (3.5 KHz) • Sediment Samples • Volume Reverberation
Navy Ocean Environmental Acoustic Data Bank (NAVDAB) NOSC	• Acoustic Propagation Loss	• Scattering and Reverberation	• Ambient Noise
DOD Bathymetric Data Library DMA HYDROGRAPHIC/ TOPOGRAPHIC CENTER	• Soundings	• Deep Scattering Layer (DSL) Depth	
Scripps Institution of Oceanography Sediment Data Bank SCRIPPS INSTITUTION	• Stations File • Manganese Nodule Analyses Files	• Sediment Analyses File • Sea Floor Photographic File	• Sediment Descriptions File • Source Reference Files
PME-124 Acoustic Data Files NAVELEX, PME-124	• Marine Environmental/ Acoustic Data		
Volume Scattering Strength Data Bank NORDA	• Volume Scattering Strength		
Long Range Acoustic Propagation Project (LRAPP) Data Bank NORDA	• Hydrocast Data • Shipping Density	• Sound Speed Profiles • Ambient Noise	• Bathymetry • Current Profiles

TABLE 4, Cont'd.

DATA BANK & CUSTODIAN	DATA BASE PARAMETERS

Fleet Numerical Weather Central
Data Files
FNWC

Marine Meteorological Data

- Ship Surface Observations
- Precipitation
- Sensible and Evaporative Heat Flux
- Total Heat Flux

- Marine Ship File
- Surface Marine Winds
- Solar Radiation

- Surface Pressure
- Surface Air Temperature
- Clouds

Oceanographic Data

- Digitized XBT
- Sea-Surface Temperature
- Primary Wave Period and Direction
- Wave Spectral Energy
- Water Temperature at 100, 200, 300, 400, 600, 800, 1000, and 1200 Ft.
- Insolation, Reflected Radiation
- Temperature 100 Ft. and 200 Ft. Below Primary Layer Depth
- Wave Direction, Period and Height

- Digitized MBT
- Current Stream Function
- Secondary Wave Period and Direction
- Primary Layer Depth
- Thermocline Gradient
- Sea-Surface Temperature Anomaly
- Ocean Fronts
- Temperature Differences Over 200 Ft. Thick Layers Between the Surface and 1200 Ft.
- Swell Direction, Period and Height

- Hydrocasts
- Current Transport
- Significant Wave Height
- White Caps
- Potential Mixed Layer Depth
- Temperature at Top of the Thermocline
- Latent and Sensible Heat, Total Heat Exchange
- Gradient 100 Ft. Above and Below Primary Layer Depth
- Combined Sea Height Direction and Period

TABLE 5
Summary of Modified Data Banks

DATA BANK & CUSTODIAN	DATA BASE PARAMETERS

Integrated Command ASW Prediction System (ICAPS) Water Mass History File
NAVOCEANO

- Temperature, Salinity and Sound Speed Profiles
- Water Depth and Bottom Provinces

Naval Underwater Systems Center (NUSC) Data Files
Used in Sonar In-Situ Mode Assessment System (SIMAS) and Optimum Mode Selection (OMS)
NUSC - NEW LONDON LAB

- Sound Speed Profiles
- Bottom Loss Provinces
- Wind Speed

- Salinity
- Biological Scattering Coefficients
- Water Depth

Synthetic Bathymetric Profiling System (SYNBAPS)
NORDA

- Bathymetric Soundings and Contours

Auto Ocean
NORDA

- Sound Velocity
- Bathymetry

- Wave Heights
- Shipping Density

Three-Dimensional Oceanographic Model Data Files
NAVOCEANO

- Temperature Model
- Sound Velocity Profile Model

- Salinity Model

REFERENCES

1. Keller, J.B., "Survey of Wave Propagation and Underwater Acoustics," *Wave Propagation and Underwater Acoustics,* Springer-Verlag, pp. 1-13 (1977).
2. DiNapoli, F.R. and Deavenport, R.L., "Computer Models of Underwater Acoustic Propagation," Nav. Underwater Syst. Ctr., Tech. Rept. 5867 (Jan. 1980).
3. Weston, D.E. and Rowlands, P.B., "Guided Acoustic Waves in the Ocean," Rep. Prog. Phys., *42,* pp. 347-387 (1979).
4. "Review of Models of Beam-Noise Statistics," Sci. Appl, Inc., SAI-78-696-WA (Nov. 1977).
5. Wilson, W.D., "Equation for the Speed of Sound in Sea Water," J. Acoust. Soc. Amer., *32* (10), p. 1357 (Oct. 1960).
6. Leroy, C.C., "Development of Simple Equations for Accurate and More Realistic Calculation of the Speed of Sound in Seawater," J. Acoust. Soc. Amer., *46* (1), pp. 216-226 (July 1969).
7. Frye, H.W. and Pugh, J.D., "A New Equation for the Speed of Sound in Seawater," J. Acoust. Soc. Amer., *50* (1), pp. 384-386 (July 1971).
8. Del Grosso, V.A., "New Equation for the Speed of Sound in Natural Waters (with Comparisons to Other Equations)," J. Acoust. soc. Amer., *56* (4), pp. 1084-1091 (Oct. 1974).
9. Medwin, H., "Speed of Sound in Water: A Simple Equation for Realistic Parameters," J. Acoust. Soc. Amer., *58* (6), pp. 1318-1319 (Dec. 1975).
10. Thorp, W.H., "Analytic Description of the Low-Frequency Attenuation Coefficient," J. Acoust. Soc. Amer., *42* (1), p. 270 (July 1967).
11. Schulkin, M. and Marsh, H.W., "Sound Absorption in Sea Water," J. Acoust. Soc. Amer., *34* (6), pp. 864-865 (June 1962).
12. Garrison, G.R., Early, E.W., and Wen, T., "Additional Sound Absorption Measurements in Near-Freezing Sea Water," J. Acoust. Soc. Amer., *59* (6), pp. 1278-1283 (June 1976).
13. Marsh, H.W., Jr. and Schulkin, M., "Report on the Status of Project AMOS (Acoustic Meteorological, and Oceanographic Survey), (1 January 1953-31 December 1954), Navy Underwater Sound Lab., Res. Rept. No. 255 (Mar. 1955).
14. Hall, H.R. and Watson, W.H., "An Empirical Bottom Reflection Loss Expression for Use in Sonar Range Prediction," Nav. Undersea Ctr., Tech. Note 10 (July 1967).
15. Chapman, R.P. and Harris, J.H., "Surface Backscattering Strengths Measured with Explosive Sound Sources," J. Accoust. Soc. Amer., *34* (10), pp. 1592-1597 (Oct. 1962).
16. Garrison, G.R., Murphy, S.R., and Potter, D.S., "Measurements of Backscattering of Underwater Sound from the Sea Surface," J. Acoust. Soc. Amer., *32* (1), pp. 104-111 (Jan. 1960).
17. Mackenzie, K.V., "Bottom Reverberation for 530- and 1030-cps Sound in Deep Water," J. Acoust. Soc. Amer., *33* (11), pp. 1498-1504 (Nov. 1961).
18. McKinney, C.M. and Anderson, C.D., "Measurements of Backscattering of Sound from the Ocean Bottom," J. Acoust. Soc. Amer., *36* (1), pp. 158-163 (Jan. 1964).
19. Love, R.H., "Predictions of Volume Scattering Strengths from Biological Trawl Data," J. Acoust. Soc. Amer., *57* (2), pp. 300-306 (Feb. 1975).
20. Wenz, G.M., "Acoustic Ambient Noise in the Ocean: Spectra and Sources," J. Acoust. Soc. Amer., *34* (12), pp. 1936-1955 (Dec. 1962).
21. Flatte, S.M., (Ed.), *Sound Transmission through a Fluctuating Ocean,* Cambridge Univ. Press (1979).
22. DeSanto, J.A., "Derivation of the Acoustic Wave Equation in the Presence of Gravitational and Rotational Effects," J. Acoust. Soc. Amer., *66* (3), pp. 827-830 (Sept. 1979).
23. Lee, D. and Papadakis, J.S., "Numerical Solutions of Underwater Acoustic Wave Propagation Problems," Nav. Underwater Syst. Ctr., Tech. Rept. 5929 (Feb. 1979).
24. Etter, P.C. and Flum, R.S., Sr., "An Overview of the State-of-the-Art in Naval Underwater Acoustic Modeling," J. Acoust. Soc. Amer., *65* S1), p. S42 (1979).
25. McGirr, R.W. and Hall, J.C., "FLIRT, A Fast Linear Intermediate-Range Transmission Loss Model," Nav. Undersea Ctr., Tech. Note 1282 (Jan. 1974).
26. Flanagan, R.P., Weinberg, N.L., and Clark, J.G., "Coherent Analysis of Ray Propagation with Moving Source and Fixed Receiver," J. Acoust. Soc. Amer., *56* (6), pp. 1673-1680 (Dec. 1974).
27. Clark, J.G., Flanagan, R.P., and Weinberg, N.L., "Multipath Acoustic Propagation with a Moving Source in a Bounded Deep Ocean Channel," J. Acoust. Soc. Amer., *60* (6), pp. 1274-1284 (Dec. 1976).
28. Flanagan, R.P. and Weinberg, N.L., "Effects of Source Motion on an Acoustic Signal in the Frequency, Time, and Space Domains," J. Acoust. Soc. Amer., *67* (5), pp. 1532-1544 (May 1980).
29. Flanagan, R.P. and Weinberg, N.L., "Effects of Source Micromotion on an Acoustic Signal in the Frequency, Time, and Space Domains," J. Acoust. Soc. Amer., *67* (5), pp. 1545-1552 (May 1980).

30. Spofford, C.W., "The FACT Model," Volume 1, Acoust. Environ. Support Detachment, Off. Nav. Res., Maury Ctr. Rept. 109 (Nov. 1974).

31. Baker, C.L. and Spofford, C.W., "The FACT Model," Volume II, Acoust., Environ. Support Detachment, Off. Nav. Res., Tech. Note TN-74-04 (Dec. 1974).

32. Bartberger, C.L., "PLRAY — A Ray Propagation Loss Program," Nav. Air. Dev. Ctr., Rept. No. NADC-77296-30 (Oct. 1978).

33. Garon, H.M., "FACTEX: FACT Extended to Range-Dependent Environments," Acoust. Environ. Support Detachment, Off. Nav. Res., Unpub. Rept. (Undated).

34. Weinberg, N.L. and Zabalgogeazcoa, X., "Coherent Ray Propagation through a Gulf Stream Ring," J. Acoust. Soc. Amer., 62 (4), pp. 888-894 (Oct. 1977).

35. Weinberg, N.L. and Dunderdale, T., "Shallow Water Ray Tracing with Nonlinear Velocity Profiles," J. Acoust. Soc. Amer., 52 (3), pp. 1000-1010 (Sept. 1972).

36. Garon, H.M., "SHALFACT: A Shallow Water Transmission Loss Model," Acoust Environ. Support Detachment, Off. Nav. Res., Unpub. Rept. (Jan. 1976).

37. Spofford, C.W., "The Bell Laboratories Multiple-Profile Ray-Tracing Program," Bell Telephone Labs. (1973).

38. Bucker, H.P., "Some Comments on Ray Theory with Examples from Current NUC Ray Trace Models," SACLANTCEN Conf. Proc. No. 5, Part I, pp. 32-36 (Dec. 1971).

39. Watson, W.H. and McGirr, R., "RAYWAVE II: A Propagation Loss Model for the Analysis of Complex Ocean Environments," Nav. Undersea Ctr., Tech. Note 1516 (apr. 1975).

40. Roberts, B.G., "Horizontal-Gradient Acoustical Ray-Trace Program TRIMAIN," Nav. Res. Lab., Rept. 7827 (Dec. 1974).

41. Cornyn, J.J., "GRASS: A Digital-Computer Ray-Tracing and Transmission-Loss-Prediction System. Volume I — Overall Description," Nav. Res. Lab., Rept. 7621 (Dec. 1973).

42. Cornyn, J.J., "GRASS: A Digital-Computer Ray-Tracing and Transmission-Loss-Prediction System. Volume II — User's Manual," Nav. Res. Lab., Rept. 7642 (Dec. 1973).

43. Yarger, D.F., "The User's Guide for the RAYMODE Porpagation Loss Program," Nav. Underwater Syst. Ctr., Tech. Memo No. 222-10-76 (Aug. 1976).

44. Gordon, D.F., "Underwater Sound Propagation-Loss Program. Computation by Normal Modes for Layered Oceans and Sediments," Nav. Ocean Syst. Ctr., Tech. Rept. 393 (May 1979).

45. Blatstein, I.M., "Comparisons of Normal Mode Theory, Ray Theory, and Modified Ray Theory for Arbitrary Sound Velocity Profiles Resulting in Convergence Zones," Nav. Ordnance Lab., NOLTR 74-95 (Aug. 1974).

46. Kanabis, W.G., "A Shallow Water Acoustic Model for an Ocean Stratified in Range and Depth," Volume I, Nav. Underwater Syst. Ctr., Tech. Rept. 4887-I (Mar. 1975).

47. Kanabis, W.G., "A Shallow Water Acoustic Model for an Ocean Stratified in Range and Depth," Volume II, Nav. Underwater Syst. Ctr., Tech. Rept. 4887-II (June 1976).

48. Lukas, I.J., Hess, C.A., and Osborne, K.R., "ASERT/ASEPS Version 4.1 FNOC User's Manual," Ocean Data Syst., Inc. (July 1980).

49. Spofford, C.W., "The ASTRAL Model Volume I: Technical Description," Sci. Appl., Inc., SAI-79-742-WA (Jan. 1979).

50. Blumen, L.S. and Spofford, C.W., "The ASTRAL Model Volume II: Software Implementation," Sci. Appl., Inc., SAI-79-743-WA (Jan. 1979).

51. Miller, J.F, and Ingenito, F., "Normal Mode FORTRAN Programs for Calculating Sound Propagation in the Ocean," Nav. Res. Lab., Memo. Rept. 3071 (June 1975).

52. Ingenito, F., Ferris, R.H., Kuperman, W.A., and Wolf, S.N., "Shallow Water Acoustics Summary Report (First Phase)," Nav. Res. Lab., Rept. 8179 (Mar. 1978).

53. Miller, J.F. and Wolf, S.N., "Modal Acoustic Transmission Loss (MOATL): A Transmission Loss Computer Program Using a Normal-Mode Model of the Acoustic Field in the Ocean," Nav. Res. Lab., Rept. 8429 (Aug. 1980).

54. Jensen, F.B. and Ferla, M.C., "SNAP: The SACLANTCEN Normal-Mode Acoustic Propagation Model," SACLANT ASW Res. Ctr., Memo SM-121 (Jan. 1979).

55. Weinberg, H. and Burridge, R., "Horizontal Ray Theory for Ocean Acoustics," J. Acoust. Soc. Amer., 55 (1), pp. 63-79 (Jan. 1974).

56. DiNapoli, F.R., "Fast Field Program for Multilayered Media," Nav. Underwater Syst. Ctr., Rept. No. 4103 (Aug. 1971).

57. DiNapoli, F.R., and Deavenport, R.L., "Theoretical and Numerical Green's Function Field Solution in a Plane Multilayered Medium," J. Acoust. Soc. Amer., 67 (1), pp. 92-105 (Jan. 1980).

58. Kutschale, H.W., "Rapid Computation by Wave Theory of Propagation Loss in the Arctic Ocean," Lamont-Doherty Geol. Obs., CU-8-73 (Mar. 1973).

59. Jensen, F. and Krol, H., "The Use of the Parabolic Equation Method in Sound Propagation Modelling," SAC-LANT ASW Res. Ctr., Memo SM-72 (Aug. 1975).

60. Brock, H.K., "The AESD Parabolic Equation Model," Nav. Ocean Res. and Dev. Activity, Tech. Note 12 (Jan. 1978).

61. Perkins, J.S. and Baer, R.N., "A Corrected Parabolic-Equation Program Package for Acoustic Propagation," Nav. Res. Lab., Memo. Rept. 3688 (Jan. 1978).

62. Tappert, F.D., "The Parabolic Approximation Method," *Wave Propagation and Underwater Acoustics,* Springer-Verlag, pp. 224-287 (1977).

63. Osborne, K.R., "DANES — A Directional Ambient Noise Prediction Model for FLENUMOCEANCEN," Ocean Data Syst., Inc. (Dec. 1979).

64. Lukas, I.J., Hess, C.A., and Osborne, K.R., "DANES/ASEPS Version 4.1 FNOC User's Manual," Ocean Data Syst., Inc. (July 1980).

65. Cavanagh, R.C., "Fast Ambient Noise Model I (FANM I)," Acoust. Environ. Support Detachment, Off. Nav. Res., Unpub. Rept. (May 1974).

66. Kuperman, W.A. and Ingenito, F., "Spatial Correlation of Surface Generated Noise in a Stratified Ocean," J. Acoust. Soc. Amer., *67* (6), pp. 1988-1996 (June 1980).

67. Wagstaff, R.A., "RANDI: Research Ambient Noise Directionality Model," Nav. Undersea Ctr., Tech. Pub. 349 (Apr. 1973).

68. Mahler, J.I., Sullivan, F.J.M., and Moll, M., "Statistical Methodology for the Estimation of Noise due to Shipping in Small Sectors and Narrow Bands," Bolt Beranek and Newman, Inc., Tech. Memo. No. W273 (June 1975).

69. Moll, M., Zeskind, R.M., and Sullivan, F.J.M., "Statistical Measures of Ambient Noise: Algorithms, Program, and Predictions," Bolt Barenek and Newman, Inc., Rept. 3390 (June 1977).

70. Moll, M., Zeskind, R.M., and Scott, W.L., "An Algorithm for Beam Noise Prediction," Bolt Beranek and Newman, Inc., Rept. No. 3653 (May 1979).

71. Zeskind, R.M. and Scott, W.L., "A Computer Program for Beam Noise Prediction," Bolt Beranek and Newman, Inc., Rept. No. 3654 (May 1979).

72. Jennette, R.L., Sander, E.L., and Pitts, L.E., "The USI Array Noise Model, Version I Documentation," Underwater Syst., Inc., USI-APL-R-8 (Mar. 1978).

73. McCabe, B.J., "Ambient Noise Effects in the Modeling of Detection by a Field of Sensors," Daniel H. Wagner Assoc. (Nov. 1976).

74. Cavanagh, R.C., "Acoustic Fluctuation Modeling and System Performance Estimation," Volume I, Sci. Appl., Inc., SAI-79-737-WA (Jan. 1978).

75. Cavanagh, R.C., "Acoustic Fluctuation Modeling and System Performance Estimation," Volume II, Sci. Appl., Inc., SAI-79-738-WA (Jan. 1978).

76. Weinberg, H. "CONGRATS I: Ray Plotting and Eigenray Generation," Navy Underwater Sound Lab., Rept. No. 1052 (Oct. 1969).

77. Cohen, J.S. and Einstein, L.T., "Continuous Gradient Ray Tracing System (CONGRATS) II: Eigenray Processing Programs," Navy Underwater Sound Lab., Rept. No. 1069 (Feb. 1970).

78. Cohen, J.S. and Weinberg, H., "Continuous Gradient Ray-Tracing System (CONGRATS) III: Boundary and Volume Reverberation," Nav. Underwater Syst. Ctr., Rept. No. 4071 (Apr. 1971).

79. Weinberg, H., "Application of Ray Theory to Acoustic Propagation in Horizontally Stratified Oceans," J. Acoust. Soc. Amer., *58* (1), pp. 97-109 (July 1975).

80. Marsh, P., "A Computer Program for Studying the Doppler Content of Reverberation," Nav. Sea Syst. Command, OD 52258 (1976).

81. Weinberg, H., "Generic Sonar Model," Nav. Underwater Syst. Ctr., Tech. Doc. 5971A (Feb. 1980).

82. Hoffman, D.W., "LIRA: A Model for Predicting the Performance of Low-Frequency Active-Sonar Systems for Intermediate Surveillance Ranges," Nav. Ocean Syst. Ctr., Tech. Doc. 259 (June 1979).

83. Hoffman, D.W., "LORA: A Model for Predicting the Performance of Long-Range Active Sonar Systems," Nav. Undersea Ctr., Tech. Pub. 541 (Dec. 1976).

84. Weinberg, H., "Navy Interim Surface Ship Model (NISSM) II," Nav. Underwater Syst. Ctr., Tech. Rept. 4527 (Nov. 1973).

85. Bachmann, W. and de Raigniac, B., "Calculation of Reverberation and Average Intensity of Broadband Acoustic Signals in the Ocean by Means of the RAIBAC Computer Model," J. Acoust. Soc. Amer., *59* (1), pp. 31-39 (Jan. 1976).

86. Princehouse, D.W., "REVGEN, A Real-Time Reverberation Generator," IEEE Int. Conf. Acoust. Speech Signal Process, pp. 827-835 (1977).

87. Marsh, P. and Poynter, A.B., "Digital Computer Programs for Analyzing Acoustic Search Performance in Refractive Waters," Volumes 1 and 2, Nav. Undersea Ctr., Tech. Pub. 164 (Dec. 1969).

88. Bertuccelli, H.C., "Digital Computer Programs for Analyzing Acoustic Search Performance in Refractive Waters," Volume 3, Nav. Undersea Ctr., Tech. Pub. 164 (Dec. 1975).

89. Lauer, R.B., "Acoustic Model Evaluation: Issues and Recommendations Incorporating the Experience of the Panel on Sonar System Models (POSSM)," Nav. Underwater Syst. Ctr., Tech. Rept. 6025 (Sept. 1979).

90. McGirr, R.W., "Acoustic Model Evaluation Procedures: A Review," Nav. Ocean Syst. Ctr., Tech. Doc. 287 (Sept. 1979).

91. Lauer, R.B. and Sussman, B., "A Methodology for the Comparison of Models for Sonar System Applications," Volume I, Nav. Sea Syst. Command, SEA 06H1/036-EVA/Most-10 (Dec. 1976).

92. Lauer, R.B. and Sussman, B., "A Methodology for the Comparison of Models for Sonar Systems Applications — Results for Low Frequency Propagation Loss in the Mediterranean Sea," Volume II, Nav. Sea Syst. Command, SEA 06H1/036-EVA/MOST-11 (Mar. 1979).

93. Etter, P.C. and Flum, R.S., Sr., "A Survey of Underwater Acoustic Models and Environmental-Acoustic Data Banks," ASW Syst. Proj. Off., ASWR-80-115 (Sept. 1980).

CHAPTER 4

THE VELOCITY OF SOUND IN THE SEA

Historical Introduction

As noted earlier, the velocity of sound — or, more properly, the *speed* of sound — was the subject of the earliest investigations of sound propagation. In the determination by Collodon & Sturm in Lake Geneva in 1827, mentioned before in Chapter 1, a bell was struck by a hammer underwater at the same instant that a light flash was produced in air. An observer in a boat 13.5 km. away determined the interval between the light flash and the arrival of the underwater signal to be 9.4 ± 0.2 seconds. Thus, the value of velocity obtained was 13,500/9.4 = 1440 meters/sec. at 8.1°C. This is doubtless a lucky result, for the modern value for distilled water at this temperature is 1439.2. A century later, Stephenson (1) found a velocity of 1453 m/sec over a distance of 15,500 meters, by measuring the arrival times of bomb explosions on a line of five hydrophones in Long Island Sound.

Complementing such direct field measurements during the period between World Wars I and II were various computations of velocity from Newton's equation using static measurements of the density of fresh and sea water at various pressures. Here may be mentioned the tables produced by Heck and Service (2), Mathews (3), and Kuwahara (4), the latter of which was regarded as the last word on the subject during the World War II years, and for some years thereafter.

Advances in electronics made possible precise measurements of sound speed in the laboratory by various kinds of *interferometers* and *pulse timing methods.* Here may be mentioned the work of Del Grosso (5), Wilson (6), McSkimmin (7), Holton (8) and Carnvale, et al. (9). Another electronic device is the *sound velocimeter*, which has been used at sea by Mackenzie (10) and Hays (11). Present values of the velocity of sound in the sea are accurate to perhaps 0.2%, and the quantity is the best known of all the variables on which the propagation of sound depends.

Newton's Equation

The sound speed — a *dynamic* quantity — can be derived from certain *static* measurements on fluids. As just mentioned, for many years this method gave the most accurate values of sound speed in sea water over a wide range of pressure, temperature and salinity. It is based on the following relationship, attributed to Newton:

$$c = \left(\rho \kappa \right)^{-\frac{1}{2}}$$

where c is the velocity of sound, ρ is the density, and κ is the adiabatic compressibility.[*] Since $\kappa = \frac{1}{v} \frac{\partial v}{\partial p}$ and $v = \frac{1}{\rho}$, where v is the specific volume (= volume of a unit mass), we can write the above expression as

$$c = v \left(\frac{\partial p}{\partial v} \gamma \right)^{\frac{1}{2}}$$

where the ratio of specific heats γ is the conversion factor from the measured isothermal quantity to the adiabatic values required in the Newton equation.

Methods of Measurement

Many methods have been used to measure the speed of sound in sea water. Table I is a summary of these methods, along with an example of their use in the literature.

The *static* laboratory method uses Newton's equation, together with values for the specific volume (v) or density (ρ) as a function of pressure in the laboratory. The tables of Kuwahara (4), for example, used values of the specific volume of water tabulated by Ekman in 1908; the tables of Heck and Service (2) used data by Bjerknes & Sanström published in 1910. Such tables are, of course, no better than the basic physical measurements on which they were based; modern-day velocity measurements show that the Kuwahara velocities, used for many years, are regularly too low by about 3 m/sec. The static method has been superceded by the various direct methods, although modern measurements (12) of the specific volume of sea water have been made for other purposes.

The *dynamic* methods (involving a moving sound wave or pulse) can be grouped into *laboratory* or *sea-going* methods. In the former category are various kinds of *interferometers*, which themselves are of two types.

---

[*]not the isothermal compressibility, since sound waves do not ordinarily allow time enough for appreciable heat flow between condensations and rarefactions.

Table I

Methods of Sound Speed Measurement

	Method	Example
LABORATORY		
STATIC		
	Newton's Formula	Kuwahara (4)
DYNAMIC		
	Interferometers	
	Variable path, Fixed Freq.	Del Grosso (5)
	Variable Freq, Fixed path	McSkimmin (7), Urick (13)
	Pulse Timing	Greenspan & Tsiegg (14), Newbauer & Dragonette (23), Wilson (15).
SEAGOING		
DYNAMIC		
	Velocimeters	Various commercial manufacturers
STATIC		
	Bathythermographs (BT)	
	Mechanical BT (Obsolete in U.S. Naval Usage)	
	Expendable BT (XBT)	
	Airborne BT (AN/SSQ-36)	

A *variable-path, fixed-frequency interferometer Fig. 1b* is one in which the frequency is held fixed and the acoustic path-length is varied so as to produce an interference pattern. In *Fig 1b*, a motion of the receiving hydrophone through one wavelength causes the output of a bridge circuit to change through one cycle, enabling the wavelength to be measured. In the interferometer used by DelGrosso (5), a reflecting plate was used instead of a receiver. In a *variable-frequency, fixed-path interferometer Fig 1a*, the frequency shift required to produce a one-cycle change in output is measured and the wavelength is computed. An interferometer of this kind was used by McSkimmin (7) for measurements on distilled water, while Urick (13) used one for velocity measurements at sea early in World War II. *Pulse timing* has been the favorite recent method for precise velocity determinations. In this method, the travel time of a short pulse through a known path length of the sample is measured. Pulse timing was employed by Wilson in accurate measurements of distilled (14) and sea (6) water, and is the basic principle of the *sing-around velocimeter,* first used by Greenspan and Tschiegg (15). Sing-around velocimeters are now made by various commercial manufacturers, and are used in research work for obtaining accurate sound speed profiles at sea. The sing-around principle is illustrated in *Fig 2*.

When the electronic complexity of the velocimeter prevents its use, various kinds of *bathythermographs* (BT's) may be employed to measure the principal variables on which sound speed depends: temperature and depth. Since salinity variations in the deep, open, ice-free sea are usually negligible, a curve of temperature vs. depth (a bathythermogram) is a faithful replica of the velocity profile in the open ocean, once it is adjusted to allow for the effect of depth.

Various kinds of BT's are in use on naval and research vessels. The *mechanical BT* was developed before World War II and was a non-electronic device lowered from, and retrieved by, a ship underway. It gave a trace of temperature vs. depth on a small smoked or gold-plated glass slide that was read on a special viewer. Its principal disadvantages were the difficulty of reading the trace and the necessity of recovering the instrument. The *expendable bathythermograph* (XBT) is a device for obtaining the temperature profile without having to retrieve the sensing unit. A cutaway view of an XBT is shown in *Fig 3*. It basically consists of a thermistor probe ejected from the moving vessel and allowed to sink at a known constant rate after launching. The probe is connected to measurement electronics on board the vessel by a fine wire contained on two reels, one remaining on board the ship underway, the other inside the streamlined probe. As the probe sinks at a fixed, known speed, both reels unwind simultaneously, leaving the wire at rest in the water with little or no tension placed upon it. The thermistor bead changes its resistance with changing temperature. On board the vessel a trace is obtained of resistance (or temperature) against time (or depth) by means of a special recorder. This system has almost completely replaced the older, retrievable mechanical bathythermograph on board U.S. naval vessels. A variant of the XBT has been developed for use from aircraft; it incorporates a radio link instead of a connecting wire, as with sonobuoys. The aircraft version is called the Airborne Bathythermograph AN/SSQ-36.

More traditionally, velocity can be computed from *Nansen casts* that provide water samples retrieved from a depth in the sea, on which temperature and salinity are measured.

Sound Velocity in Sea Water

Three independent variables determine the velocity of sound. These are

1. *temperature*
2. *salinity* (weight of dissolved solids in grams contained in 1 kilogram of sea water, expressed in parts per thousand (ppt or 0/00))
3. *pressure*.

However, the functional dependence of velocity on these quantities is complex. Various workers who have computed or measured velocity as a function of one or more of these parameters have published different empirical expressions for the dependence. For zero depth, some examples are

Kuwahara (4) (1939)
   $c = 1445.5 + 4.664T - .0554T^2 + 1.307 (S-35) + . . .$
Del Grosso (5) (1952)
   $c = 1448.6 + 4.6618T - .0523T^2 + 1.25 (S-35) + . . .$
Wilson (6) (1960)
   $c = 1449.2 + 4.623T - .0546T^2 + 1.391 (S-35) + . . .$

In these expressions, c is the velocity in meters per sec, T is the temperature in degrees C, and S is the salinity in parts per thousand. The + . . . means that higher order and cross-product terms follow, such as terms in T^3, $(S-35)^2$, $(S-35)T$, etc. The differences between various formulas are discussed by Mackenzie (16) and are less than about 3 meters/sec, or 0.3%.

The search for accurate empirical expressions for c as a function of temperature, salinity and depth is not at an end. A more recent example is an expression by Del Grosso (17) containing 19 terms, each with coefficients to 12

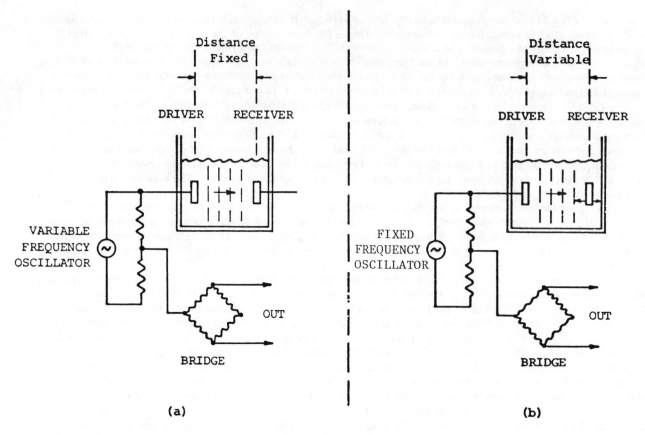

Fig. 1.   Two types of interferometers: a) variable-frequency, fixed-path; b) variable path fixed-frequency.

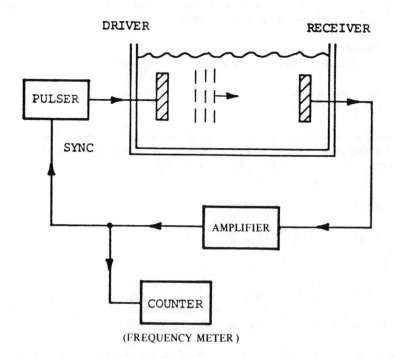

Fig. 2.   The sing-around principle

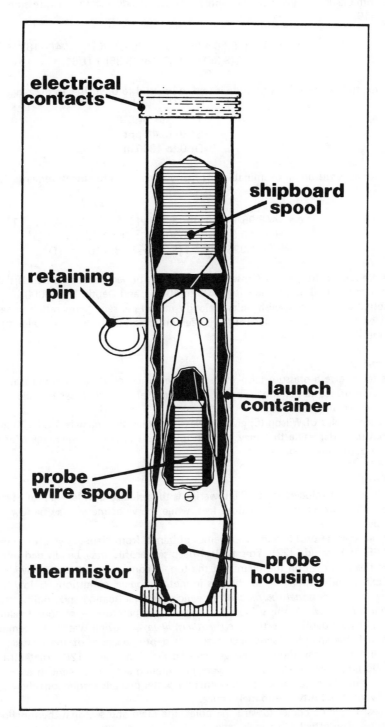

electrical contacts

shipboard spool

retaining pin

launch container

probe wire spool

probe housing

thermistor

Fig. 3.   Cutaway View of an XBT. A special launcher and an electronics — recorder unit complete the system.

significant figures. This deceptive accuracy is included for computer applications. Del Grosso (18) has published some tables based on his formula that may be useful when precise velocities are required and when computerization of a complex formula is not justified. For most practical needs a simpler expression is adequate, such as the one given by Leroy (19):

$$c(m/sec) = 1493.0 + 3(T-10) - .006(T-10)^2 - .04(T-18)^2 +$$
$$1.2(S-35) - .01(T-18)(S-35) + D/61.$$

where D is the depth in meters. This formula is said to be valid to 0.2 m/sec in the range

$$T: -2° \text{ to } 24.5°C.$$
$$S: 30 \text{ to } 42 \text{ ppt}$$
$$D: 0 \text{ to } 1000 \text{ m}$$

Another expression, based on an examination of many oceanographic measurements, has been given by Mackenzie (20):

$$c = 1448.96 + 4.591T - 5.304 \times 10^{-2} T^2 + 2.374 \times 10^{-4} T^3$$
$$+ 1.340(S-35) + 1.630 \times 10^{-2} D + 1.657 \times 10^{-7} D^2$$
$$- 1.025 \times 10^{-2} T(S-35) - 7.139 \times 10^{-13} TD^3$$

These 9 terms are said to fit the Del Grosso expression mentioned above to a standard deviation of 0.07 m/sec over the range: Temperature T: 0 to 30°; Salinity S: 30 to 40 ppt; and Depth D: 0-8000 m.

Tables of sound velocity in English units (velocity in feet per sec., temperature in degrees Fahrenheit, and depth in feet) converted from Wilson's tables (6) have been published (21). Curves of velocity against depth, with temperature as a parameter, are given in *Figure 4.*

Pressure Dependence

Kuwahara's tables give a pressure term that, expressed in terms of depth in the sea, amounts to + 0.0181 meters/sec per meter, or feet/second per foot. That is, the sound velocity *increases* by 1.81 feet per second in 100 feet, or by 1.81 meters per sec. in 100 meters.

The more recent tables of Wilson (6) give a lower value than this, namely + 0.0170 sec.$^{-1}$. This is a large percentage change from the older value that may have an important effect in long-range deep-sea propagation, such as to change the distance of convergence zones.

The Velocity Profile

The end-product of a velocimeter or BT lowering is the velocity profile — a plot of sound velocity vs. depth. The BT gives the profile down to several hundred feet, while the velocimeter may be lowered to as great a depth as the available cable permits.

Fig 4 shows an average profile and its extremes obtained from Nansen casts taken over a 9-year period at a location 15 miles SE of Bermuda (22). This typical deep-sea profile may be divided into a number of layers having different properties as shown on the figure. At the top, in contact with the air above, is the *diurnal layer* exhibiting day-night variability and responding to changes in meteorological conditions. Below it, down to a depth of a few hundred meters, lies the *seasonal thermocline* in which seasonal heating and cooling effects take place. Next comes the *main thermocline* in which the principal change of temperature — or sound velocity — in the water column occurs. At deep abyssal depths lies the *deep isothermal layer* having water at a temperature near 4°C; since this layer is isothermal, the sound velocity increases with depth. Because of the reversal of velocity gradient in the profile there is a depth of minimum sound velocity (in Fig. 5 it lies at 1200 meters) having a profound effect on long-range sound propagation. Not all the layers just mentioned are present in every profile; for example, in the Arctic, the upper three layers are absent and isothermal water prevails throughout the water column below a shallow surface layer of variable salinity due to melting ice.

Since the oceans become cooler toward the poles, the main and seasonal thermoclines become less pronounced in higher latitudes. The effect is to make the depth of the velocity minimum (or the "axis" of the Deep Sound Channel) more shallow with increasing latitude, so as to lie just under the ice in the Arctic. Examples of the effect of latitude in the South Pacific Ocean may be seen in *Fig 6.*

Charts giving the depth of minimum velocity and the minimum velocity itself in the Atlantic and Pacific Ocean have been published in the Journal of Geophysical Research (23) (24). The velocity profile in various areas of the North Atlantic Ocean, as determined mainly by reduction of oceanographic data, may be found in Refs. (25) and (26).

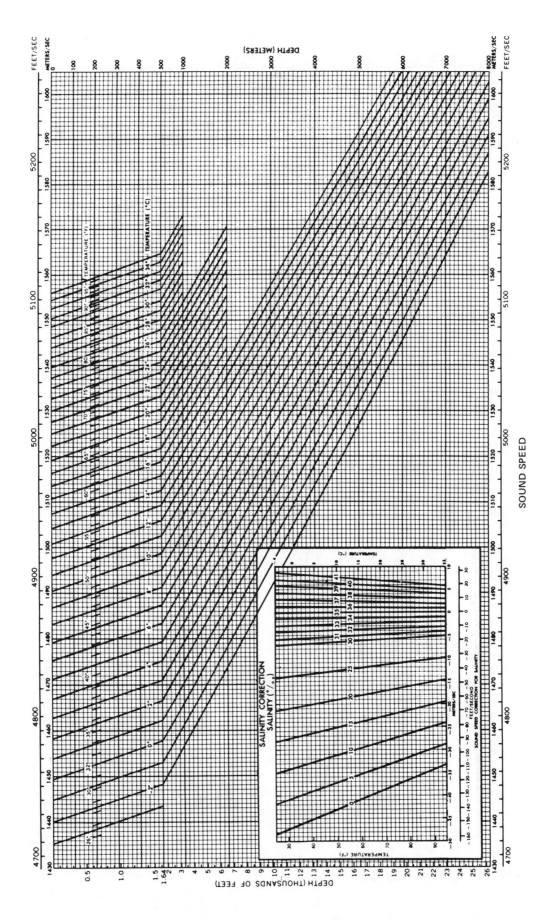

Fig. 4   Sound velocity vs. depth for different temperatures (30).

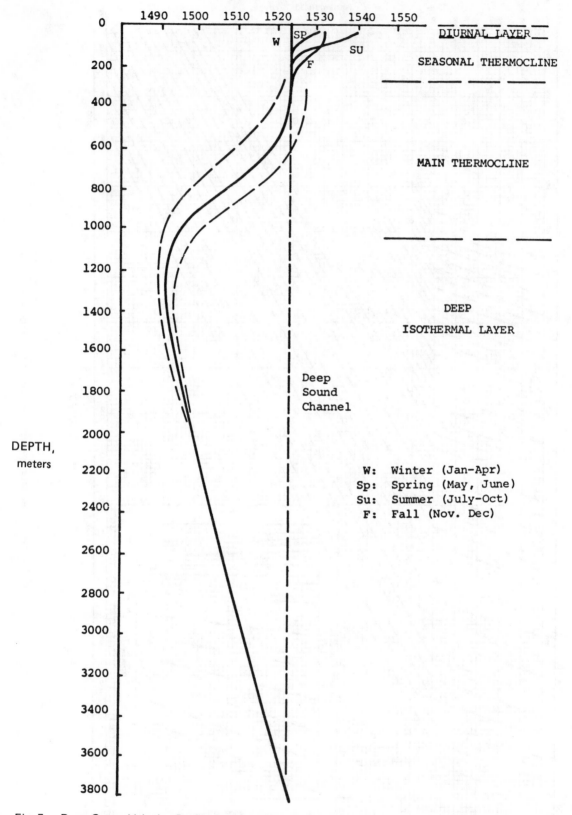

Fig. 5. Deep Ocean Velocity Profile Based on Nansen casts taken every two weeks over a 9 year period at a location 15 miles SE of Bermuda. (24).

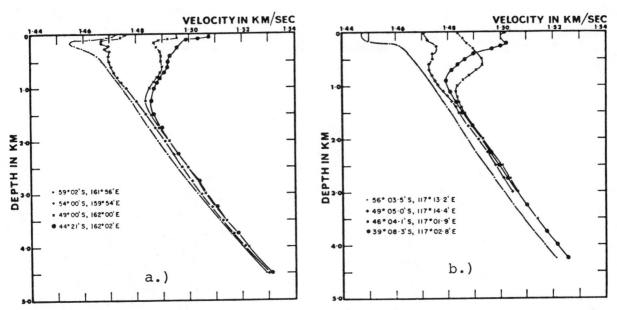

Fig. 6. Velocity profiles in different latitudes along two meridians in the South Pacific. a) 160°E, b) 117°E. Reference 31.

Ray Tracing

Once the velocity profile is known, the paths of sound rays in that profile can be found using various ray tracing techniques. The earliest of these was a slide rule (27) developed by the Woods Hole Oceanographic Institution during World War II. It used the same principle as that employed in some modern computer programs. The velocity profile is broken up into layers having a *linear gradient*, in which the rays are arcs of circles, as shown in the Appendix. In each layer, a circular arc is drawn of the appropriate radius of curvature. A ray is "traced" by starting it off at the source at a given angle and following it along from layer to layer. Alternatively, the profile may be broken up into *isovelocity* layers and Snell's Law used to trace the straight line segments of a ray from layer to layer. Once a pair of rays have been drawn using the basic ray postulate of ray theory that energy does not cross rays, the intensity I_r at range r of the pencil of rays can be computed from the vertical separation of the rays Δh, according to the expression (28)

$$I_r = \frac{I_o}{r} \cdot \frac{\triangle \theta}{\triangle h} \cdot \frac{v_s}{v_r}$$

where $\triangle\theta$ is the angular separation of the two rays in radians at the source and v_s/v_r is the ratio of the velocity at the source to that at the receiver. This simple formula is rigorous within the limitations of ray theory as long as $\Delta h \neq 0$, that is, away from caustics and foci. Every laboratory appears to have its own ray trace program embodying these principles in one form or another. When the profile can be assumed to approximate a suitable analytic mathematical form, the ray parameters (range, depth, travel time) may be expressed analytically. Some of these expressions are listed in Table I.

Need for Accurate Values

Accurate sound velocities are needed whenever a *travel time* in the sea has to be converted to a *distance*. This need arises in *fathometry* (which, as we have seen, was the original incentive to determinations of sea water velocity) and in *fire control*, where an accurate target range is needed from sonar data to launch a missile, such as a torpedo. A third application is in *missile impact location* by "Sound Fixing and Ranging" (SOFAR) triangulation, where the time of a signal axially travelling in the Deep Sound Channel is to be converted to a distance, where it serves to locate the point of impact.

Table I

Ray Parameters for Various Profile Functions

From Reference 29

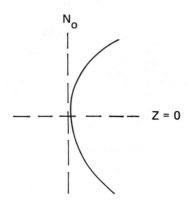

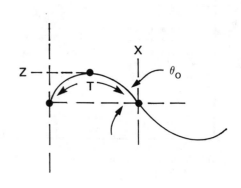

A = a functional parameter

Function	Axial Range X	Vertex Distance Z	Travel Time T
$v_z = v_o e^{AZ}$	$\dfrac{1}{A}\,(\pi - 2\theta_o)$	$\dfrac{1}{A}\,\log \operatorname{cosec}\theta_o$	$\dfrac{2 \cos \theta_o}{Av_o}$
$= v_o \cosh AZ$	π/A	$\dfrac{1}{A}\cosh^{-1}(\operatorname{cosec}\theta_o)$	$\pi/v_o A$
$= v_o\,(1+AZ)$	$\dfrac{2 \cot \theta_o}{A}$	$\dfrac{1}{A}\operatorname{cosec}\theta_o - 1$	$\dfrac{2}{Av_o}\,\log \cot(\theta_o/2)$
$= v_o\,(1-Z^2/A^2)$	$\pi A \sin\theta_o$	$A \cos\theta_o$	$\dfrac{\pi A}{2v_o}\,(1+\sin^2\theta_o)$

APPENDIX

A Short, Clever Proof of the Circularity of Rays in a Linear Gradient

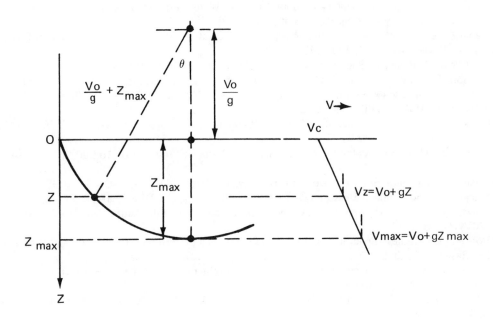

Referring to the figure, consider a medium in which the velocity varies with depth according to $v_z = v_o + gZ$, where $Z = o$ is selected arbitrarily. In this medium, consider a ray which becomes horizontal at a depth z_{max} where the velocity is v_{max}. Now, at any other depth Z where the velocity is v_z, this ray has a grazing angle θ given by

$$\cos \theta = \frac{V_o + gZ}{V_o + gZ\,max} = \left(\frac{V_o}{g} + Z \right) \Big/ \left(\frac{V_o}{g} + Z\,max \right)$$

An inspection of the figure will show that this relationship is satisfied only by a circle having its center at a distance v_o/g above $z = o$. This proof is given in L. L. Nettleton, *Geophysical Prospecting for Oil*, 1st Ed., McGraw Hill Book Co., 1940 pp. 257-8.

"V" and "Z" of this figure correspond to "**c**" and "**y**" of Figure 1 in Chapter 2.

REFERENCES

1. E. B. Stephenson, Velocity of Sound in Sea Water, Phys. Rev. *21*, 181, 1923.
2. N. H. Heck and J. H. Service, Velocity of Sound in Sea Water, USC&GS Special Publication 108, 1924.
3. D. J. Mathews, Tables of the Velocity of Sound in Pure Water and Sea Water for Use in Echo Sounding and Sound-Ranging, Admiralty Hydrographic Dept., 1939.
4. S. Kuwahara, Velocity of Sound in Sea Water and Calculation of the Velocity for use in Sonic Sounding, Hydrographic Review *16*, No. 2, 123 (1939).
5. V. A. Del Grosso, Velocity of Sound at Zero Depth, NRL Report 4002, 1952.
6. W. D. Wilson, Speed of Sound in Sea Water as a Function of Temperature, Pressure and Salinity, JASA *32*, 641, June 1960. See also extensions and revised formulas in JASA *32*, 1357, Oct 1960 and in JASA *32*, 1357, Oct 1960 and in JASA *34*, 866, June 1962.
7. H. J. McSkimmin, Velocity of Sound in Distilled Water for the Temperature Range 20°-75°C, JASA *37*, 325, 1965.
8. G. Holton et al, Ultrasonic Velocity Measurements in Water at Pressures of 10,000 kg/cm^2, JASA *43*, 102, 1968.
9. A. Carnvale et al, Absolute Sound Velocity Measurement in Distilled Water, JASA *44*, 1098, 1968.
10. K. V. Mackenzie, Sound Speed Measurements Using the Bathyscaph TRIESTE JASA *33*, 85, 1961.
11. E. E. Hays, Comparison of Directly Measured Sound Velocities with Values Calculated from Hydrographic Data, JASA *33*, 85, 1961.
12. W. Wilson and D. Bradley, Specific Volume of Sea Water as a Function of Temperature, Pressure and Salinity, Deep Sea Research *15*, 355, 1968.
13. R. J. Urick, An Acoustic Interferometer for the Measurement of Sound Velocity in the Ocean, U. S. Navy Radio and Sound Lab. (now NOSC) Report S-18, 1944.
14. W. D. Wilson, Speed of Sound in Distilled Water as a Function of Temperature and Pressure, JASA *31*, 1067, Aug 1959.
15. M. Greenspan and C. E. Tschiegg, Rev. Sci. Instr. *28*, 897, 1957; also JASA *31*, 1038, July 1959; also, Tables of the Speed of Sound in Water, JASA *31*, 75, Jan 1959.
16. K. V. Mackenzie, Formulas for the Computation of Sound Speed in Sea Water, JASA *32*, 100, Jan 1960.
17. V. A. Del Grosso, New Equations for the Speed of Sound in Natural Water, JASA *56*, 1084, 1974.
18. V. A. Del Grosso, Tables of the Speed of Sound in Open Ocean Water, JASA *53*, 1384, 1973.
19. C. C. McLeroy, Simple Equations for Accurate and More Realistic Calculation of the Speed of Sound in Sea Water, JASA *46*, 216, 1969.
20. K. V. Mackenzie, Effect of Sound Speed Equations on Critical Depths in the Ocean, JASA *62* (S1), S(19)A, 1977.
21. A. M. Lyons (Miss), Sea Water Sound Speeds Expressed in English Units, Naval Ordnance Lab Tech Rept. 63-168, 1963.
22. L. M. Jones & W. A. VonWinkle, Sound Velocity Profiles in an Area South of Bermuda, Underwater Sound Lab Rept. 632, 1965.
23. J. Northrop and J. G. Colborn, Sofar Channel Axial Sound Speed and Depth in the Atlantic Ocean, J. Geoph. Res. *79*, 5633, 1974.
24. R. Johnson and R. Norris, Geographic Variation of Sofar Speed and Axis Depth in the Pacific Ocean, J. Geoph. Res. *73*, 4695, 1968.
25. Oceanographic Atlas of the N. Atlantic Ocean, Part VI: Sound Velocity, USN Oceanographic Office Pub. No. 700, 1967.
26. "Velocity Profile Atlas of the N. Atlantic" (2 vols), USN Air Development Center, 1966.
27. Calculation of Sound Ray Paths Using the Refraction Slide Rule, Bur. of Ships, Navy Dept. May 1943.
28. R. J. Urick, *Principles of Underwater Sound*, McGraw Hill Book Co., New York, 2nd Ed. 1975, p. 120.
29. H. Kaufman, Velocity Functions in Seismic Prospecting, Geophysics, *18*, 289, 1953.
30. Handbook of Oceanographic Tables, USN Oceanographic Office Special Publ. 68, 1966.
31. R. N. Denham and A. C. Kibblewhite, Sound Velocity Structure etc., art. in *Antarctic Oceanology* II, *Antarctic Research Series*, *19*, Am. Geophysical Union, 1972, pp. 41.

CHAPTER 5

ATTENUATION AND ABSORPTION

Introduction

The various sources of loss of a sound wave may be grouped into two types: *spreading loss* and *attenuation loss*. *Spreading* includes focussing and defocussing effects and is depicted by the ray diagram. *Attenuation* includes the losses due to absorption, leakage out of ducts, scattering and diffraction. With one exception, these are all processes wherein the energy radiated by a sound source is *redistributed* in space and they are not shown in a ray diagram. The exception is *absorption*, which involves the conversion of the elastic energy of a sound wave into heat and results in a heating up of the medium in which it occurs.

Theory

In an absorptive medium, a certain fraction of the intensity of a sound wave is lost — converted to heat — in a given distance. If this fraction is dI/I then in the distance dx we can write for a plane wave

$$\frac{dI}{I} = -n dx$$

where n is a proportionality coefficient and the minus sign denotes a loss of intensity. On integration, we find that in travelling from x_1 to x_2 the intensity I_2 of the plane wave at x_2 is related to its intensity I_1 at x_1 by

$$I_2 = I_1 \exp\left[-n(x_2 - x_1)\right]$$

Taking logs to the base 10 and writing $10n \log_{10} e = \alpha$, we obtain

$$10 \log(I_2/I_1) = -\alpha(x_2 - x_1)$$

By custom in underwater sound, in order to avoid small values, α is expressed in db per kiloyard (1000 yds) in much of the literature. In metric units, as in the recent literature, α is expressed in db per kilometer. At very low frequencies where α in even these units is a small quantity, a better unit would be db per *megayard* or *megameter*. (One megayard is approximately 500 nautical miles).

In reading the physics literature it is necessary to be careful about whether α refers to *intensity* or *pressure*. Since pressure is proportional to the square-root of intensity in a plane wave, the pressure coefficient is one-half of the intensity coefficient. A detailed theoretical description of absorbtion is given in the Appendix to this chapter.

Historical Summary

The earliest work on α for sea water was done in 1935 by Stephenson (1) of NRL. Sea measurements at 30 kc gave a value of 6.5 db/ky, though much variability was found. Other measurements at sea were made just prior to and during World War II. During the post-war years a number of sources of attenuation have been discovered and many additional measurements of attenuation coefficient have been made, mostly at frequencies below 10 kHz. Measured values at lower frequencies throughout the years have always been higher than would have been expected by extrapolating higher frequency values downward, and have pointed to new and unsuspected attenuation-producing processes.

Our knowledge of the magnitude of the attenuation coefficient extends from about 20 Hz to 300 kHz in the open-ocean environment. No measured data exists outside this range in the natural deep-sea medium, although there are a number of laboratory measurements at frequencies beyond 60 kHz in fresh water and in simulated sea water.

Frequency Dependence

The dependence of α on frequency is complicated, indicating that in different frequency bands various different processes are involved. That is, different processes or mechanisms are dominant over others in different parts of the spectrum.

In Fig 1, the solid curve shows approximately the variation of α vs f for sea water over the range 1 Hz to 10 MHz. Over this large frequency range, it is convenient to divide the curve into four parts, in each of which it may be suspected, from the shape of the curve, that different processes operate. These will be discussed in reverse order, highest first.

Region IV

The classic sources of absorption in fluids are *heat conduction* and *viscosity*. *Heat conduction* creates a loss by a heat-flow from the compressed parts of a sound wave to the rarefactions; this contribution to the total absorption is negligibly small for water. *Viscosity* was shown by Rayleigh (2) to result in an amplitude absorption coefficient equal to $\dfrac{8\pi^2\mu}{3\lambda^2\rho c}$. The intensity coefficient is twice this, or $\dfrac{16\pi^2\mu}{3\rho c^3}\,f^2$, in units of cm^{-1} when cgs values are used. The theoretical basis of these results is given in the Appendix. On substituting values for fresh water and converting α to db/ky, we obtain

$$\alpha = 6.1 \times 10^{-5}\ f^2\ \text{(kHz)}\ ,\ \text{db/ky}$$

Thus, α is proportional to f^2 and amounts to 61 db/ky at 1 MHz. In Fig 1, this is the curve BB'.

However, subsequent measurements on distilled water did not agree with this theory. For example, Fox and Rock (3) in 1941, by measuring the pressure exerted on small beads and discs by a sound wave at different distances, found appreciably higher values. The measured coefficients were two to four times higher than would be predicted by classical theory and are shown by the line A-A^l in Fig 1.

This excess absorption has been accounted for by Hall (4) by postulating a two-state structure for water. The lower energy state is the normal state; the higher energy state is one where the molecules have a more closely packed structure. A compressional wave causes molecules to transfer from the more open state to the closely packed state; there is a *time-delay* involved in this process and its reverse, causing *dissipation* of acoustic energy. Liebermann (5) showed that this could be taken care of by postulating a volume *viscosity-coefficient* for water μ'. If $\mu' = 2\,\mu$, where μ is the ordinary *shear* viscosity coefficient, then the excess absorption is correctly accounted for. These two coefficients are included in the classical theory of viscosity; see Lamb (6). Hall (4) computed a time constant of 1.6×10^{-12} sec at 30°C for this *relaxation process*.

Region III

While the absorption of *pure water* can be explained in this way, an additional process is required for *sea water*. At frequencies between 5 kHz and 100 kHz, measurements of α in sea water, made during World War II, showed α to be about *30 times* its value in fresh water at the same frequency.

An explanation for this major discrepancy was soon found in terms of another relaxation process having a longer time constant or *relaxation time*. Generally speaking, in acoustic terms, a relaxation process is one in which some equilibrium condition is distributed by a passing sound wave, with a phase or time lag between the alternations of pressure and the "response" of the medium. At low frequencies, a near-equilibrium condition is maintained throughout the pressure cycle, resulting in small absorption; as the frequency increases, the process lags further behind, resulting in increased absorption; at frequencies well above the reciprocal of the relaxation time, the process is unable to "follow" the rapid variations and a constant value of α results.

The specific relaxation process invoked for sea water is *ionic relaxation* of one of its dissolved ionized salts. At first, it was thought that sodium chloride (NaCl), because it is the principal dissolved salt in sea water, was responsible (5); later measurements on NaCl solutions by Wilson and Leonard (7), however, showed *no* additional absorption. The culprit was eventually found to be magnesium sulphate (MgSO$_4$). Kurtze and Tamm (8) assumed the existence of MgSO$_4$·H$_2$O complexes which split up into ions of Mg, OH, H and SO$_4$ on the passage of a sound wave; the dissociation takes time, and thereby extracts energy from the sound wave. The relaxation time at 20°C is 1/130 kHz, i.e., 1/130,000 sec. The expression for α vs. frequency was given by Liebermann (5) as

$$\alpha = \frac{A\omega^2\theta}{1 + \omega^2\theta} + B\omega^2$$

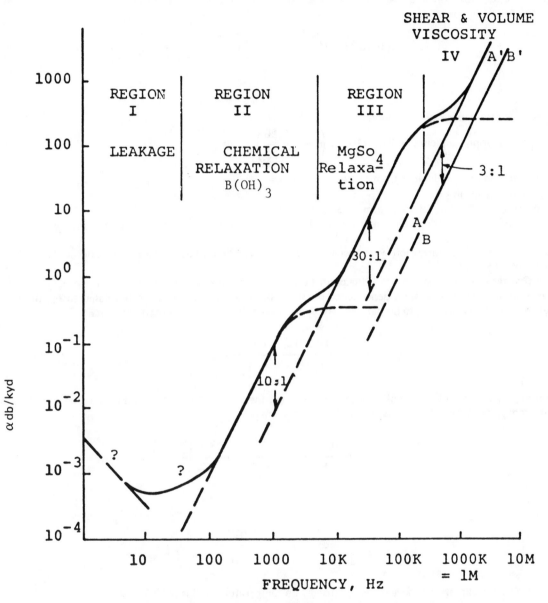

Fig. 1.   Regions of Different Dominant Processes of Attenuation of Sound in Sea Water.

where $\omega = 2\pi f$, $A = 2.9 \times 10^{-5}$ sec/cm, $B = 1.2 \times 10^{-17}$ sec^2/cm, θ = relaxation time $\approx 1.1 \times 10^{-6}$ sec. The units of α are cm^{-1}. A, B and θ are functions of temperature and pressure. The first term is the part of the coefficient due to ionic relaxation; the second is that due to viscosity.

Subsequently, Schulkin and Marsh (9) reviewed the theory and the literature on sea water absorption and presented the following formula:

$$\alpha = \left[\frac{2.34 \times 10^{-6}\, S f_T f^2}{f_T^2 + f^2} + \frac{3.38 \times 10^{-6}\, f^2}{f_T} \right] \cdot \left[1 - 6.54 \times 10^{-4}\, P \right]$$

where

S = salinity in parts per thousand

f_T = relaxation frequency $= 21.9 \times 10 \exp\left(6 - \frac{1520}{T+273} \right)$ kHz

T = temperature in degrees Centigrade
f = frequency in kHz
P = pressure in atmosphere (1 atm = 33 ft of water)
α = absorption coefficient in nepers/meter. To convert to db/ky, it is necessary to multiply by 7.943×10^3.

The coefficients in this expression were based on field data yielding 30,000 values for α between 2 and 25 kHz out to ranges of 24 kiloyards.

The first term in the first bracket is the contribution of the magnesium sulphate relaxation process; the second is that of viscosity, the temperature dependence of which turns out to be conveniently related to f_T, the relaxation process of MgSO$_4$. Converting to db per kiloyard and with S = 35 parts per thousand we obtain

$$\alpha = \frac{0.65 f^2 f_T}{f_T^2 + f^2} + \frac{0.027 f^2}{f_T} \quad \text{db/ky}$$

at zero depth. On inspection it will be seen that for $f \ll f_T$, the first, or MgSO$_4$, term is proportional to the square of the frequency, while when $f \gg f_T$ it is constant. Thus, for $f \ll f_T$

$$\alpha = \frac{0.65 f^2}{f_T} + \frac{0.027 f^2}{f_T} = \frac{0.677 f^2}{f_T}$$

while for $f \gg f_T$

$$\alpha = 0.65 f_T + \frac{0.027 f^2}{f_T} \quad .$$

f_T as given by the expression above depends strongly on temperature, and is plotted in *Fig 2.*

The effect of pressure is given by the second bracketed term. In 15,000 ft of water (P = 460 atm) this coefficient is

$$(1 - 6.54 \times 460 \times 10^{-4}) = .70$$

Thus, the absorption at 15,000 feet is only 70% of its near-surface value. This pressure effect is important for long range propagation via deep acoustic paths in the sea.

More recently, measurements by Bezdek (10) in the Pacific Ocean at 75 kHz over vertical and horizontal paths at depths of 700 and 3400 meters have shown the pressure coefficient to be about twice as great as thought previously, or to decrease by 4 percent per thousand feet of depth. The cause of this discrepancy has not been determined. If true, it means that the attenuation of high frequency sound over deep paths is significantly less than had been anticipated.

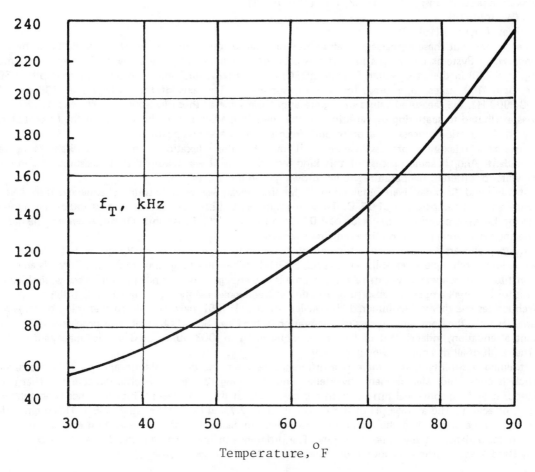

Fig. 2. Magnesium Sulphate Relaxation Frequency vs Temperature in Sea Water, according to the relation $f_T = 21.9 \times 10^{(6-x)}$; $x = 1520 \div (T + 273)$ given by Schulkin and Marsh (9).

Region II

At frequencies below 1 kHz, it was found by Thorp (11), on compiling measured data, that measured values of α were nearly an order of magnitude higher than the above formulas, when extrapolated downward in frequency, would predict. *Fig 3* is taken from this paper.

Various processes have been put forth to account for this excess attenuation. They have been:
- explosive transmission effects (Marsh) (12)
- diffraction out of the base of the DSC (Brown & Raff) (13)
- scattering by inhomogeneities (Urick) (14)
- eddy viscosity (Schulkin) (15)
- relaxation process, unspecified (Urick) (16) (Thorp) (17)
- fish (Weston) (18)
- particles (Duykers) (19).

In order to sort out these processes, an ambitious program of direct measurement was undertaken by the U.S. Navy Underwater Systems Center. As part of this program, measurements of α using TNT charges were made by Browning et al (20) in the Deep Sound Channel (DSC) of Lake Superior, which has a minimum depth of 500 feet over the path 100 miles long used for the measurements. The axis of the DSC was at 100 feet. In the range 700-8900 Hz, the measured values of α were about the same as those in sea water. The excess over expected values was attributed to scattering by variations in the thermal gradients near the surface of the Lake. Later, some yet unspecified relaxation process common to both fresh and sea water was postulated (21).

In a chemical relaxation process, whatever it may be, the relaxation frequency is likely to be temperature-dependent. And, if some process of this kind indeed exists, it was reasoned that measurements in different bodies of water of different temperature should throw light on the process.

With this in mind, field data were obtained in the Mediterranean Sea, where a sound channel exists in the summer season with an axial temperature of 13°C. These measurements (22) were interpreted as indicating a relaxation frequency of 1.7 kHz, compared to a value of 1.0 kHz in the cooler (4°C) Atlantic Ocean. However, the nature of a process having such a long relaxation time remained a mystery.

The mystery appears to have been dissipated by laboratory measurements of Yeager et al (23) who used the temperature-jump technique to establish boric acid, $B(OH_3)$, as having a long relaxation time. Boron is an extremely minor constituent of sea water; yet its relaxation-time is low enough and its concentration in sea water high enough to account for the small amount of absorption existing at frequencies below 1 kHz (less than 0.1 db per kyd).

At frequencies less than a few hundred Hz. Mellen, et al (24) (25), have postulated scattering by large-scale inhomogeneities to be the dominant process of attenuation in the Deep Sound Channel. This process is said to produce a constant attenuation, independent of frequency, amounting to .003 db/ky or 3 db per megayard in the open ocean. The result of all this may be seen in *Fig 4*.

An intriguing possibility is that there is a difference between the deep Atlantic and Pacific Oceans, as far as attenuation is concerned. Measurements by Mellen and Browning (26) in the Pacific indicate a smaller α than in the Atlantic, suggesting some real difference in the chemistry of the two oceans. This difference is postulated to be one of pH, or acidity. The average pH of the Pacific is about 7.7 and that of the Atlantic 8.1. This slight difference (the Pacific is more acidic than the Atlantic) is sufficient to cause the Pacific attenuation coefficient to be only half that in the Atlantic at the same frequency. The difference in the pressure dependence of the coefficient, reported by Bezdek and mentioned above, is doubtless the result of this same cause.

Region I

Here we enter the realm of speculation in seeking an explanation for the suggestion of higher values of α at frequencies of 20 Hz and below. Such observations are few in number. One explanation is that below 20 Hz, leakage occurs out of the Deep Sound Channel (within which the measurements must necessarily be made) because of the failure of such frequencies to be trapped in the Channel. A calculation (15) using a formula taken from the radio literature shows that the first mode fails to be trapped, or is just cut-off — at a frequency of a few cycles per second. The formula is

$$\lambda_{max} = \frac{16}{9} (2)^{1/2} \left(\frac{\Delta v}{v}\right)^{1/2} d$$

where λ_{max} is the maximum trapped wavelength, occurring at the cutoff frequency, d is the depth of the axis of the sound channel and $\Delta v/v$ is the proportional change in sound velocity or the "strength" of the channel. Using d = 3000 ft, $\Delta v/v = 100/5000 = .02$, we get $\lambda_{max} = 1066$ ft, corresponding to a frequency of 4.69 Hz.

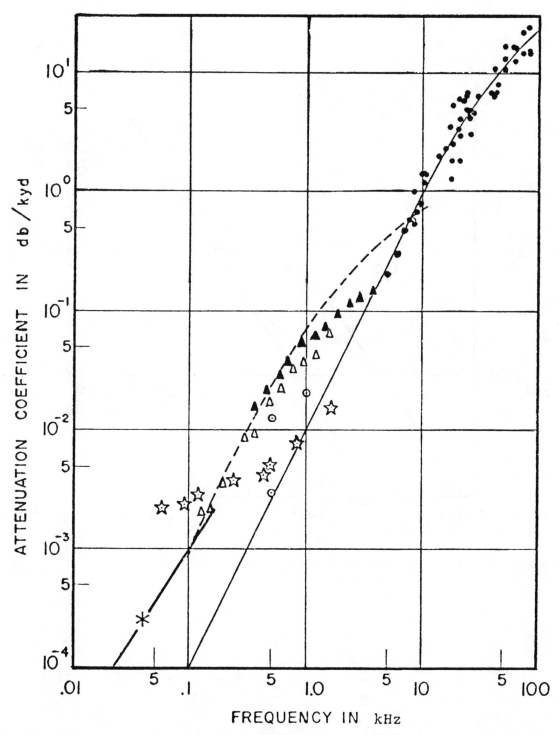

Fig. 3. Measured Coefficients vs Frequency as Compiled by Thorp (11). Symbols are at-sea data points taken from the literature.

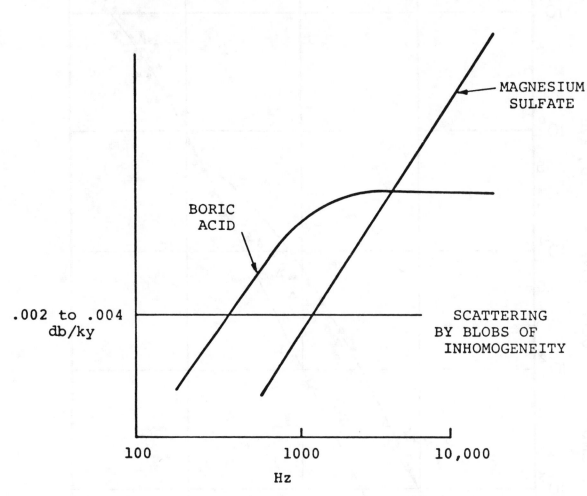

Fig. 4.   Diagrammatic View of the Attenuation Processes in the Region 100-10,000 Hz.

Methods of Measurement

The attenuation coefficient can be measured *at sea* or in *the laboratory* using samples of real or simulated sea water. The *at sea* measurements are made as a *transmission run*, where a receiver is held fixed and the source is varied in range, followed by rectification of the data (Chap 1) after playback in the laboratory. The slope of the rectified line is the desired attenuation coefficient. This is the only method suitable at frequencies below about 10 kHz, where the coefficients are so small that long distances are required for the measurement. In the *laboratory* an equivalent range-run, using pulses and a moveable source or receiver, can be made for attenuation determinations above a few hundred kilohertz, and even an acoustic interferometer can be used for the purpose at such frequencies. A number of investigators have used a nearly-spherical glass flask filled with water and excited by a pulse; the decay of a resonance of the spherical volume is proportional to the absorption coefficient of the fluid inside. This method was employed by Leonard and colleagues in their discovery of $MgSO_4$ as the cause of the excess attenuation in sea water at kilohertz frequencies.

Attenuation as a Function of Frequency, Temperature and Pressure

At various times over the years, various empirico-theoretical expresssions have been published for α in terms of the variables on which it depends. One of the most useful and easy to understand is the following

$$\alpha(db/ky) = 0.003 + \frac{0.1f^2}{1+f^2} + \frac{40f^2}{4100+f^2} + 0.000275f^2$$

The four terms are, in order, 1) a constant term due to large scale-scattering (mentioned above), 2) boric acid relaxation 3) magnesium sulphate relaxation 4) viscosity — another relaxation process having a very short integration time. There is no temperature or pressure dependence in this expression, and it is useful only as an approximation.

Based mostly on a review of laboratory measurements, Fisher and Simmons (27) have proposed the following expression for a constant salinity of 35 ppt and a pH equal to 8:

$$\alpha = A_1 \frac{f_1}{f_1^2+f^2} f^2 + A_2 P_2 \frac{f_2}{f_2^2+f^2} f^2 + A_3 P_3 f^2$$

where A_1, A_2, A_3, f_1, f_2 are complicated functions of temperature and P_2 and P_3 are functions of pressure. The three terms give the effects of boric acid, magnesium sulphate and viscosity, respectively. A pressure dependence factor for the boric acid relaxation (the term P_1) was not given, due to lack of data. *Fig 5* is a plot of this expression for zero depth, while *Fig 6* shows the effect of pressure for two depths (3000 and 6000 meters approximately) and at two temperatures (4° and 30°C) in terms of the ratio relative to the absorption coefficient at the surface. Finally, from this same paper *Fig 7* summarizes very well the frequency dependence of the three constituent causes of sea water absorption.

Schulkin and Marsh (28) have made a review of the available theory and data for the boric acid relaxation somewhat similar in scope to the earlier review of the magnesium sulphate effect made by these same authors many years earlier (9). The low frequency excess absorption due to the presence of boron in the sea (α_{BA}) was found to be

$$\alpha_{BA} = \frac{Qf_r f^2}{f_r^2+f^2} \times 10^3 \text{ nepers/meter}$$

where

$$Q \times 10^5 = 3.1 \times 10^{0.69(pH-6)} \text{ nepers/wavelength,}$$

$$f_r = 6.1(\frac{S}{35})^{\frac{1}{2}} 10^{(3-1051/T)} kHz$$

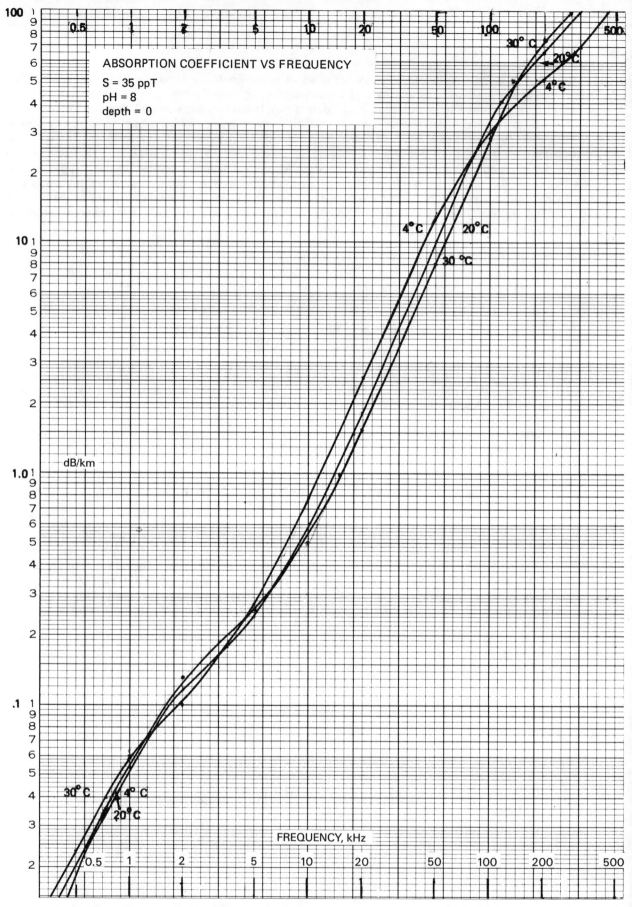

Fig. 5.   Absorption Coefficient vs. Frequency at Three Temperatures according to Formula Given by Fisher and Simmons (27) S = 35 ppT, pH - 8, depth zero.

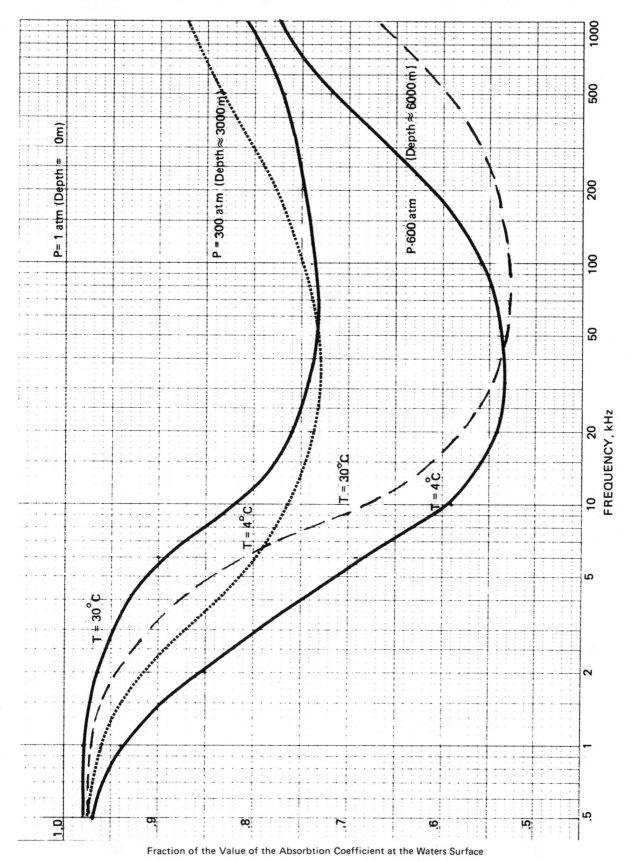

Fig. 6. Relative Effect of Pressure (Depth) on the Absorbtion Coefficient according to the Formulas of Fisher and Simons (27) for S = 35 ppt, pH = 8, and depth zero. There is no pressure dependence of the boric acid absorbtion.

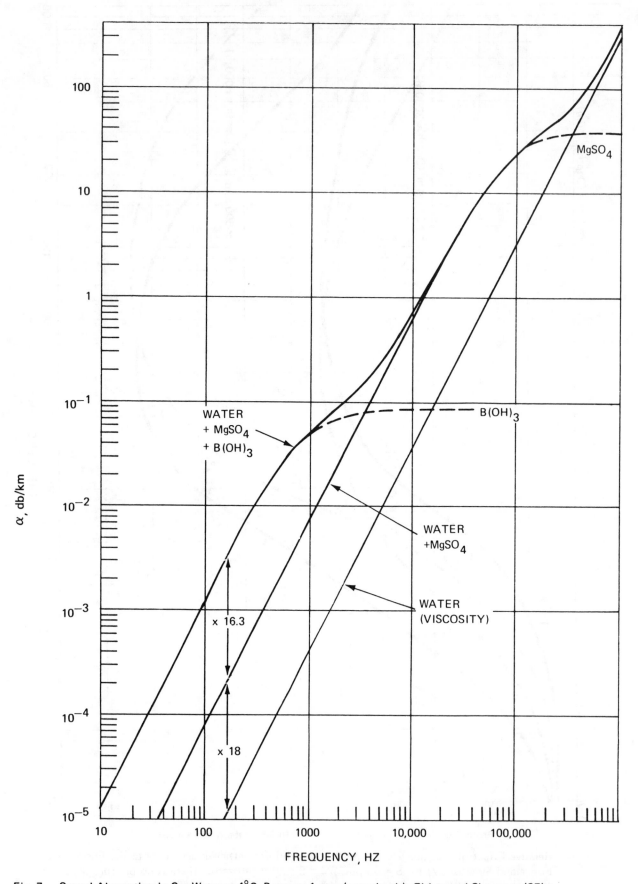

Fig. 7.   Sound Absorption in Sea Water at 4°C, Pressure 1 atm (zero depth). Fisher and Simmons (27).

This expression, said to fit existing laboratory and sea data very well, includes the effects of temperature, pH, and salinity, with pressure believed to have only a secondary effect. A somewhat more convenient functional description of the boric acid absorption has been provided by Mellen and Browning (29):

$$\alpha_{BA} = \frac{Af^2}{1+(f/f_r)^2} \ db/km$$

$$A = 0.11 \ 10^{[pH - 8]}$$

$$f_r = 10^{(T-4)/100}$$

where T is in degrees C and f is in kHz.

For a number of temperature and pH values, A and f_r are evaluated in the following table:

T($^\circ$C)	f_r(kHz)	A(pH = 7.6)	A(pH = 8.0)	A(pH = 8.2)
4	1	.044	.110	.174
10	1.15	.038	.096	.151
20	1.45	.030	.076	.104
30	1.82	.024	.060	.096

APPENDIX*

The equation of state for a *perfect* fluid is

$$p = ks$$

$$= \rho_0 c^2 s \qquad \qquad 1)$$

where k = the bulk modulus
       s = the condensation, or proportional change in density.

When viscosity is added, this equation is modified (Kinsler and Frey, p. 220) to

$$p = ks + \mu \frac{\partial s}{\partial t} \qquad \qquad 2)$$

This inclusion of viscosity, attributed to Stokes, adds an additional term to the wave equation which becomes for plane waves

$$\frac{\partial^2 p}{\partial t^2} = c^2_o \frac{\partial^2 p}{\partial x^2} + \frac{\mu}{\rho_o} \frac{\partial^2 p}{\partial x \partial t}$$

Here μ is an effective total viscosity coefficient. The viscosity term causes the pressure and condensation in a sinusoidal wave to have a phase difference. To show this, we may take $p = P_o e^{i\omega t}$ and assume $s = S e^{i\omega t}$, where S may be complex. Substitution in the Stokes equation yields a relation between S and P_o:

$$P_o = (k + i\omega\mu)S \qquad \qquad 3)$$

and the condensation *lags* the pressure by a phase angle equal to

$$\varphi = \tan^{-1} \frac{\omega\mu}{k} = \frac{\omega\mu}{k}, \varphi \ll 1$$

and the equivalent relaxation time is

$$\tau = \frac{\varphi}{\omega} = \frac{\mu}{k}, \varphi \ll 1$$

which means that the velocity of sound is reduced by viscosity. For water, this effect is extremely small. Comparing Equations 1) and 3) we note that

_____

 *   Drawn from pages 220-225 of Reference (30).

which means that the velocity of sound is reduced by viscosity. For water, this effect is extremely small. Comparing Equations 1) and 3) we note that

$$\rho_o c_o^2 = k + i\omega\mu = c^2 + i\omega\mu$$

$$\rho_o C^2 = \rho_o c_o^2 - i\omega\mu$$

$$c^2 = c_o^2 \left(1 - \frac{i\omega\mu}{\rho_o c_o^2} \right)$$

$$c = c_o \left(1 - \frac{1}{2} \frac{i\omega\mu}{\rho_o c_o^2} \right)$$

$$\frac{1}{c} = \frac{1}{c_o} \left(1 - \frac{1}{2} \frac{i\omega\mu}{\rho_o c_o^2} \right)^{-1}$$

$$= \frac{1}{c_o} \left(1 + \frac{1}{2} \frac{i\omega\mu}{\rho_o c_o^2} \right)$$

Introducing the above complex expression for c into the solution of the one-dimensional wave equation, we get

$$p = P_o e^{i\omega(t - x/c)} = P_o e^{i\omega[t - \frac{x}{c_o}(1 + \frac{1}{2}\frac{\omega\mu}{\rho_o c_o^2})]}$$

$$= P_o e^{-\frac{\omega^2}{2\rho_o c_o^3}} \cdot e^{i\omega(t - x/c_o)}$$

$$= P_o e^{-k x} e^{i\omega(t - x/c_o)}$$

where

$$k = \frac{\omega^2}{2\rho_o \omega_o^3} = \frac{2\pi^2 f^2 \mu}{\rho_o c_o^3}$$

Here μ includes all sources of viscosity. Going back to the basic hydropdynamic equations, it turns out that

$$\mu = \mu_L + 2\mu_s$$

where μ_L is a *longitudinal or volume viscosity* coefficient and μ_s the *ordinary shear* coefficient. Stokes assumed that the fluid shows no viscous effects under uniform compression, whence it follows in theory that $\mu = 4/3\ \mu_s$. Putting this in the expression for k, we find

$$k = \frac{8}{3} \frac{\pi^2 f^2}{\rho_o c_o^3} \mu_s$$

The intensity coefficient is twice this or

$$k = \frac{16}{3} \frac{\pi^2 f^2}{\rho_o c_o^3} \mu_s$$

where k is in units of cm^{-1} with CGS units. To convert to db/ky, it is necessary to multiply k by $(10 \log_{10} e)$ **times** (no. of cm. in one ky) = $4.34 \times 91.4 \times 10^3 = 4 \times 10^5$. On substituting $\mu_s = .01$ poise; $c_o = 1.5 \times 10^5$ cm/sec; $\rho_o = 1$, we find

$$\frac{k}{f^2} = 1.53 \times 10^{-16} \; cm^{-1} \; or$$

$$\frac{\alpha}{f^2} = 6.1 \times 10^{-11} \; db/ky$$

or at 1 mHz, $\alpha = 61$ db/kyd.

REFERENCES

1. E. B. Stephenson, Naval Research Lab Report S-1204, 1935.
2. Lord Rayleigh, *Theory of Sound*, vol. II, p. 316.
3. F. E. Fox and G. D. Rock, Ultrasonic Absorption in Water, JASA *12*, 505, 1941.
4. L. Hall, The Origin of Ultrasonic Absorption in Water, Phys. Rev. *73*, 775, 1948.
5. L. N. Liebermann, Origin of Sound Absorption in Water and in Sea Water, JASA *20*, 868, 1946; also, Sound Propagation in Chemically Active Media, Phys. Rev. *76*, 1520, 1949.
6. H. Lamb, *Hydrodynamics*, pp. 574-77, 1932.
7. O. B. Wilson and R. W. Leonard, Measurements of Sound Absorption in Aqueous Salt Solutions by a Resonator Method, JASA *26*, 223, 1954.
8. G. Kurtze and K. Tamm, Measurements of Sound Absorption in Water and in Aqueous Solutions of Electrolytes, Acustica *3*, 33, 1953.
9. M. Schulkin and H. Marsh, Absorption of Sound in Sea Water, J. Brit. I.R.E. *25*, 493, 1963; also, same title, JASA *34*, 864, 1962.
10. H. F. Bezdek, Pressure Dependence of Sound Attenuation in the Pacific Ocean, JASA *53*, 782, 1973.
11. W. H. Thorp, Deep Ocean Sound Attenuation in the Sub- and Low-Kilocycle Region, JASA *38,* 648, 1965.
12. H. Marsh, Attenuation of Explosive Sound in Sea Water, JASA *35*, 1837, 1963.
13. C. B. Brown and S. J. Raff, Theoretical Treatment of Low Frequency Sound Attenuation in the Deep Ocean, JASA *35*, 2007, 1963.
14. R. J. Urick, Low Frequency Sound Attenuation in the Deep Ocean, JASA *35*, 1413, 1963.
15. M. Schulkin, Eddy Viscosity as a Possible Acoustic Absorption Mechanism in the Ocean, JASA *35,* 263, 1963.
16. R. J. Urick, Long Range Deep Sea Attenuation Measurement, JASA *39*, 904, 1966.
17. W. H. Thorp, Analytic Description of the Low Frequency Attenuation Coefficient, JASA *42*, 270, 1967.
18. D. E. Weston, Fish as a Possible Cause of Low Frequency Attenuation in Deep Water, JASA *40*, 1558, 1966.
19. L. R. B. Duykers, Sound Attenuation in Liquid-Solid Mixtures, JASA *41*, 1330, 1967.
20. D. G. Browning and others, Project Hiawatha — Long Range Shallow Water Sound Propagation in Lake Superior, USL Memo 2211-173-68, June 1968. Abstract in JASA *44*, 381(A), 1968.
21. D. G. Browning and others, Attenuation of Low Frequency Sound in Fresh Water, Science, *162*, 1120, 1968.
22. E. N. Jones and others, Effect of Temperature on Low Frequency Sound Attenuation in Fresh and Salt Water, USL Memo 2213-435-68, Dec 1968. Abstract in JASA *45*, 306, 1969.
23. E. Yeager, et al, Origin of the Low Frequency Sound Absorption in Sea Water, JASA *53*, 1705, 1973.
24. R. H. Mellen, D. G. Browning and J. M. Ross, Attenuation in Randomly Inhomogeneous Sound Channels, JASA *56*, 80, 1974.
25. R. H. Mellen and others, Diffsuion Loss in a Stratified Sound Channel, JASA *60*, 1054, 1976.
26. R. H. Mellen and D. G. Browning, Variability of Low Frequency Sound Absorption in the Ocean: pH Dependence, JASA *61*, 704, 1977.
27. F. H. Fisher and V. P. Simmons, Sound Absorption in Sea Water, JASA *62*, 558, 1977.
28. M. Schulkin and H. W. Marsh, Low Frequency Sound Absorption in the Ocean, JASA *63*, 43, 1978.
29. R. H. Mellen and D. G. Browning, Attenuation in Surface Ducts, JASA (in press) 1978.
30. L. Kinsler and A. Frey, *Fundamentals of Acoustics,* J. Wiley and Sons, New York, 1962.

CHAPTER 6

THE SURFACE DUCT

Introduction

The surface duct occurs just below the sea surface whenever the processes of stirring by the wind and convection caused by surface cooling and evaporation produce a layer of quasi-isothermal water. Within this layer, called the *mixed-layer* by oceanographers and the *surface duct* by acousticians, sound is *trapped*, though sometimes poorly so because of losses at the boundaries. While the mixed layer has long been known to be an acoustic trap, the causes and magnitude of the losses within it have been of interest only since the post-World War II advent of long-range sonars. A literature summary of the nature and acoustics of the surface duct may be found in a doctoral thesis by Schulkin (1).

Occurrence

The mixed layer is a characteristic feature of the temperate, windy regions of the world's oceans. The thickness of the layer varies with the seasons; the median layer depth in the North Atlantic between latitudes 40°N & 50°N is 200 ft in the Winter (Jan-Mar), 90 ft in Spring (Apr-June), 70 ft in Summer (July-Sept) and 150 ft in Autumn (Oct-Dec). However, an appreciable fraction, perhaps 20%, of the BT's that are judged to have a mixed layer really do not qualify as having an acoustic surface duct because of the occurrence of a small negative gradient within the layer.

Processes of Formation

Two processes originating at the sea surface act to cause mixing of the upper water of the sea. One is the process of mixing by the *turbulent wind*, which transfers some of its energy to wave motion and thence to turbulence in the sea below. As the wind continues to blow, this turbulence extends to deeper and deeper depths. If a temperature gradient extends up to the surface and the wind rises, the heat of the upper part of the gradient layer, or *thermocline*, is carried downward by the wind-caused turbulence. If, in addition, heating from above occurs, and if a deep isothermal layer is present initially, a mixed layer of warmer water develops on top of the thermocline. This progressive development of the layer occurs in the spring and early summer, as illustrated in Fig. 1.

The other process of mixing is *cooling* at the top by (a) a lower air temperature and (b) evaporation, producing instability and convection; stirring now exists due to convection as well as to wind-caused turbulence. As the cooling takes place, the layer deepens. This occurs in the autumn (Fig 1).

On calm, sunny days, the near-surface waters heat-up and wind stirring is negligible. During the day a thermocline develops in the first tens of feet of water and the *Afternoon Effect* of surface-ship sonars occurs. During the night, cooling occurs and the near-surface thermocline disappears.

These processes often cause the base of the mixed layer to be sharp and well-developed. When a persistent wind has prevailed for a long time, field measurements show that layer is indeed well-mixed and is isothermal to within a few-hundredths of a degree centigrade.

When the layer lies on top of a strong thermocline, a sharp break in the BT occurs at the base of the mixed layer, producing an extremely strong gradient of temperature. At other times, under transitory conditions, the break at the base of the layer is ill-defined and the layer is often no longer strictly isothermal.

A well-developed mixed layer may be likened to the atmosphere below a deck of cumulus clouds on a warm summer afternoon.

Other characteristics of the layer affecting propagation are 1) the rough sea surface, 2) the presence of air bubbles just under the surface and 3) the occurrence of internal waves at the base of the layer. All of these act to scatter, absorb and diffract sound so as to destroy the effectiveness of the duct as an acoustic trap.

Conditions for Ducting

For a surface duct to exist, the negative temperature gradient within it (if — as is usual in the deep open sea — salinity gradients are negligible) must not exceed a certain value determined by the effect of pressure on sound velocity. In isothermal water, the pressure gradient of sound velocity amounts to .017 m/sec/m = .017 ft/sec/ft = .017 sec^{-1}, as mentioned in Chap. 4. The temperature gradient at 15°C that happens to produce this particular velocity gradient is 1°C in 180 m. If a negative gradient less than this should exist, a duct will be formed; if greater, ducting will be absent. When the negative gradient just happens to equal this value, an iso-velocity condition, with straight-line propagation paths, exists. The gradients associated with the surface duct are so small that a small change of gradient laterally, or over a period of time, can either produce or destroy the mixed-layer duct.

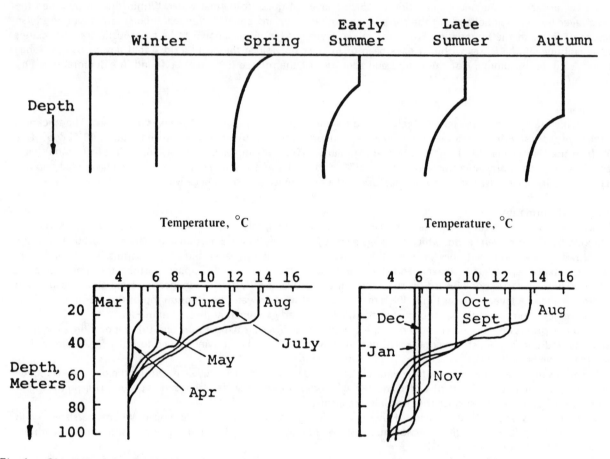

Fig. 1. Generalized Seasonal BT's and Monthly BT's at an open ocean location. From Ref. 1, quoted from another source.

Radio Ducts in the Atmosphere

There is a close analogy with the ground-base ducts of radio transmission in the atmosphere. These have been studied more extensively, and at an earlier date, than their underwater counterparts. For example, in a 1947 paper, Pekeris (2) applied normal mode theory to transmission measurements made by NRL in 1944, and determined the attenuation coefficients for the first and second modes responsible for long-distance propagation. The modern underwater analog of this kind of work is the elaborate theory of Pedersen and Gordon (3) published some twenty years later.

Ray Theory Model

The surface duct may be viewed as a half-channel with its sound channel axis at the surface and with an image half-channel above the surface. Ray theory is readily applied to such a channel.

Let there be a point source of sound in a duct with plane boundaries as shown in Fig. 2. At *short* ranges, *spherical spreading* (TL = 20 log r) must occur, while at *long* ranges, *cylindrical spreading* (TL = 10 log r) must occur. Let the two regions, equivalent to the *near-field* and the *far-field* of the source in the duct, be separated a range r_o; thus, there is spherical spreading out to r_o and cylindrical spreading from r_o to a range r. r_o is sometimes referred to as the *transition range* (between the two types of spreading). The transmission loss can therefore be written

$$TL = 20 \log r_o + 10 \log r/r_o$$

$$= 10 \log r_o + 10 \log r$$

In order to estimate r_o we invoke ray theory plus an assumption concerning the distribution of sound in the duct at ranges well beyond r_o. Assuming 1) that all of the sound radiated between angles $+ \theta$ and $- \theta$ stays within the duct and 2) that the intensity of sound is uniform throughout the duct at long ranges, it is easy to show (4) that for small θ,

$$r_o = \frac{H}{2 \sin \theta} \approx \frac{H}{2\theta}$$

where θ is the angle in radians with the horizontal at the source of the maximum trapped ray and H is the duct thickness. Leakage out of the duct is taken care of in this model by an attenuation coefficient α_L in addition to the ordinary volume absorption coefficient α. Adding leakage and absorption, we obtain for the average transmission loss in the duct

$$\boxed{TL = 10 \log r_o + 10 \log r + (\alpha_L + \alpha)\, r \times 10^{-3}}$$

where r_o and r are in yards and α_L and α are in db/ky. This is a general expression applicable to all sound channels.

Since θ decreases with increasing source depth, the average intensity in the duct should decrease with source depth, once the source gets below the depth at which the pressure-release effect of the surface is negligible (about $\lambda/4$). In a layer of depth H and source depth d_s, it follows from geometry that

$$\theta^2 = \frac{2\,(H-d_s)}{R}$$

where R is the radius of curvature of the rays in the linear gradient of the layer. Hence we have for the average intensity in the duct

$$\bar{I}_r = \frac{I_o}{rH} \cdot 2\theta = \frac{2I_o}{rH} \left[\frac{2(H-d_s)}{R} \right]^{\frac{1}{2}}$$

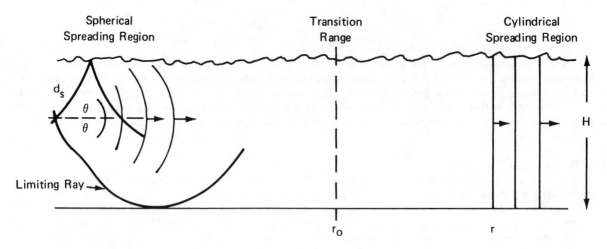

Fig. 2.   Conceptual Model for Duct Transmission. On the assumption of uniform intensity in the duct at a long range, it can be shown that $r_o = H/2\theta$.

where I_o is the source intensity at 1 yd. If now we assume symmetry in depth dependence between source and receiver, and normalize by reciprocity to obtain the same average intensity when sound and receiver and interchanged, it can be shown (5) that for a receiver depth d_r

$$\overline{I}_r = \frac{I_o}{r} \left[\frac{3}{H^{1/2}} \left(\frac{2}{R} \right)^{1/2} \left(1 - \frac{d_s}{H} \right)^{1/2} \left(1 - \frac{d_r}{H} \right)^{1/2} \right] = \frac{I_o}{rr_o}$$

where $1/r_o$, the reciprocal of the transition range, is the factor in the brackets. This shows that the intensity varies as $H^{-1/2}$, becoming greater as H becomes smaller for the same d_s/H and d_r/H. A thin duct is a better trap than a thick duct when leakage is negligible.

Wave Theory Models

On the other hand, wave theory is extremely complicated and has only been worked out exactly for a smooth non-scattering) surface. In one case, for transmission at 530 and 1030 Hz out to 10 kyds (6), as many as 40 modes for the bi-linear gradient case were summed on a computer and compared with ray theory summations. Ray theory was found to produce caustics and shadow zones where none existed in mode theory or in the observed data. At short ranges the accuracy of the mode approach was limited to the number of modes summed.

On the other hand, when mode theory is compared to field data such as the comprehensive Lockheed measurements (7), the results are poor, probably due to the neglect of the effects of the rough sea surface. This particular comparison was summarized in a short JASA paper by Eden and Nicols (8), but the agreement between mode theory and the field data is strikingly poor even though the authors claim success in their attempt to fit an elaborate theory to the real world.

Wave theory predicts that for any kind of ducted propagation there should be a *cut-off-frequency* below which the duct ceases to act as a trap. The wavelength then becomes too great to "fit" in the duct, and the attenuation becomes large. Near the cut-off frequency only a single mode is well-propagated. The relation between maximum trapped wavelength λ_{max} and duct thickness H was worked out long ago for the ground-base ducts of radio(9) (10) to be

$$H = 36 \, \lambda_{max}^{2/3}$$

where λ_{max} and H are in feet. For λ_{max} = 10 ft (500 Hz), H = 160 ft; for λ_{max} = 100 ft (50 Hz), H = 770 ft. Fig 3 is a plot of this expression.

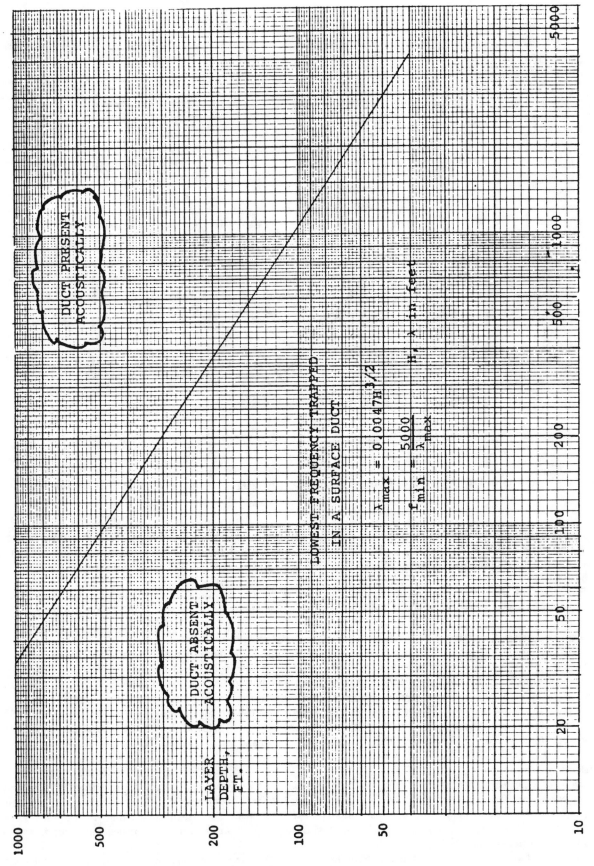

Fig. 3.   Lowest Frequency Trapped in a Duct of a Given Depth or Thickness.

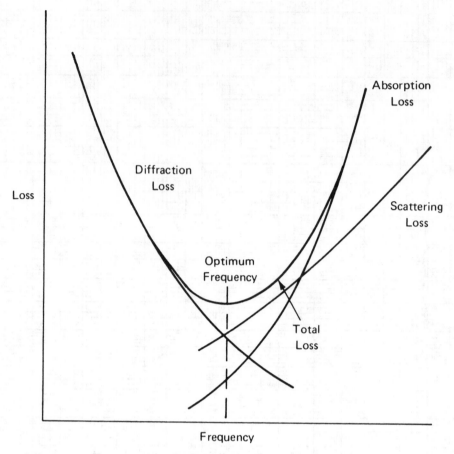

Fig. 4. Loss to a fixed range in a surface duct. The optimum frequency is that at which the total loss is a minimum.

The complete series of modes, and their attenuation coefficients, were worked out by Voorhis (11) for the case of a smooth sea surface. The results, however, are all but meaningless for the real sea whose roughness so greatly determines the propagation. A more elaborate theoretical treatment is given by Brekhovskikh (12), again for the smooth surface.

Ray diagrams show the presence of caustics and foci in the surface duct, similar to those in the Deep Sound Channel; these have not been observed in field data, probably because they are "washed out" by surface scattering.

Leakage by Surface Scattering

Schweitzer (13) has shown a way by which the scattering by elements of the rough surface can be added up intensity-wide to give the intensity below the layer. He used a scattering function given in a book by Beckman and Spizzichino (14), together with values of sea surface slope as a function of wind speed due to Cox and Munk (15). Agreement was found with certain measured data. The source of sound below the duct was believed to be those parts of the surface not far from the receiver in the direction toward the source.

In addition to roughness scattering, the sea surface sometimes has a layer of air bubbles beneath it that have been hypothesized (16) to contribute to duct losses by absorption and scattering.

Leakage by Diffraction

Even for a perfectly calm sea there will be some leakage due to diffraction, or "transverse diffusion" out of the lower boundary. This has been the subject of theoretical (17) and experimental (18) Russian papers. The latter employed artificial ducts in laboratory tanks with an un-ruffled surface. Yet it seems likely that when the sea is even slightly rough, the roughness must overwhelm the loss by diffraction so as to make it of negligible significance at relatively high frequencies.

The upshot of all of this is that there exists an optimum frequency for any duct, at which the total loss is a minimum, as illustrated diagramatically in Fig. 4. Above the optimum, a higher frequency results in higher losses due to absorption and leakage; below the optimum, the loss increases with decreasing frequency due to diffraction; low frequencies and long wavelengths can no longer "fit" into the duct.

Internal Waves

The lower surface of the mixed layer is characterized by the presence of *internal waves*. These are crenulations of the temperature structure, wherein a particular temperature occurs at different depths at different places; hence, a surface of constant temperature in the sea is wavy. These waves are not stationary but travel with a characteristic speed. In the Pacific, a common deep water internal wave pattern in the main thermocline shows wavelengths of about 12 miles with an amplitude of 50-100 feet, decreasing with depth.

A vast literature exists on the subject (19). Not too much is known of their acoustic effects. They are unlikely to have much effect on α_L unless the duct is thin, but would produce large fluctuations in the sound field below the duct.

A moving sonar, such as a minehunting set echo-ranging on a bottom mine, would experience echo fluctuations as the target passed in and out of shadow zones. Ray diagrams for such refractive effects have been drawn (20-21), and an acoustic variability in transmission said to be caused by internal waves has been reported (22). An exhaustive tank and theoretical study is available (23). Yet, while internal waves are fascinating to oceanographers, it is likely that their acoustic effects are limited to adding to the many sources of variability in the sea.

Magnitude of the Leakage Coefficient

Expressions for the leakage coefficient as a function of the three variables on which it depends — frequency, duct thickness, and surface roughness or sea state — have been published by several investigators through reduction of measured field data. The three extant expressions have different ranges of validity, and are not entirely concordant.

I. A leakage coefficient α_L^1 has been deduced by *Schulkin* (24) from extensive measurements made in the 1950's, to be

$$\alpha_L^1 = 1.64 \, (fh)^{1/2} \ \text{db/limiting ray cycle}$$

where f is in kHz, h is the mean wave height in feet, and α_L^1 is the loss in the distance of one bounce of the limiting ray of the duct. Calling this distance x_o, we have $x_o = \sqrt{8RH}$, and using R = 5000/.017 = 3 x 10^5 ft = 100 ky, we have $x_o = 0.52 \sqrt{h_{ft}}$ (x_o in kyds, H in ft) so that

$$\alpha_L = \frac{1.64 (fh)^{1/2}}{0.52 H^{1/2}} = 3.18 \left(\frac{fh}{H} \right)^{1/2} \text{db/ky}$$

where f is in kHz, h in feet, H in feet. This expression was said to be valid over the range 3<fh<70 kHz ft. Relating h to the sea state s by the expression h = $0.4s^2$ we get

$$\alpha_L = 2s \left(\frac{f}{H} \right)^{1/2} \text{db/ky}$$

II. A somewhat different empirical formula was obtained by *Saxton, Baker and Shear* (25) from NRL field data at 10 kHz. They fitted their data by the relationship $\alpha_L = 1200 \, (1.4)^s \, (RH)^{-1/2}$ db/ky, where the radius of ray curvature R and the layer depth H are in yards. If we take R = 10^5 yds and convert the layer depth to feet, we obtain

$$\alpha_L = 6.6 \, (1.4)^s \, H^{-1/2}$$

for a frequency of 10 kHz. While different in form from the Schulkin expression given above, the two expressions give substantially identical values for α_L (near 1.9 db/ky) at 10 kHz for a 100 ft layer in sea state 3.

III. A third empirical expression for the leakage coefficient has been published by *Baker* (26). Based on 4 sets of field data at 3.25, 3.5 and 7 kHz, for sea state 2 to 5, for layer depths 80 to 220 ft, source and receiver depths 30 to 60 ft., the expression is

$$\alpha_L = \frac{26.6f}{[(1452 + 3.5T)H]^{\frac{1}{2}}} \cdot (1.4)^S \text{ db/ky}$$

where f and H are in kHz and ft, respectively, and s is the sea state. T is the temperature in $^\circ$C (the term 3.5T is negligible for practical work). The formula is said to fit the data on which it is based to a mean error of 2 db and a standard deviation of 7 db.

Transmission Loss Prediction

For estimating the loss to be expected at a given range in a duct characterized by a surface roughness (such as the sea state) and thickness, the design engineer and performance predictor have available a number of models. All are based on field data and have restricted ranges of validity, but, unfortunately, are often discordant.

I. Model Expressions with Leakage Coefficient

This prediction model uses the simple near-field far-field expression given above, plus one of the above expressions for α_L:

$$TL = 10 \log r_0 + 10 \log r + (\alpha + \alpha_L) r \times 10^{-3}$$

where the transition range is

$$r_0 = \frac{(RH)^{\frac{1}{2}}}{2\sqrt{2}} \cdot (1 - d_s/H)^{-\frac{1}{2}} \cdot (1 - d_r/H)^{-\frac{1}{2}}$$

where   R = ray radius of curvature in yards $\approx 10^5$ yds
        H = layer depth, yards
        d_s = source depth, yards
        d_r = receiver depth, yards
        α = volume absorption coefficient, db per kiloyard. See Chap. 4
        α_L = leakage coefficient, db per kiloyard

II. AMOS Data

In the early 1950's the USN Underwater Sound Laboratory (now NUSC) and the USN Hydrographic Office (now NAVOCEANO) carried out a two-ship transmission survey at various frequencies between 2.5 to 25 kHz at many locations in the North Atlantic. The data were fitted to theoretico-empirical expressions by Marsh & Schulkin (27) that were subsequently evaluated and plotted for a number of frequencies and depth combinations by R.P. Delaney (28). The transmission loss values from this source for 2, 5, and 10 kHz are given as tables in the Appendix for a number of depth combinations.

III. TRW-Lockheed Data

In 1967, The Lockheed Company and the Navy Electronics Laboratory made an exhaustive series of transmission measurements using two ships. Pings at 7 different frequencies between 500 and 8000 Hz were received at 28 hydrophones on a string extending down to 1500 ft at ranges from 4 to 20 miles with layer depths 100-400 ft. The resulting data was analyzed and fitted (7) to the theory of Pedersen and Gordon (3).

A subsequent analysis of this same data was made by TRW, Inc., (29) in order to use it for predictive purposes. Surprisingly, no dependence in the data on any of the expected variables (frequency, layer depth, sea state) could be found. The loss in the range 10-30 kyds, for source and receiver near the surface, could be represented by a single curve equivalent to

$$TL = 20 \log r + 0.25r \times 10^{-3}$$

This expression is plotted in Fig. 5. The effect of source or receiver, depth is shown by the separate "correction" curve of Fig 6 along with curves for $\pm\delta$ and $\pm 2\delta$ relative to the average (AVE).

IV. Baker Expressions

W.F. Baker (26) in 1975 published expressions for the loss in a surface duct using essentially the model expression given above. The field data fitted by the expressions cover the frequency band 3.25 to 7.5 kHz, the ranges from 1 to 30 kyds and layer depths from 80 to 220 ft. These formulas are given in Appendix II.

V. Loss Below the Duct

Once a value for TL *in* the duct is obtained, the additional loss to a point in the shadow zone far *below* the duct (below about twice the layer depth) can be obtained from

$$TL = 28 - 2.5s$$

where TL is the excess loss to a below-duct receiver and s is the sea state. This expression was obtained by Roebuck (30) from theoretical arguments based on the sea surface scattering as the principal loss mechanism and supported by field data at frequencies between 3 and 10 kHz and at ranges from 2 to 20 kyds.

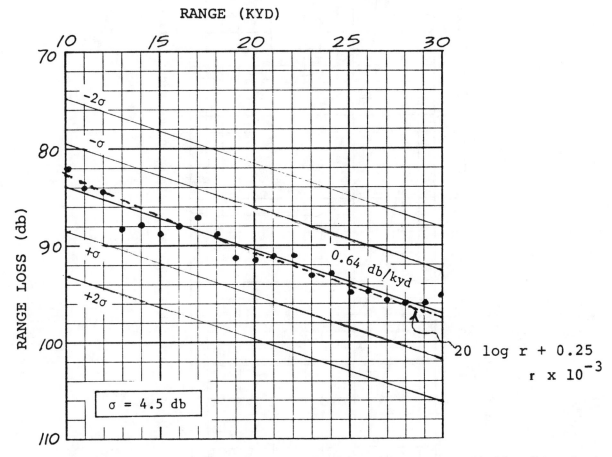

Fig. 5.   Loss vs. range in a surface duct as given in Ref. 7 based on an analysis of a field trial carried out by the Navy Electronics Laboratory.

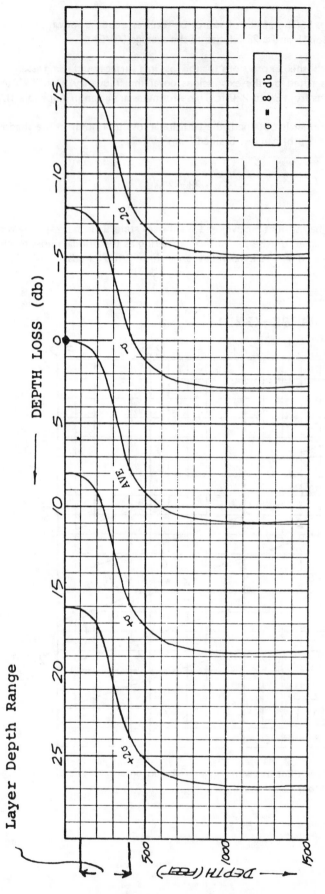

Fig. 6. Relative loss vs. depth curves from Ref. 7. "Depth loss" gives the loss in the duct for a fixed source depth and a variable receiver depth.

APPENDIX I

AMOS TRANSMISSION LOSS TABLES

The following three tables give the transmission loss at 2, 5, and 10 kc for a number of different layer depths and transducer combinations. The values were read from machine-computed plots obtained by R. P. Delaney in 1960 from the semi-empirical equations originally derived by Marsh and Schulkin (27) from the AMOS transmission data. The three tables are given for one transducer (the "source") at depths of 50, 250, and 900 feet; the other transducer (the "target") is located at depths of 50, 300 and 600 feet. Dashes indicate a loss too high to be read from the plots.

Some hesitancy should be felt in relying too heavily on these values for prediction purposes. Neither the sea state, nor the temperature gradient below the layer, appear as determining factors for the transmission loss. It has been found that the AMOS equations have a probable error of 5 to 10 db when used to predict actual losses. The values given should therefore be regarded as only rough guides to the loss that might be experienced in the field under the stated conditions.

50 FT. SOURCE

Layer Depth		50 ft. Target			300 ft. Target			600 ft. Target		
		5 ky	10 ky	20 ky	5 ky	10 ky	20 ky	5 ky	10 ky	20 ky
0'	2 kc	87	107	—	85	102	—	82	99	—
	5 kc	95	—	—	90	—	—	85	—	—
	10 kc	105	—	—	98	—	—	90	—	—
20'		90	107	—	86	103	—	81	100	—
		96	—	—	90	—	—	82	107	—
		106	—	—	99	—	—	91	—	—
50'		82	90	110	87	105	—	80	103	—
		85	95	—	88	—	—	81	110	—
		88	105	—	102	—	—	92	—	—
100'		77	85	95	84	100	—	78	100	—
		79	87	103	86	105	—	80	107	—
		82	95	—	94	—	—	88	—	—
150'		75	84	93	78	92	100	77	98	—
		76	86	99	81	96	108	79	105	—
		79	92	—	85	102	—	86	—	—
250'		74	83	90	76	86	95	77	93	107
		75	84	95	78	90	100	79	97	—
		78	89	—	81	95	110	84	105	—
400'		74	82	88	75	84	92	76	87	97
		75	83	93	76	88	96	79	90	101
		78	88	105	80	91	108	83	96	—

APPENDIX I, Contd.

250 FT SOURCE

Layer Depth		50 ft Target			300 ft. Target			600 ft. Target		
		5 ky	10 ky	20 ky	5 ky	10 ky	20 ky	5 ky	10 ky	20 ky
0'	2 kc	85	102	—	81	99	—	77	95	—
	5 kc	90	—	—	85	105	—	79	102	—
	10 kc	97	—	—	91	—	—	85	—	—
20'		86	104	—	78	99	—	77	95	—
		92	—	—	79	106	—	78	102	—
		99	—	—	81	—	—	82	—	—
50'		87	105	—	77	100	—	77	96	—
		94	—	—	78	107	—	79	104	—
		101	—	—	79	—	—	84	—	—
100'		83	100	—	76	101	—	75	97	—
		85	105	—	76	107	—	77	105	—
		89	—	—	79	—	—	81	—	—
150'		78	92	100	75	96	107	75	99	—
		80	94	107	76	100	—	77	105	—
		83	100	—	80	105	—	81	—	—
250'		77	87	94	75	90	97	75	95	106
		78	88	100	72	92	103	78	99	—
		81	94	—	82	97	—	81	105	—
400'		75	83	92	75	85	94	75	87	97
		76	85	96	78	87	97	77	88	101
		79	90	108	80	92	110	80	94	—

900 FT. SOURCE

Layer Depth		50 ft. Target			300 ft. Target			600 ft. Target		
		5 ky	10 ky	20 ky	5 ky	10 ky	20 ky	5 ky	10 ky	20 ky
0'	2 kc	80	97	—	75	91	—	74	90	—
	5 kc	82	106	—	77	98	—	75	95	—
	10 kc	86	—	—	80	106	—	78	102	—
20'		78	97	—	75	92	—	73	86	—
		81	105	—	76	100	—	74	90	—
		85	—	—	80	107	—	77	100	—
50'		77	97	—	75	93	—	73	85	—
		81	106	—	76	100	—	74	90	—
		86	—	—	80	—	—	75	99	—
100'		77	97	—	75	95	—	73	85	—
		81	105	—	76	105	—	74	90	—
		85	—	—	83	—	—	75	97	—
150'		76	96	—	75	95	—	72	85	—
		80	105	—	76	102	—	73	90	—
		85	—	—	83	—	—	75	97	—
250'		76	95	—	75	95	—	72	85	—
		78	100	—	77	100	—	73	90	—
		84	—	—	80	—	—	75	95	—
400'		76	90	105	75	88	105	73	84	106
		77	94	—	76	91	—	74	87	—
		83	102	—	79	97	—	77	93	—

APPENDIX II

DUCT EXPRESSIONS ACCORDING TO W. F. BAKER
(J.A.S.A. *57*, 1198, May 1975)

Prediction Formulas
Short Ranges:

$$r < 350H^{\frac{1}{2}} \text{ where } r, \text{ range in yards} \quad H, \text{ depth in feet}$$

$$
\begin{aligned}
TL &= 20 \log r + (\alpha + \alpha_L)\, r \times 10^{-3} \\
r &= \text{range in yds} \\
\alpha, \alpha_L &= \text{dB/ky.}
\end{aligned}
$$

Long Ranges:

$$TL = 10 \log r_o + 10 \log r + (\alpha + \alpha_L)\, r \times 10^{-3}$$

$$(r > 350H^{\frac{1}{2}}) \qquad r \text{ in yards, } H \text{ in feet}$$

$$10 \log r_o = 20.9 + 5 \log H$$

Leakage Coefficient

$$\alpha_L = \frac{26.6f}{[(1452 + 3.5t)H]^{\frac{1}{2}}} (1.4)^{ss} \text{ dB/kyd}$$

f in kHz, t in deg. centigrade, H in ft., ss sea state

Limits of Test Data

freqs   : 3.25-7.5 kHz
r   : 1-30 kyds
Layer depth : 80-220 ft
Source and receiver depth : 30-60 ft

REFERENCES

1. M. Schulkin, Propagation of Sound in Imperfect Ocean Surface Ducts, Underwater Sound Laboratory Rept. 1013, 1969.

2. C. L. Pekeris, "Wave Theoretical Interpretation of Propagation of 10 cm and 3 cm Waves in Low-Level Ocean Ducts" Proc IRE, Institute of Radio Engineers 35, 453, 1947.

3. M. A. Pederson and D. F. Gordon, A Normal Mode Approach to Underwater Sound Propagation, Naval Electronics Laboratory Rep 1407, Sept '66 (Conf.)

4. R. J. Urick, *Principles of Underwater Sound*, 2nd Ed. McGraw Hill Book Co., New York, 1975 p. 140

5. M. Schulkin, Propagation of Sound in Imperfect Ocean Surface Ducts, Underwater Sound Laboratory Rept 1013, 1969 p.

6. M. A. Pederson and D. F. Gordon, Normal Mode Theory Applied to Short-Range Propagation in an Underwater Acoustic Surface Duct, JASA 37, 105, 1965.

7. Normal Mode Propagation Study (5 vols), Lockheed Aircraft Corp. Report 20556, May 1967 (conf.)

8. H. F. Eden and J. Nicol, Acoustic Transmission in an Ocean Surface Duct, JASA 53, 819, 1973.

9. NDRC Summary Tech. Report, Committee on Propagation, Vol 1, 1947, p. 207.

10. D. E. Kerr (ed.) *Propagation of Short Radio Waves*, MIT Rad Lab Series 13, McGraw Hill, 1951.

11. A. Voorhis, Sound Transmission in the Surface Isothermal Channel, WHOI Ref 52-90, 1952.

12. L. N. Brekhovskikh, *Waves in Layered Media*, Academic Press, New York, 1960, Section 39.

13. B. J. Schweitzer, Sound Scattering into the Shadow Zone below an Isothermal Layer, JASA 44, 525, 1968.

14. P. Beckmann and A. Spizzichino, *Scattering of Electromagnetic Waves from Rough Surfaces*, Pergamon Press, New York, 1963, p. 89.

15. C. Cox and W. Munk, Measurement of the Roughness of the Sea Surface from Photographs of the Sun's Glitter, J. Opt. Soc. Am. 44, 838, 1954.

16. M. Schulkin, Surface Coupled Losses in Surface Sound Channel Propagation II, JASA 45, 1054, 1969.

17. L. M. Brekhovskikh and I. D. Ivanov, Concerning One Type of Attenuation of Waves Propagating in Inhomogeneously Stratified Media, Soviet Physics Acoustics 1, 23, 1955.

18. A. N. Barkatov, Measurement of Sound Attenuation in a Surface Isothermal Layer of Water, Soviet Physics Acoustics 1, 327, 1955; also, the Sound Field in a Medium with a Homogeneous Surface Layer, Soviet Physics Acoustics 4, 11, 1958.

19. Internal Waves, Bibliography, Report 4090265, 1965; also Internal Waves — Their Influence on Naval Operations, Arthur D. Little Inc. Report 4090266, 1966.

20. O. S. Lee, Effect of an Internal Wave on Sound in the Ocean, JASA 33, 677, 1961.

21. E. J. Katz, Effect of the Propagation of Internal Water Waves on Underwater Sound Transmission, JASA 42, 83, 1967.

22. O. S. Lee and W. F. Batzler, Internal Waves and Sound Pressure Level Changes, Proc. 1st Navy Symposium on Military Oceanography, June 1964.

23. P. Barakos, Acoustic Wave Scattering and Refraction by Internal Waves in a Model Tank, Underwater Sound Laboratory Rep. 905, 1968.

24. M. Schulkin, Surface Coupled Losses in Surface Sound Channels, JASA 44, 1152, 1968.

25. H. L. Saxton, H. Baker and N. Shear, 10-Kilocycle Long Range Search Sonar, Naval Research Laboratory Report 4515, 1955.

26. W. F. Baker, New Formula for Calculating Acoustic Propagation Loss in a Surface Duct, JASA 57, 1198, 1975.

27. H. W. Marsh and M. Schulkin, Report on the Status of Project AMOS, Underwater Sound Laboratory Research Rep 255, 1955.

28. R. P. Delaney, Glenn L. Martin Co. Report EL 11024, July, 1960.

29. Surface Channel Propagation Loss, TRW, Inc. Report 10555-6035-R7-00, 1968.

30. I. Roebuck, Propagation of Sound to Long Ranges in the Shadow Region Below Oceanic Surface Ducts Adm. Underwater Weapons Establishment Tech. Note 412/70, 1970 (unpublished)

CHAPTER 7

THE DEEP SOUND CHANNEL

Introduction

The Deep Sound Channel (DSC) is sometimes referred to as the *SOFAR*[*]channel from its earliest use in acousti-cally locating aviators downed at sea. It is now used for locating missiles instead of aviators, as part of the MILS (Missile Impact Location System) network for missile-impact location (1). Its existence has been well known since World War II, when the earliest investigations were made and a SOFAR net was established in the Pacific. In later years it has provided the necessary long range transmission paths for investigations of the attenuation coefficient in the sea at low frequencies. Today it remains the best natural non-radio channel for long distance communication, should such communication become necessary. However, as will be seen, the transmission distortion of the DSC, caused by multipath effects, is severe. Yet the sound from a small (1-2 lb.) explosion can be heard easily above background at distances of thousands of miles.

The DSC is caused by the fact that the deep sea is warm on top and cold below. The surface warming effect is not sufficient to extend all the way to the bottom and is limited to the upper part of the water column where it forms the main thermocline. Below it, the sea is nearly isothermal (near 40° F) and therefore has a positive velocity gradient (Fig. 5, Chap. 3).

Accordingly, a depth of minimum velocity exists, called the "axis" of the DSC, toward which sound rays are continuously bent by refraction.

In the DSC, the ray-path propagation is by a series of upward and downward arcs, alternately concave and convex, that are the result of the reversal of the velocity gradient at the axis. These ray paths are illustrated by the now classic ray diagram of *Fig 1*, drawn by hand (2) during World War II, showing the propagation from a source on the axis of the DSC, and, incidentally, showing a convergence zone at a range of 32 miles.

The upper and lower limits of the DSC are determined by the velocity profile and the water depth. Usually the near-surface region of the profile has the highest velocity. If the water depth is great enough, there is a depth below the axis where the velocity is the same as that at the surface. This depth is sometimes called the *critical depth* and forms the lower limit of the DSC. It is "critical" in that a receiver *below* it will *not* receive low-loss refracted sound from a distant shallow source, but instead only weak sound travelling via bottom reflected or RSR[**]paths. When the water depth is less than critical, a near-surface source similarly lies outside the DSC and cannot transmit to long ranges via low-loss ducted paths. These considerations are illustrated in *Fig 2*.

Transmission Loss in the DSC

The loss expression for surface ducts applies also for the DSC; namely

$$TL = 10 \log r_o + 10 \log r + (\alpha + \alpha_L)r \times 10^{-3}$$

where r_o is the transition range between spherical and cylindrical spreading, and α_L is the duct leakage coefficient. In the DSC, signal stretching caused by multipath propagation requires that TL be the energy-density transmission loss, in which all multipath contributions are added up, rather than the intensity transmission loss. Also, between a deep source and a deep receiver in the DSC, it is not (yet) possible to separate α and α_L; low-frequency attenuation coefficients (Chap. 4) measured in the DSC always tacitly assume $\alpha_L = 0$.

As mentioned in Chap. 1, r_o and α can be found from field measurements of TL by "rectifying" them by plotting (TL+10log r) against r, as described in Chapter 1 and illustrated by a published example in *Fig 3*. For the DSC, the rectified plot will be sensibly linear, with a slope equal to α and intercept equal to 10 log r_o. α depends only on relative measurements (it is a slope), but r_o involves all the system calibrations and its value is correspondingly uncertain in any series of experiments. For example, 10 log r_o was found (3) to lie between 32 and 36, depending on frequency band while another series of measurements (4), with another velocity profile, found values between 46 and 51. Additional measurements of 10 log r_o for the DSC are 35 db by Webb and Tucker (5) and 50 to 54 db by Sussman et al (6). The great disparity in the measurements of r_o stems not only from calibration uncer-tainties, but also from lateral variations of the velocity profile along the transmission path.

We should note here that TL as found by the above expression is the average TL over the width of the chan-nel at range r. Ray diagrams show that the DSC is full of foci, caustics and shadow zones, causing TL to change markedly with depth and range. We will consider these irregularities in dealing with convergence zones in the next chapter.

* Sound Fixing and Ranging   **Refracted-Surface-Reflected

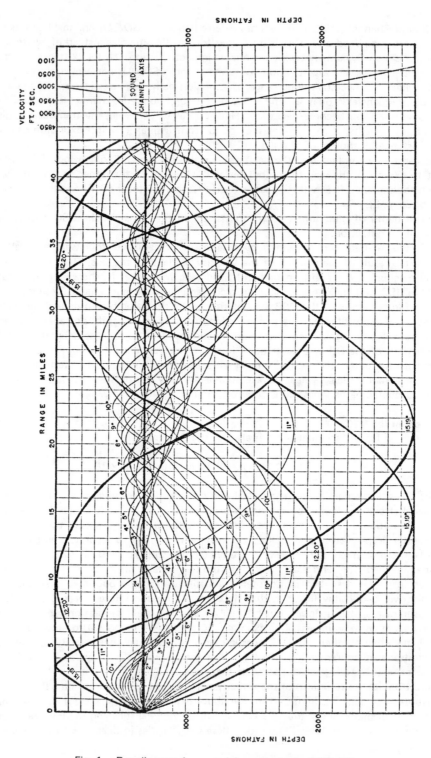

Fig. 1.　Ray diagram for an axial source in the DSC. **(2)**.

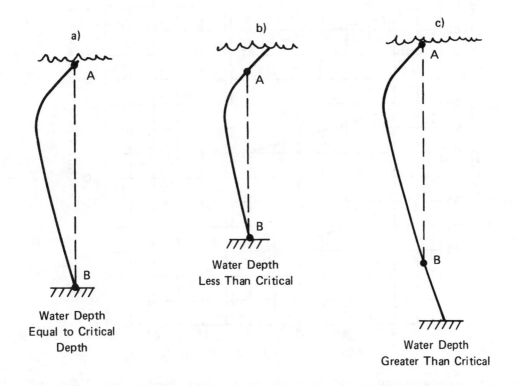

Fig. 2   Velocity profile and the critical depth. in a) the water depth equals the critical depth and the entire water column forms the DSC. In b) and c), sound sources shallower than A in b) and deeper than B in c) would lie beyond the DSC. Condition c) is required for the formation of a CZ (next chapter).

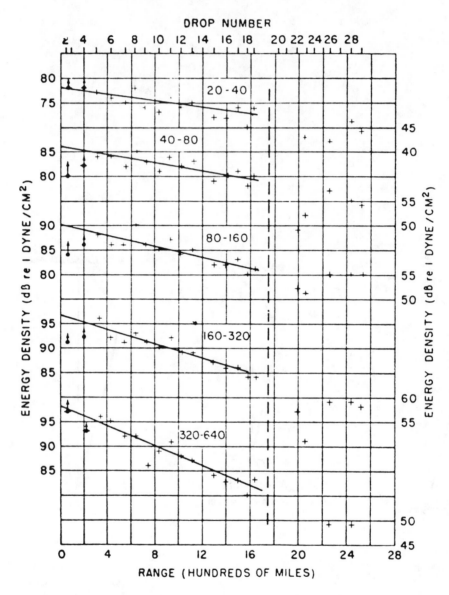

Fig. 3. Energy density levels plus 10 log r, in units of dB relative to the energy density of a 1-dyne/cm² plane wave for a period of 1 sec (dB re 1 dyne/cm²) in octave bands. The vertical dashed line shows location of Mid-Atlantic Ridge. Different level scales are used for the plots on each side of the ridge. (3).

Attenuation Coefficient

Most studies of the DSC have been done with explosive sources because of their high-level, broad frequency band and convenience of use. In analyzing field recorded data, the shot signals are filtered, squared and integrated before conversion to TL. The earliest determinations of attenuation coefficient were made long ago by Ewing and Worzel (2), who found values between 25 and 50 db per my (1my = 10^6 yds) at frequencies between 14 and 4000 cps; for example, one particular value was 49.8 db/my in the band 56-350 Hz. These are far too high by modern values which average only about 1 db/my in this range. Examples of some more modern measurements are those of Refs (3) (7) and (8).

Signal Envelope — On Axis

When both source and receiver are on the axis, the sound from a distant axial explosion in the DSC has a characteristic envelope. The received signal is a long, drawn-out blob of triangular envelope that rises gradually out of noise, reaches a peak, and then suddenly ceases.

In the SOFAR method of aviation rescue, aviators downed at sea were supposed to launch an explosive sound signal detonating on the axis of the DSC that was received by widely separated shore stations. Using triangulations based on the instant of cessation of the received signals, the position of the source could be found to within a few miles. In MILS, where the approximate point of impact is known beforehand and the horizontal velocity to various receiving stations can be determined, better accuracies can be obtained.

The *front end* of an axial signal is caused by ray arrivals leaving the source at high angles, extending up and down near to the limits of the channel, and taking a relatively small number of path oscillations about the axis. The *rear end* represents energy travelling near the axis of the channel and making many, though small, oscillations about the axis. The density of ray arrivals (number of arrivals per unit time) increases with time during the signal duration and becomes infinite at the instant of peak intensity. The axial ray itself is a caustic and has, in ray theory, an infinite intensity. Individual ray arrivals can sometimes be identified near the beginning of an axis-axis signal (if the S/N is large), but the tail always has a smooth build-up caused by the high density of ray arrivals. A series of signal envelopes from an axis source to an axial receiver at different ranges between Bermuda and the Azores may be seen in *Fig 4*. Note the increasing signal duration with increasing range.

It can be shown theoretically (8) that the time duration of the axial signal in a bi-linear channel is related to the angle of the limiting ray of the channel according to

$$D = \frac{r\theta^2 L}{6C_o}$$

where D is the signal duration at range r, θ_L is the inclination of the limiting ray trapped in the channel, and C_o is the axial velocity. Taking, as an example, θ_L = 1/5 radian (a typical value) and C_o = 1490 m/sec. (1/C_o = 1240 sec/kilomile), the rate of increase of duration with range (= D/r) becomes 1240/(6x25) = 8.3 seconds per kilomile. In rough confirmation of the theory, a value of 10 sec/kilomile was found in the Atlantic (2) between Eleuthera and Bermuda and 9.4 sec/kilomile was measured (3) between Bermuda and the Azores; in the Pacific, in one experiment, values of only 4 sec/kilomile were observed (9), possibly because of the ubiquitous presence of seamounts in the area.

Signal Envelope — Off Axis

When source and/or receiver depart from the axis, individual ray arrivals begin to be discernable, and the smooth cresendo of the axial signal disappears. In one experiment (10), a series of drops were made around a semi-circle 600 miles from Bermuda, as shown in *Fig 5*. In this series, air-dropped explosive charges detonating at 800 feet were received by a hydrophone on the DSC axis at 4000 feet. The received signals, shown in *Fig 6*, were found to consist of individual arrivals that occured in pairs over a time interval of about 5 seconds. These arrivals could be identified by ray calculations. The arrival pairs were identified as (11, 12) — (12, 12); (12, 13) — (13, 13) etc. to (15, 16) — (16, 16), where (11, 12) stands for a ray having 11 crests and 12 troughs in its oscillating path between source and receiver. A characteristic envelope persisted for most of the drops, and pointed to an essentially uniform oceanic environment, at least over the east and south of Bermuda. Only very weak signals were received from the northeast, probably because of the pressure of seamounts in the area. Ray calculations also gave fairly good agreement with the observed intensities of the arrivals.

The arrival pattern varies with source and receiver depth combination. In another experiment (11), a series of explosive charges were air-dropped in clusters at locations 150 miles apart between Bermuda and Antigua. The shot signals were received on axial and bottomed hydrophones at Bermuda, Antigua and Eleuthera. The detonation depths were 800, 1500, 3000, 4000, 6000, 8000, 10,000 and 12,000 feet. The received signals were found to lose their smooth triangular envelope completely when they were off-axis, and to acquire a "character" that

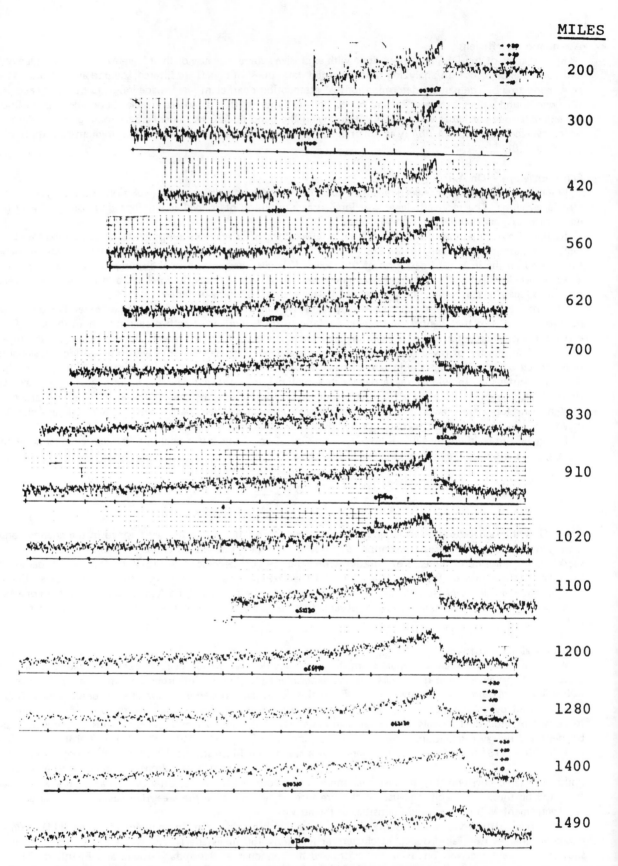

MILES

200

300

420

560

620

700

830

910

1020

1100

1200

1280

1400

1490

Fig. 4. DSC Shot Signal Envelopes Received at Different Ranges between Bermuda and the Azores. Source depth, 4000 ft; receiver depth 4000 feet at Bermuda. 1-Second Time Ticks. (3).

7-6

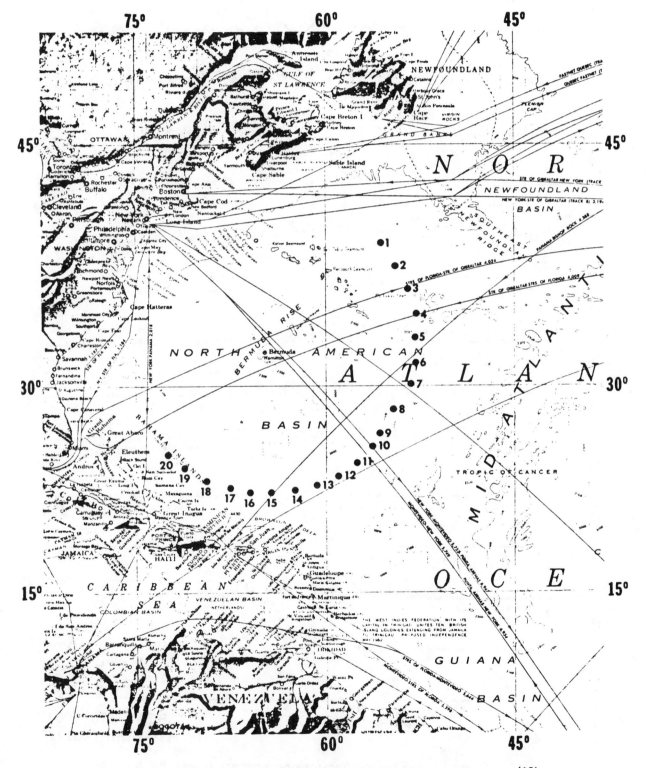

Fig. 5. Chart of Drop locations circling Bermuda at a distance of 600 miles. (10).

7-7

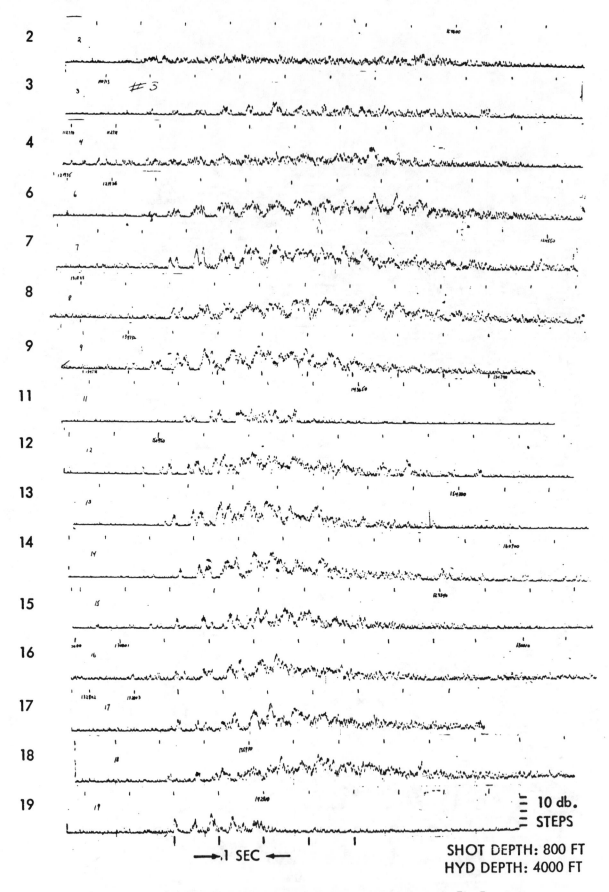

Fig. 6. Received Signal Envelopes from the various stations shown in Fig. 5. (10).

was sensitive to depth, but not greatly sensitive to distance, as may be seen in *Fig 7*. This "character" represents simply the time and intensity pattern of the various ray arrivals. The 12,000 foot depth was beyond the limit of the channel so that only weak refracted-surface-reflected paths occurred.

Effect of Bottom Topography

When a portion of the bottom extends up into the DSC, some of the ray paths will be intercepted and a "shadow" of the bottom will be manifested in the received signals. The most striking example of this occurs when an island lies between source and receiver. The shadowing effect of Bermuda was said (9) to have been observed in 1945 by Ewing and Worzel in their early SOFAR experiments. They are said to have found that signals were not received at Bermuda from bombs detonated in the shadow of Bermuda at ranges less than 700 miles, but were received beyond 700 miles. This may have been due to horizontal refraction or else to diffraction, as in an optical shadow.

However, a bottom obstacle penetrating the DSC only part-way will obstruct only some of the ray paths. If it does not extend up to the axis, only certain high-angle rays will be affected and the front end of the received signal will be reduced in amplitude.

If a ridge or a seamount should completely intercept the axis, the rear, high-amplitude tail will be eliminated and a profound effect on the level of the signal will occur. For example, crossing the Mid-Atlantic Ridge between the Azores and the UK was found (3) to reduce the energy density of the signals on the other side by about 30 db. The signals recorded at Bermuda on the other side of the Ridge were shortened and reduced in intensity so as to be just barely above noise, as illustrated in *Fig 8*. This is more strikingly shown by the two sample signal envelopes of *Fig 9*. The effect of the Ridge is to cut off all but a short piece of the signal, which, across the Ridge, just barely is perceptible above the background of noise.

Effect of a Changing Velocity Profile Along the Path

Not much is known about the effect of non-uniform velocity structure for long-distance SOFAR transmission. In one case (3), the channel axis became shallower during a run and low values of attenuation were reported. In another (9), the duration of SOFAR signals was found to reach a maximum, and then begin to decrease with increasing range instead of the normal linear increase, an effect that was attributed to poor sound channel conditions along part of the path.

Northward from Hawaii the channel axis becomes shallower with increasing latitude, so that a shallow source finds itself closer to the axis of the DSC as the range increases northward. As a result, the transmission becomes better than it would be if the axis of the DSC were at constant depth. This is illustrated by *Fig 10* which shows the velocity profile and measured transmission loss for 60 ft shots dropped at various distances northward from an axial hydrophone at Hawaii.

It is becoming increasingly clear that the ocean is by no means as laterally uniform as had been tacitly assumed for many years. Recently, the effects of horizontal non-uniformity have received considerable attention. It has been found (12), for example, that deep hydrophones at Bermuda receive more sound, by about 10 dB, from 800-foot shots fired on the other side of the Gulf Stream than on the near side in the Sargasso Sea. This is essentially the same as the latitude effect, in that the change in the profile, when going across the Gulf Stream, is such as to carry sound downward to a deep receiver and away from a shallow receiver. In another measurement (13), a different attenuation coefficient was found in the North Pacific between latitudes 30-40 N and 50-60 N, the latter being higher than the former; this is likely to be again due to the profile, which has its axis shallower in the North than in the South, causing shallower transmission with higher attenuation in the more northerly latitudes. Essentially this same effect was found off Australia and New Zealand in the South Tasman Sea (14). In this same area also (15), differences in transmission in different directions out to 3000 km from a hydrophone off New Zealand were found to be correlated with the properties of the different water masses encountered in different directions. Apparently, in making propagation predictions out to long ranges, great care has to be used to properly account for variations in the velocity profile along the transmission paths.

Signal Stretching and Range Computation in the DSC

The distinction between energy density and intensity is particularly important for the DSC. Because of stretching, amounting to about 10 sec per kilomile in mid-latitudes, the peak intensity of an axial explosive shot signal should fall-off more rapidly with distance by a factor of $1/r$ than the fall-off due to spreading alone. Thus, when the energy density spreads like r^{-1}, the intensity should fall-off like r^{-2}. A pseudo-spherical spreading law results when cylindrical spreading is combined with a time-stretching proportional to range.

Measured peak intensities of axial SOFAR signals at 1 kilomile have been reported (3) to be 128 db re 1 μPa in the band 50-150 cps for a 4-lb charge, and 140 db re 1 μPa in another experiment (16) in an unspecified band for

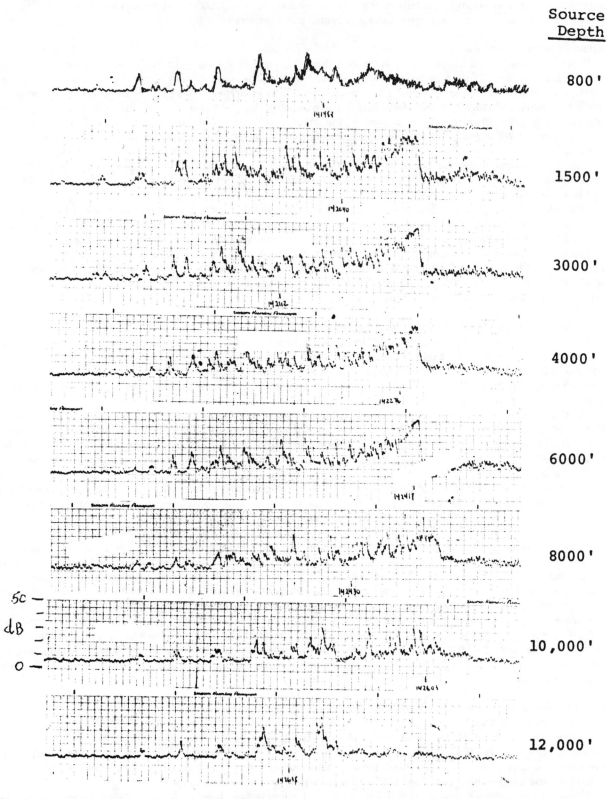

Source Depth

800'

1500'

3000'

4000'

6000'

8000'

10,000'

12,000'

Fig. 7. Signal envelopes from shots fired at different depths at a signal location. Distance 400 miles. Receiver was an axial hydrophone at 4000 ft at Bermuda. The arrival structure is determined by the available ray paths from the source. (11).

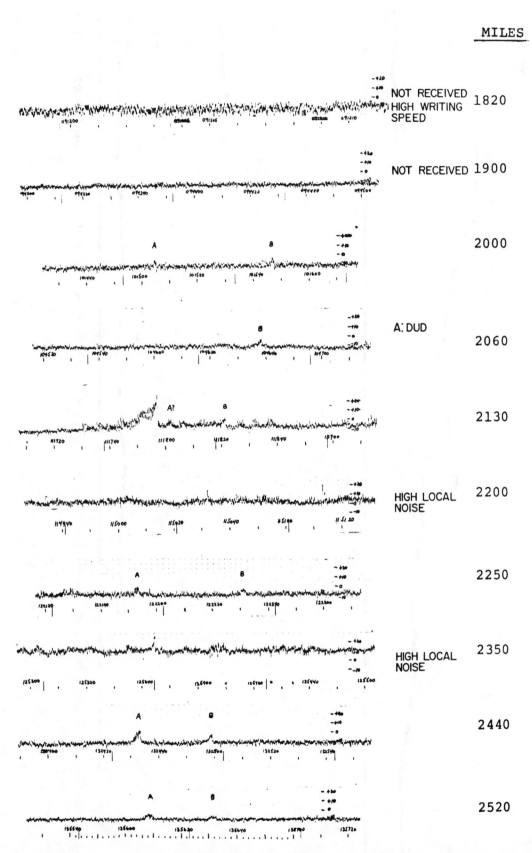

MILES

NOT RECEIVED 1820
HIGH WRITING
SPEED

NOT RECEIVED 1900

2000

A: DUD 2060

2130

HIGH LOCAL 2200
NOISE

2250

HIGH LOCAL 2350
NOISE

2440

2520

Fig. 8.   A continuation of Fig 4, but on the other side of the Mid-Atlantic Ridge. Two shots were dropped at each
range shown on the right. A is a 1500 ft. shot; B is a 3500 ft shot near the axis of the DSC. (7).

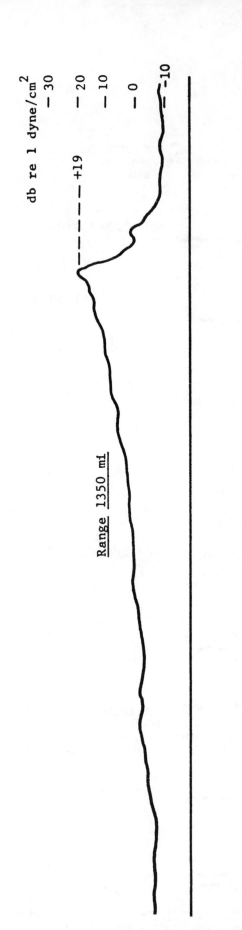
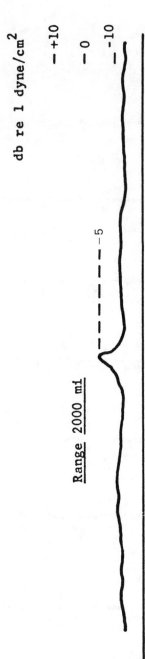

Fig. 9. SOFAR Signal Envelopes from Shots on either Side of the Mid-Atlantic Ridge from Bermuda. Shot Depth: 3500' hyd. Depth: 4000'. Freq. Band: 50-150 Hz Approx.

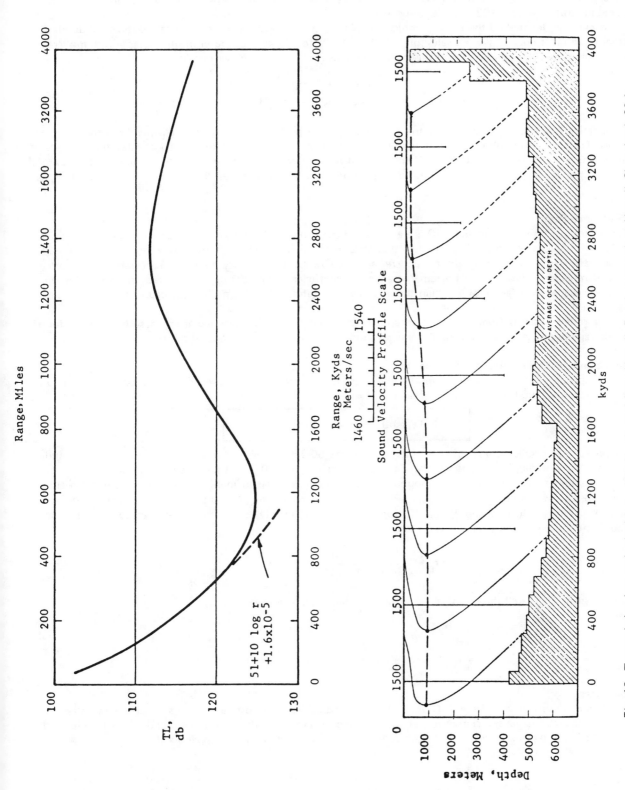

Fig. 10. Transmission loss and velocity profiles Northward from Hawaii. Receiver on **axis** at Hawaii. Shot depth 60 ft.

7-13

a 4-lb charge. Taking the latter to be 10-200 cps, and converting to a 1-lb charge by applying a correction of −10 log (charge weight in lbs), and to a 1 Hz band by applying a correction of −10 log (bandwidth in Hz), the two measured intensities become 102 and 108, respectively.

As an exercise, let us find the range at which the peak spectrum level of the shot signal becomes 10 db above the level of ambient noise. Taking a value of +71 db re 1 μPa for the ambient level in the deep sea with moderate shipping, and using 105 as the average of the measured intensities at 1 kilomile, we obtain

$$10 = (SL - TL) - NL,$$
$$= 105\text{-}20 \log r - \alpha r - 71,$$

where spherical spreading is taken to be the range-law for the peak intensity of the signal, and r is the range in kilomiles. Taking α = .001 db/ky = 2 db/kilomile, we find $20 \log r + 2\ r = 24$, so that r = 5 kilomiles, the computed range at which the peak of a 1 lb. SOFAR shot should be 10 db above ambient noise. As a crude verification of this is the observation (17) that a 4-lb depth charge detonated off Australia was "heard" at Bermuda 12 kilomiles away.

Non-Refracted Paths

Not all propagation paths in the DSC are entirely refracted paths. When source or receiver or both lie beyond the limits of the channel, only reflected paths that encounter either surface or bottom, or both, are possible. *RSR* paths are *reflected above* by the surface, and *refracted below* by the velocity gradient. *RBR* paths are *refracted above* and *reflected below* by the bottom. Attenuation coefficients for RSR paths have been measured (18) and found to be higher by a factor of 1.5 than those for entirely refracted paths, probably because of losses at or near the sea surface.

Doubly reflected paths from both surface and bottom, together with scattering from these boundaries, form the weak, rapidly decreasing tail beyond the time of sudden cessation of long range SOFAR signals.

Transmission Loss-Shallow Source and Receiver

For CW propagation — i.e. when all multipaths are summed — a working expression for TL between a shallow source and receiver (1000 ft.) in the deep ocean is

$$\boxed{TL = 40 + 10 \log r + \alpha r \times 10^{-3}}$$

This approximates a large number of field tests in the range 50-250 Hz beyond a range of about 10 miles. It indicates cylindrical spreading plus absorption beyond a transition range of 10,000 yds. (10 log r_0 = 40 db).

The maximum trapped ray in a deep sound channel 5000 yds. deep in mid-latitudes has an inclination angle of about ±15°. If we assume 1) that the sound emitted by the source within ±15° is trapped in the duct and the sound beyond ±15° is lost to the duct and 2) that the trapped sound is uniformly distributed in depth throughout the duct, we find, using the expression given in the preceding chapter,

$$r_0 = \frac{H}{2 \sin \theta} = \frac{5000}{2 \sin 15°} = 9700 \text{ yds},$$

confirming surprisingly well the empirical value for r_0 in the above expression.

Special Cases

The Arctic is a special case of the DSC where the channel axis lies at, or just below the sea surface and is essentially a half-channel. Its transmission characteristics are described in Appendix I. Internal sound channels of limited extent and of only seasonal occurrence exist in various areas; two examples are in Appendix II.

APPENDIX I: THE ARCTIC, A SPECIAL CASE
OF THE DEEP SOUND CHANNEL

Introduction

The Arctic has some of the characteristics of both the Mixed Layer Channel and the Deep Sound Channel. It is a half-channel with its axis at the surface, which, typically, is ice-covered. One boundary, to which sound is continually refracted, is the rough surface underneath the ice cover. It is this feature which gives the Arctic its unique propagation characteristics. *Fig 11* is a ray diagram for propagation in the Arctic Ocean for a typical velocity profile.

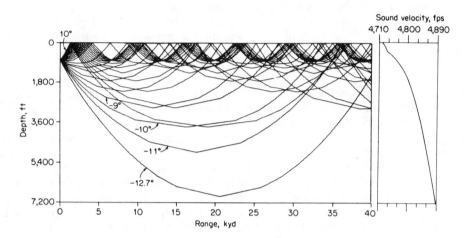

Fig. 11. Typical profile and ray diagram in the Arctic.

The Arctic Ocean

The Arctic is a roughly circular sea extending in depth down to 1500-2000 fathoms and divided into two parts by a partition called the Lomonosov Ridge. Large portions of its area are less than 1000 fathoms deep. It is bordered by various major indentations like the White Sea, Chukchi Sea and Bering Sea less than 100 fathoms in depth. Its major characteristic is its cover of sea-ice that occurs everywhere in winter and over much of it in summer. Within this cover are floating ice islands, in particular one called Ice Iceland T3, that have served as measurement platforms for much of the acoustic work that has been done.

The lack of solar heating in the area causes the main thermocline of the temperate oceans to be absent. Positive-gradient water extends up to shallow depths in summer and all the way up to the ice in winter. The axial depth is shallow, often within a few hundred feet of the surface. In the summer in open water, a small negative gradient extending to 100 feet or more is often present. Strong salinity gradients occur due to melting ice and river discharges and may serve to accentuate the positive velocity gradient and destroy any shallow negative that might otherwise be present.

Acoustic Advantages of Working in the Arctic

Although the Arctic presents many difficulties to research workers, because of its low temperatures, high winds and isolation, it has a number of favorable qualities from an acoustic standpoint. The ice forms a stable platform for gathering acoustic data, and sensors and arrays can be readily deployed through leads or man-made holes in the ice. The velocity profile is free from diurnal and seasonal effects below a shallow surface layer, and tends to be uniform over great distances. Finally, a low ambient noise level often exists, especially with an unbroken shore-fast ice cover, low wind speeds, and rising temperatures.

Propagation Measurements

In deep water, Arctic transmission data were collected by the U S Navy Underwater Sound Laboratory from 1958-1962 and were reported by Mellen and Marsh (19), and Marsh and Mellen (20). The work was continued by General Motors and reported by Buck and Greene (21) and Buck (22) (23). In shallow Arctic waters the Canadians have been most active, with reports by Milne (24) (25) (26) and Macpherson (27).

The U.S. measurements were made using the drifting ice island T-3 as the receiving platform; other ice islands, as well as ships and aircraft, have been used as platforms for sound sources.

Attenuation

Most observed Arctic transmission loss data can be fitted by an equation of the form

$$TL = constant + 10 \log r + \alpha r x 10^{-3}$$

where the constant can be interpreted as 10 log (transition range). Values of α over a range of frequencies as computed from this model are plotted in *Fig 12*, based on measurements reported by Buck [23]. The data from various sources show no agreement at all as to the constant term; various measurements give values between 30 and 50 (r_0 = 1–100 kyds).

Note from Fig 12 how much greater α is in the Arctic than in the Deep Sound Channel, on which our low-frequency attenuation values rest. Also, there is a suggestion, in the small amount of data below 20 Hz, for α to level off at frequencies near 10-20 Hz; in work by Milne [25], the transmission for the octave 12-24 Hz was poorer than in the octave 25-50 Hz.

Causes of Losses

The excess attenuation over that of the ice-free DSC is obviously due to the ice-cover. In the DSC, paraxial rays carry most of the energy; in the Arctic, these rays encounter many reflections from the under-ice surface and are highly attenuated. Thus, roughness-produced scattering is the dominant cause of Arctic attenuation. A minor cause of loss is the sea bed, which is shallower than it is in the deep ocean basins. Although many Arctic transmission encounter water of 1000-foot depth over a part of their distance, the existence of upward refraction and the dominant effect of the ice cover cause the bottom to be unimportant as a source of loss in the Arctic.

Because of the overwhelming effect of ice on the propagation, the magnitude of the excess attenuation in the Arctic should be determined by the statistics of the under-ice surface. Diachok [28] modelled this surface as an ensemble of half-cylinders, representing sea-ice ridges, for which the theory of scattering had previously been worked out by Twersky [29]. Good agreement was found between measured transmission data out to 300 miles and the theory using reasonable values for the size and number per unit distance of the cylinders.

Signal Characteristics

Arctic-transmitted signals have features both similar to, and different from, those of the Deep Sound Channel. Explosive signals show the characteristic elongation of SOFAR signals, but do not show the steep buildup and sudden cessation. The signal duration in one reported series [20], amounted to 15 seconds per kilomile.

Arctic explosions also show frequency dispersion, with high frequencies occurring at the beginning of the signal and low frequencies toward the tail. This has been interpreted in terms of normal modes; low order mode arrivals have been identified in Arctic signatures [27],[30],[31]

Comparison with Ice-Free Waters: A Summary

Relative to non-Arctic acoustics, Arctic acoustics may be qualitatively characterized in the following way:

Transmission: *Better*, due to prevailing upward refraction and the shallow depth of the channel axis.
                                     Less Variable, due to more constant meterological conditions.
Ambient Noise: *Lower* under a continous ice cover with rising temperatures. *Higher* in a non-continuous cover or in falling temperatures.
Surface Scattering: *Higher*, because of the rough under-ice surface.
Volume Scattering: *Lower*, due to a smaller amount of marine life.

In another way, we can compare the Arctic with the ice-free ocean of lower latitudes by its two principal distinguishing characteristics: its *ice cover* and its *velocity profile*:

EFFECTS RELATIVE TO THE OPEN SEA

PERMANENT ICE COVER
1. An increased transmission loss due to scattering, especially at frequencies greater than about 30 Hz.
2. An increased reverberation level at low sea states.
3. A more variable ambient noise level, sometimes very quiet and at other times and places, very noisy.

COLD SURFACE WATER
(Positive Velocity Gradient)
1. Upward refraction at all depths.
2. No convergence zones.
3. A scattering layer just under the ice with an annual, rather than a diurnal, migration.

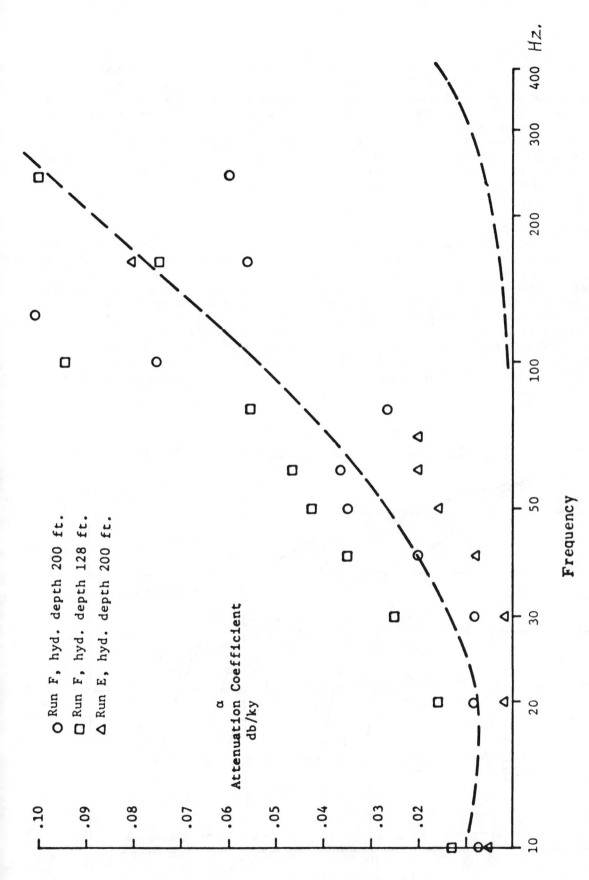

Fig. 12. Attenuation Coefficient in the Arctic, as determined by data in Reference 5, fitted to the expression TL = 10 log r_o + 10 log R + αrx10^{-3} with r_o taken to be 50 kyds. Receiver depths 128 and 200 ft, explosive source depth 800 ft, ranges 22-420 mi. The lower dashed curve shows α in the Deep Sound Channel.

Loss Prediction in the Arctic

The available Arctic loss data have been summarized by Buck (**32**) in a form useful for prediction purposes (*Fig 13*). These curves give the average measured transmission loss in the Arctic at a number of frequencies, based on the available data; the standard deviation of the various data points from the smooth curve is stated for each frequency. The dashed line shows spherical spreading (TL = 20 log r). It is evident that the transmission in the Arctic degrades rapidly with increasing frequency above 20 Hz. As a function of range, the transmission is better than it would be in the free-field (i.e., with spherical spreading) out to some range, and is poorer beyond. As in shallow water (Chap. 8) this peculiarity is the result of opposing influences on the propagation. At short and moderate ranges, ducting improves the transmission; at long ranges the repeated encounters with the under-ice surface degrades it. Subsequent data confirming the validity of the curves of Fig 13 has been reported by Bradley (**33**) for the marginal ice zone East of Greenland.

The Matched Filter of the Arctic

In the DSC, as we have seen, a short pulse is received on the axis at long ranges as a long, drawn-out pulse with an envelope of increasing amplitude until its sudden cessation. The Arctic is essentially a limiting, or special case of the DSC, having two important peculiar features: 1) its axis lies at the surface so as to form a half-channel and 2) the surface is covered with ice. Feature 1) causes a short pulse from a shallow source to be received at a shallow receiver as a long pulse, just as in the DSC in lower latitudes, as long as the surface is smooth and free of ice. But, with the ice-cover of Feature 2), the build-up of amplitude toward the tail of the pulse is lessened or absent altogether, since it is due to shallow ray arrivals undergoing many surface encounters and therefore suffering severe attenuation by scattering. The latter process is frequency-selective, with high frequencies attenuated more than low. The result is that a broadband pulse, as from an explosion, is received as an elongated pulse showing frequency dispersion, with lower frequencies occurring toward the tail of the pulse and higher frequencies toward the front.

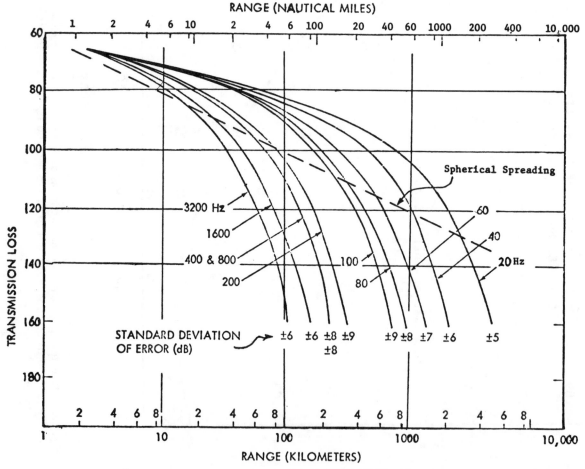

Fig. 13. Curves of Arctic transmission loss vs. range based on measured data. (14)

A filter "matched" to the Arctic would have the same characteristics of elongation and dispersion, but reversed in time; it compresses an elongated pulse into a short pulse of greater amplitude, giving a greater signal-to-noise ratio when used as part of the processing system at a distant receiver. For a given range interval, the matched filter would be valid over much of the Arctic Ocean, since both the ice-cover and the velocity profile are uniform over wide areas, and the bathymetry, though variable, plays no part in the transmission.

APPENDIX II: TRANSITORY INTERNAL CHANNELS IN DEEP WATER

Intermediate in depth between the Deep Sound Channel, with its axis at a depth between 3000 and 4000 feet (about 1000 meters) in mid-latitudes, and the ice-covered Arctic where its axis lies at or just below the surface, are sound channels of a more restricted area and of a seasonal occurrence. Such channels have their axes at a shallow depth, and although they are of a more local transitory nature, they often have a strong effect on Naval operations.

Two examples may be mentioned. One occurs during the summer between Long Island and Bermuda where the peculiar conditions of the Gulf Stream cause a reversal of the normal velocity gradient and a velocity minimum or channel axis near 300 feet (100 meters).

Another shallow summertime channel exists in the Mediterranean Sea. In this region the heating by the sun of the upper layers of water, together with an absence of mixing by the wind, causes a strong near-surface negative gradient to develop during the summer and early autumn months. This thermocline overlies isothermal water at greater depths. The result is a strong sound channel with its axial depth near 300 feet (100 meters). During the late autumn, the profile gradually **returns to its** wintertime conditions, wherein isothermal water and a positive velocity gradient extend throughout the water column all the way up to the surface. During the summer season the near-surface negative gradient and the resulting strong downward refraction greatly limit the range of surface ship sonars. By way of compensation, the summertime channel in the Mediterranean produces convergence zones for a near-surface source in the same way as does the deep-ocean sound channel, although the zone range is much less (typically, 20 miles or 37 km) because of the smaller thickness of the channel. The critical depth is, in summer, only about half that of the Atlantic Ocean, ranging from zero in winter to about 1800 meters in summer. In most of the basins into which the Mediterranean is partitioned by shallow sills, the critical depth is less than the water depth, so that convergence zones regularly occur. At the same time, reliable surface ducts do not exist from April to September. A good summary of Mediterranean propagation has been published by Leroy (34).

REFERENCES

1. H. H. Baker, Missile Impact Locating System, Bell Tel. Lab Rec. *39*, 195, 1961.
2. M. Ewing and J. L. Worzel, Long Range Sound Transmission, Geological Soc. of America Memoir 27, 1948.
3. R. J. Urick, Low Frequency Sound Attenuation in the Deep Ocean, JASA *35*, 1413, 1963.
4. H. A. Thorp, Deep Ocean Sound Attenuation in the Sub- and Low Kilocycle per Second Region, JASA *38*, 648, 1965.
5. D. C. Webb and M. J. Tucker, Transmission Characteristics of the SOFAR Channel, JASA *48*, 767, 1970.
6. B. Sussman and others, Low Frequency Attenuation Studies, Underwater Sound Lab. Tech. Memo. 911-16-64, 1964.
7. R. J. Urick, Long Range Deep Sea Attenuation Measurement, JASA *39*, 904, 1966.
8. A. C. Kibblewhite, R. N. Denham and P. H. Barker, Long Range Sound Propagation Study in the Southern Ocean-Project Neptune, JASA *38*, 628, 1965.
9. T. P. Condron, Effect of Sound Channel Structure and Bottom Topography on SOFAR Signals, Navy Electronics Lab. Rep. 233, 1951.
10. R. J. Urick, Ray Identification in Long-Range Sound Transmission in the Ocean, Naval Ordnance Lab. Tech. Rep. 65-104, 1965.
11. R. J. Urick, The Signatures of Distance Explosions at Different Depths in the Deep Sea, Naval Ordnance Lab. Tech. Rep. 68-20, 1968 (unpublished).
12. C. Levenson and R. Doblar, "Long Range Acoustic Propagation through the Gulf Stream", JASA *59*, 1134, 1976.
13. A. C. Kibblewhite and others, "Regional Dependence of Low Frequency Attenuation in the North Pacific Ocean", JASA *61*, 1977.
14. A. C. Kibblewhite and others, "Effects of Temperature Microstructure on Low Frequency Propagation in the South Tasman Sea", JASA *61*, 1977.
15. R. H. Bannister and others, "Project Tasman Two: Low Frequency Propagation in the South Tasman Sea", JASA *61*, 1977.
16. G. M. Bryan, M. Truchan and J. Ewing, Long-Range SOFAR Studies in the South Atlantic Ocean, JASA *35*, 273, 1963.
17. Note, Trans. Am. Geophys. Union *41*, 670, 1960.
18. R. J. Urick, Attenuation over RSR Paths in the Deep Sea, JASA *36*, 786, 1964.
19. R. H. Mellen and H. W. Marsh, Underwater Sound Propagation in the Arctic Ocean, AVCO Marine Electronics Report MED-65-1002, 1965.
20. H. W. Marsh and R. H. Mellen, Underwater Sound Propagation in the Arctic Ocean, JASA *35*, 552, 1963.
21. B. M. Buck and C. R. Greene, Arctic Deep Water Propagation Measurements, JASA *36*, 1526, 1964.
22. B. M. Buck, Arctic Acoustic Transmission Loss and Ambient Noise, GM Def. Res. Labs. TR 66-20, June 1966.
23. B. M. Buck, Low Frequency Underwater Acoustic Measurements in the Arctic Ocean, AC Electronics Def. Res. Labs. TR 69-10, 1969.
24. A. R. Milne, Acoustics under Arctic Sea Ice, Pac. Nav. Lab. Report 63-1, 1963.
25. A. R. Milne, A 90 km Sound Transmission Test in the Arctic, JASA *35*, 1459, 1963.
26. A. R. Milne, Shallow Water Under Ice Acoustics in Barrow Strait, Pac. Naval Lab. Report 14, Oct. 1959.
27. J. D. Macpherson, Effect of Ice on Long Range Underwater Sound Propagation, Jour. Brit. IRE *26*, 293, 1963.
28. O. I. Diachok, "Effects of Sea-Ice Ridges on Sound Propagation in the Arctic", JASA *59*, 1110, 1976.
29. V. Twersky, Scattering of Sound by Rough Surfaces, JASA *29*, 209, 1957.
30. K. Hunkins and H. Kutschale, Shallow Water Propagation in the Arctic Ocean, JASA *35*, 542, 1963.
31. H. Kutschale, Long-Range Sound Transmission in the Arctic Ocean, Jour. Geophys. Res. *66*, 2189, 1961.
32. B. M. Buck, Arctic Acoustic Transmission Loss and Ambient Noise, paper in Arctic Drifting Stations (J. E. Sater, editor), Arctic Inst. of North Am., 1968.
33. D. L. Bradley, Long Range Acoustic Transmission Loss in the Marginal Ice Zone North of Iceland, U.S. Naval Ordnance Lab. Rept. 72-217, 1973.
34. C. C. Leroy, Sound Propagation in the Mediterranean Sea, paper in *Underwater Acoustics*, vol 2, V. M. Albers, ed. Plenum Press, New York, 1967.

CHAPTER 8

CAUSTICS AND CONVERGENCE ZONES

Introduction

This chapter concerns the distribution of sound throughout the Deep Sound Channel (DSC). This distribution is by no means uniform, but is characterized by a complex series of *shadow zones* and *convergence zones* (CZ's) whose presence and extent are determined by the velocity profile and the location of surface, bottom and source relative to the profile. The various shadow zones are never completely "dark" but are insonified to some extent by sound travelling over reflected paths. The various convergence zones, bounded by caustics, are regions of high intensity having great practical importance for Naval sonars.

The existence of convergence zones and their associated caustics in the Deep Sound Channel is readily demonstrated by drawing a ray diagram. The ray diagram (Fig 1, Chap. 6) published in the open literature in 1947 by Ewing and Worzel (1) clearly shows convergence at a range of 32 miles. Yet the existence of CZ's was considered as classified information in this country for nearly 15 years thereafter. In an anonymous review written to glorify the Russian advances in acoustics since the "Great October Socialist Revolution" of 1917, CZ's are said to have been discovered in the Black Sea by the Soviets (2) (by A. L. Sosedova) in 1954. In this country a landmark paper on CZ's by F. E. Hale (3) appeared in the open literature in 1961.

Caustics Generally

In one dictionary (4) a *caustic* is defined as "the envelope of rays emanating from a point and reflected or refracted by a curved surface". In our case, the "curved surface" is the reverse bending of rays occurring in the DSC. A caustic may be thought of as a *surface* formed by the envelope of the intersections of the 3-dimensional rays from the source; alternatively, in a 2-dimensional ray-diagram, a caustic is a *curve* formed by the intersections of adjacent rays in the diagram. A *focus* occurs when a caustic degenerates to a point or to a small region of space.

In conventional ray theory, the intensity of sound on a caustic is infinite. In modified ray theory using the W.K.B. Wentzel-Kramers-Brillouin approximation (amounting to a hybrid ray-wave theory) the sound field at and near a caustic is finite and calculable. In this theory the sound field on one side turns out to be oscillatory and on the other, exponentially decaying. The oscillatory side, in our case, is the CZ, the other lies on the other side. The field near a caustic is given by Brekhovskikh (5).

Convergence Gain

Let the intensity at a point, at distance r from a source, be I_r and the intensity at unit range be I_o. Then we can write

$$I_r = F \frac{I_o}{r^2}$$

where F is a *focussing factor*. $10 \log F$ may be called the *convergence gain*. In terms of transmission loss,

$$10 \log F = 10 \log r^2 + 10 \log \frac{I_r}{I_o}$$
$$= 10 \log r^2 - TL$$

The convergence gain is thus the difference between the loss due to spherical spreading and the observed loss. It is the negative of the transmission anomaly defined and used during World War II to quantify the departure of measured data from what would be expected in the ideal medium. Convergence gain is the amount of improvement in transmission produced by convergence. Sometimes it is taken to be difference relative to spherical spreading *plus absorption*, rather than to spherical spreading alone.

Caustics in the DSC

There is a definite pattern to the caustics of the refracted rays from a source within the DSC. This caustic pattern is illustrated diagrammatically in *Fig 1*. It has the following features:
1. The horizontal ray leaving the source is itself a caustic, beyond a distance of one whole loop from the source (A-A).
2. From its crests and troughs, pairs of caustics radiate in upward and downward directions (B-B).
3. The entire pattern moves in range and depth as the source depth changes.

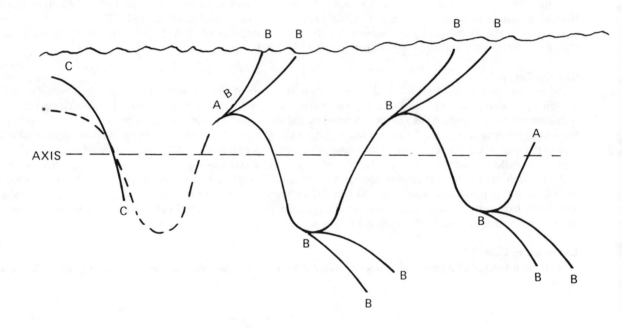

Fig. 1.   Caustic pattern for a source above the axis. A similar pattern exists for a source below the axis, but the caustics are displaced in depth and range. When the source is *on* the axis, the caustics radiate in pairs from the straight-line path along the axis, which is itself a caustic.

4. Often, depending on the details of the velocity profile at shallow depths, there is a caustic formed at short ranges by the upward-going rays leaving the source after they start downward (C-C).

5. There is a focus (intersection of caustics) at successive crests and troughs of the horizontal ray leaving the source. The source thus appears to have an "image" at these focal points.

6. Other caustics exist, such as those formed by reflected paths such as RSR (Refracted, Surface-Reflected).

The pattern thus amounts to a complex system of caustics, foci, and associated convergence zones that exists throughout the entire extent of the DSC.

Source near the Surface

To understand what happens for a near-surface source, it is necessary to consider the upward- and downward-going rays separately.

Fig 2 shows the caustic formed by the *downward-going* rays from a shallow source. The various rays A, B . . . E leaving the source in *downward* directions are turned around by upward refraction below the axis of the DSC and intersect on the other side. The locus of the intersections AB, BC, CD, and DE of rays infinitely close together at the source forms a caustic having a *convergence zone* on the far side. When the sea surface gets in the way, before intersection can take place, the rays are reflected and a reflected caustic is produced beneath the surface. Thus the sea, with its peculiar velocity profile, acts like a lens, bringing rays together that would otherwise continue to diverge.

Upward-going rays from the source are drawn in *Fig 3*. Often, depending on the profile above the depth of the source, a downward-going caustic is formed at the outer boundary of the direct sound field, while, as before, after reversal at deep depths, an upward-going caustic is formed at longer ranges with a high-intensity, or convergence, zone at the far side. The CZ formed by the upward-going rays lies at a longer range than the CZ formed by down-going rays. Between the direct sound field and the caustic is a shadow-zone to which only bottom-reflected rays can penetrate.

When the source is quite close to the surface, the convergence zones of the upward and downward-going rays overlap and merge together. The result is an extremely complicated sound field having numerous caustics at shallow depths. This single convergence zone is commonly called *the* convergence zone; the two zones of which it is composed are called *half-zones*.

Effects of Changing Source Depth

Fig 4 is a series of ray diagrams for a succession of source depths for a typical velocity profile with the axis at 4500 feet. The first pair of half-zones are indicated by x and y, while the shadow zones between such pairs of half-zones are designated by a and b. Let us imagine that the source is descending, and, following the succession of ray diagrams, see what happens as the source descends:

(1) The half-zones x, y separate, the inner half-zone moving inward, the outer half-zone moving outward.

(2) The shadow zones a, b (insonified only by bottom-bounce paths) at shallow depth fill up and disappear when the source reaches the *critical depth* (Chap. 6) here at 12,000 feet.

(3) The shadow zone between half-zones deepens and widens.

(4) When the source reaches the critical depth, no caustics appear at ranges shorter than the range to the first "image" of the source.

The rays from a source at critical depth are shown in *Fig 5*. Ray paths from any deep source are sometimes called *Reliable Acoustic Paths* because they are not subject to the near-surface vagaries of shallow-going ray-paths.

Fig 6 shows the movement of the caustics from a descending source, as deduced from ray diagrams like those of the previous figure. A caustic diagram for a source on and above the axis of the DSC similar to Fig 6 has appeared in a Russian paper (6).

Conditions for Convergence

The primary condition for convergence is that the source must lie within the DSC. There must exist, as a refracted ray, the ray leaving the source horizontally. If this ray is reflected at either boundary, the caustic pattern is destroyed and no convergence is possible. *Another requirement for convergence is that the water depth be greater than the critical depth*, in order that there be room, so to speak, for deep-going rays to be turned around and converge. There must be a *depth excess* in the velocity profile as related to the water depth. When the depth excess exceeds a few hundred meters, a CZ is likely to occur. For water depths less than critical, the rays that would converge if the water were deeper are cut off by the bottom and become bottom-reflected without convergence.

Because of the fact that the *deep* depths of the sea are essentially at the same temperature the world over, the velocity of sound at a given depth is nearly the same in all oceans and depends only on the depth. On the other hand, at shallow depths, the velocity of sound is determined essentially by the surface temperature. These two properties, surface temperature and water depth, determine whether or not a depth excess exists and, therefore, whether or not a CZ will occur. Thus, oceangraphic charts of surface temperature and water depth are the prediction tools for the existence of a CZ at any location.

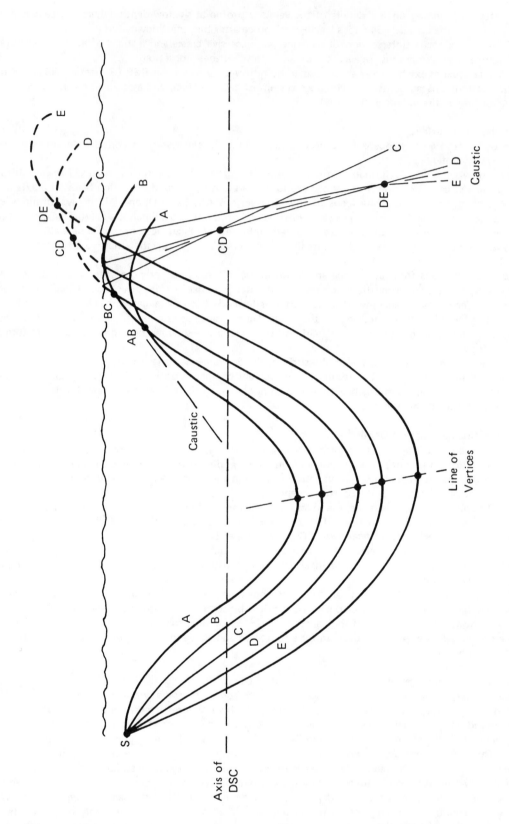

Fig. 2.   Caustics produced by downward-going rays from a shallow source.

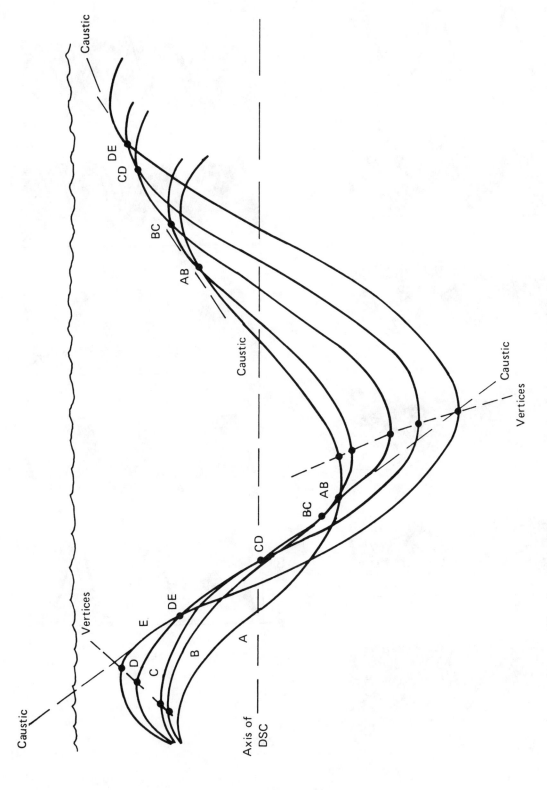

Fig. 3.   Caustics produced by upward-going rays from a shallow source.

Source depth

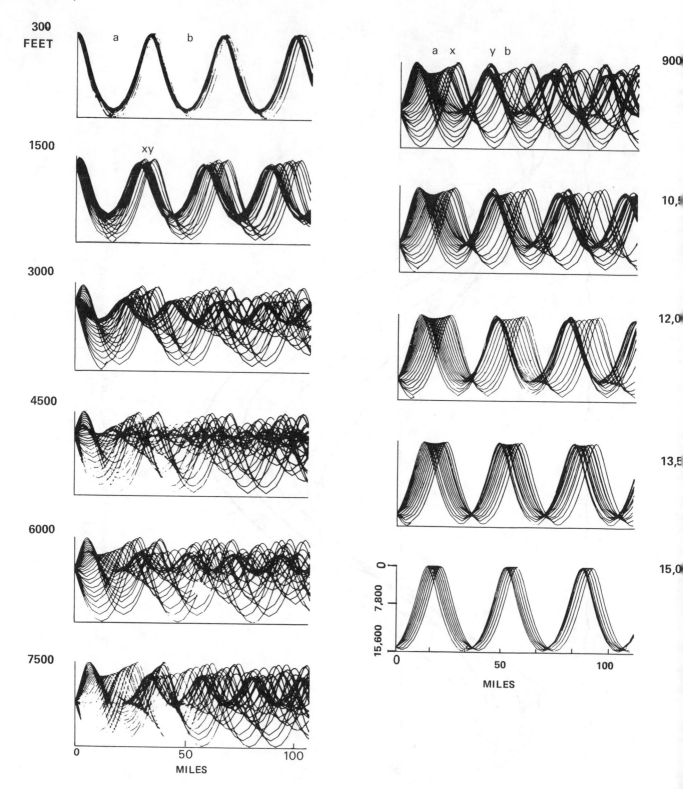

Fig. 4. Ray diagrams for different source depths for a profile having the same sound velocity at the surface and at 10,500 ft., and with channel axis at 4500 ft.

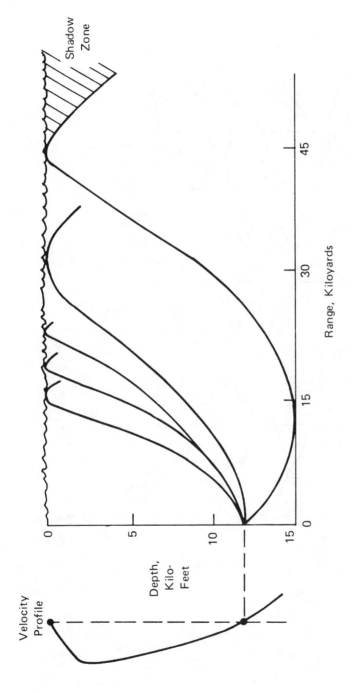

Fig. 5 Rays from a source at critical depth producing complete coverage near the surface out to 45 kyds.

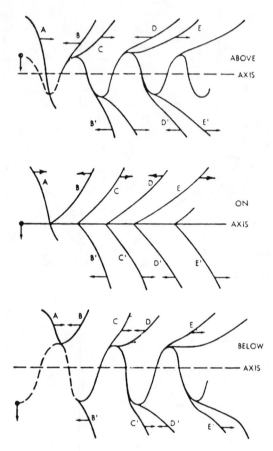

Fig. 6.   Caustic patterns for a source above, on and below the axis. The arrows show their movement in range as a source descends.

It becomes apparent that CZ's are less likely to occur for a shallow source in summer than in winter at any one location.

Although the existence of a CZ depends on whether the critical depth is greater or less than the water depth, the *range* to the first CZ, if it does exist, depends only on the critical depth itself. The shallower the critical depth the shorter the range to the first CZ.

In temperate latitudes of the North Atlantic, the CZ range is near 30 miles and decreases northward. In the Mediterranean the CZ range is only 10 to 20 miles due to the shallowness of the critical depth. In the Arctic the CZ range is very short or absent altogether.

The solid curve of *Fig 7* is a curve of critical depth vs. surface temperature for mid-latitudes in the North Atlantic and North Pacific Oceans. When entered with water depth on the left and surface temperature horizontally, the point so located determines the presence or absence of a CZ for a given surface temperature. Should a CZ be present, the range to the first CZ can be found from the dashed curve and the range scale on the right. Slight variations exist between major oceans. The Underwater Sound Laboratory (now Naval Underwater Systems Center) has issued a CZ slide rule giving these relationships for the N. Atlantic, the N. Pacific, Mediterranean and Norwegian Seas.

Effect of Range on CZ's

Successive CZ's get wider with increasing range, until at a range beyond a few hundred miles they coalesce. The result is a smooth variation of loss with range, with cylindrical spreading plus attenuation determining the transmission loss.

This was most graphically observed in shot signals recorded by Nutile and others (7) between Antigua and Newfoundland. Beyond 600 km, successive CZ's formed by ray paths taking between 10 and 45 loops, overlapped and coalesced so as to form a smooth curve of transmission loss vs. range, without the CZ maxima observed at shorter ranges.

Results of Field Studies

The peculiarities of the sound field in the deep sea at ranges out to 110 miles were investigated in a succession of field trips, carried out by the Naval Ordnance Laboratory (now Naval Surface Weapons Center) over a period of years. The work was done at a single spot East of Eleuthera, where the depth excess in 16,000 feet of water amounted to about 1000 feet. The field observations tend to verify the general features of convergence as described above.

The field work was done with a surface ship and deep hydrophones, together with an aircraft to drop explosive charges. Two kinds of source patterns were employed: (1) charge drops at constant depth at close range intervals (½ to 1½ mi) and (2) drops at different depths at a few different ranges. Results have appeared in a number of reports (8) (9) (10) (11). Some of the findings were as follows:

1. Convergence gains in the half-zones average about 5 to 10 db, with half-zone widths of 3 to 5 miles. The second half-zones show a slower fall-off of intensity with range than do the first half-zones, presumably because of scattered sound trapped in the surface duct.

2. Convergence was observed in different bands down to the 25-100 Hz band, though with a somewhat lower gain and with less sharp zone boundaries.

3. The inner boundaries of the zones are extremely sharp, and show an increase of intensity of 10-15 db or more within a small fraction of a mile.

4. At ranges less than the first CZ, four bottom-bounce ray arrivals (B, BS, SB, SBS)*occur. As the caustic of the first half-zone is approached with increasing range, the first two (B, BS) draw together in time and reach a maximum as the caustic is crossed; in the second half-zone, the same happens to the other pair of arrivals (SB, SBS).

5. At longer ranges, the pattern of ray arrivals becomes more complex and at 80 mi becomes difficult to interpret without help from travel-time computations.

6. The observed transmission losses agree roughly with the spacing of rays in the ray diagram.

7. The total energy flux density computed by adding the flux densities of seven charges detonating over the thickness of the DSC falls off with distance according to cylindrical spreading plus absorption, with an absorption coefficient about the same as that generally accepted for the DSC.

8. Using a string of 6 hydrophones 2000 ft apart, an 800 ft source was found to be in a CZ at all ranges, with different hydrophone depths "picking up" the zone signals at different ranges. As the source range increased, the strong zone-signals progressed up the string and down again in successive half-zones, as illustrated in *Fig 8*.

---

* These letters refer to the four paths making one encounter with the bottom between a source and a receiver: B=Bottom, S= Bottom-Surface, SB=Surface-Bottom, SBS=Surface-Bottom-Surface. See Fig. 6, Chapter 14.

9. The vertical coherence of CW sound (using a 1120 Hz CW source) was greater within the half-zones than outside them because of the existence of essentially a single propagation path in the half-zones. *The practical result of this finding is the likelihood of a higher array gain for a vertical array located within a CZ than outside it.* A vertical array in a CZ would accordingly have a higher signal-to-noise ratio because of the combined effects of convergence gain and coherence.

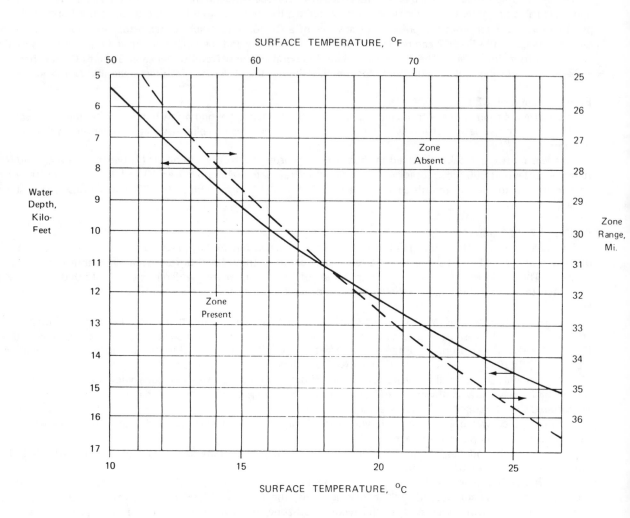

Fig. 7.   CZ prediction curves. Water depth and surface temperature determine the presence or absence of a CZ (solid curve). Dashed curve and the right-hand scale gives the zone range. Near surface source, North Atlantic and North Pacific Oceans.

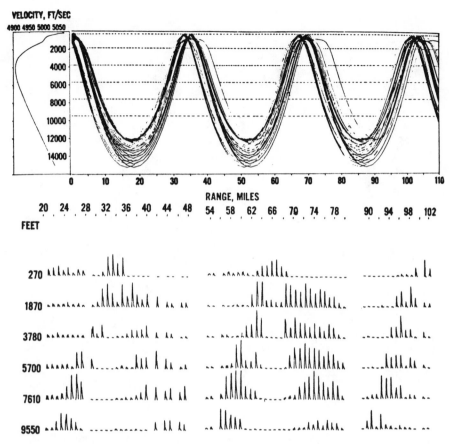

Fig. 8.   Shot signals received by a string of hydrophones at the indicated depths. The ray diagram for a source at 800 feet is shown above.

REFERENCES

1.   M. Ewing and J. L. Worzel, Long Range Sound Transmission, Geol. Soc. Am. Mem. *27*, 1948.
2.   Anon., Soviet Acoustics During the Last Fifty Years, Soviet Physics Acoustics *13*, 415, 1968.
3.   F. E. Hale, Long Range Sound Transmission in the Deep Ocean, J. Acoust. Soc. Am. *33*, 456, 1961.
4.   Webster's Seventh New Collegiate Dictionary, 1966.
5.   L. N. Brekhovskikh, *Waves in Layered Media*, Academic Press, New York, 1960, pp 483-492.
6.   L. Brekhovskikh, Propagation of Sonic and Infrasonic Waves in Natural Waveguides over Long Distances, Uspekhi Fiz. Nauk. *70* 351, 1960.
7.   D. A. Nutile and others, "Long-Range Acoustic Propagation Paths", Antigua, Newfoundland, JASA *59*, 1150, 1976.
8.   R. J. Urick, Caustics and Convergence Zones in Deep Water Sound Transmission, J. Acoust. Soc. Am. *38*, 348, 1965.
9.   R. J. Urick, Observations of the Sound Field in the Deep Sea, NOLTR 67-103, 1967.
10. R. J. Urick, Amplitude and Coherence of Sound at Long Ranges in the Deep Ocean, Proc. 6th Int. Congress on Acoustics, 1968.
11. R. J. Urick and G. R. Lund, Coherence of Convergence Zone Sound, J. Acoust. Soc. Am. *43*, 723, 1968.

CHAPTER 9

SHALLOW WATER DUCTS

Introduction

The acoustics of shallow water is a subject beset by contradictions. Of all aspects of propagation in the sea, it has the largest literature. It presents fascinating problems to the theoretician. It has accumulated a surprising number of transmission runs, made all over the world by British, Canadian, New Zealand and U.S. sea-going scientists. Yet, this accumulation of theory and measurement has failed to give us the quantitative understanding required for long-range prediction and optimum sonar design. This understanding is far less than we now have for deep water. The reason is the complexity of the problem: in shallow water the surface, volume and bottom properties all are important, are spatially and temporally variable and cannot be modelled realistically in a satisfactory way.

What is Shallow Water?

Two definitions of shallow water may be made. One is *hypsometric*, the other *acoustic*. The hypsometric definition is based on the fact that some continents have *continental shelves* of gentle slope, generally bordered by the 100-fathom (200 meters) contour line, beyond which the bottom rapidly falls off into deep water. By this definition "shallow" water means continental shelf water bordered by the 100-fm line on the off-shore side and by about 100 feet on the in-shore side, the shallowest depth for submerged submarine operations. In the following, we restrict ourselves to *coastal waters* and to frequencies useful for *submarine detection and surveillance*, neglecting the waters of bays and harbors and problems of mines and mine countermeasures.

The *acoustic* definition is that shallow water exists whenever the propagation is characterized by numerous encounters with *both* surface and bottom. By this definition, some "shallow" water environments are acoustically deep. Most torpedo problems are acoustically deep water problems, and some environments, such as the Gulf of Maine and the Scotian Shelf, where strong internal sound channels exist, are deep water environments. On the other hand, the deep ocean may be considered "shallow" at long ranges when the propagation is by repeated surface and bottom reflections.

Transmission Runs

A total of some 4000 transmission runs has been estimated to exist in the unclassified literature. These have been (and are being) made in many areas of the world since World War II. *Fig. 1* is a sampling of transmission loss data (1) obtained in different areas by different investigators under conditions of a negative gradient in the frequency band 0.5 to 1.5 kHz. The heavy straight line is the line (on a logarithmic range scale) of spherical spreading.

Two features of Fig. 1 are of immediate interest. One is the spread of the data, amounting to about 40 db at 10 miles (20 kyds) under the rather broad range of gradient and frequency included. The other feature is for the transmission to be *better* than in the free field (spherical spreading) at *short and moderate ranges* and to be *worse* at *longer ranges*. This peculiarity is caused by trapping in the shallow water duct, which improves the transmission at short ranges, and by boundary losses at long ranges, which degrade the transmission.

High-Frequency Measurements

Except for the German work described on page 1-1, the earliest shallow water transmission runs were made at 12 and 24 kHz during World War II, and the results were summarized in two reports, based on work done off the West Coast (2) and East Gulf Coasts (3) of the United States. Appendices I & II repeat verbatim some of the conclusions stated in these reports. Although dating from World War II, they summarize much of our current understanding of shallow-water transmission at high frequencies.

As a short summary of these findings, the transmission at 12 kHz and 24 kHz may be said to depend in the following way on the following eight factors:

1. Frequency — Improves between 24 kHz and 12 kHz.
2. Bottom type — Improves between mud (worst) and sand (best).
3. BT Gradient — Improves with smaller gradient.
4. Water depth — Improves with water depth between 60 and 600 ft. with a negative gradient. From 600-1200 ft., becomes worse.
5. Layer depth — Improves with layer depth when source and receiver are in-layer at low wind speeds (Beaufort wind force 1), at high wind speeds (Beaufort wind force 3), no change.
6. Wind speed — Improves with lower wind speeds.
7. Receiver depth — Improves with increasing receiver depth with a negative gradient.
8. Salinity — Improves with a salinity gradient (off the Mississippi delta).

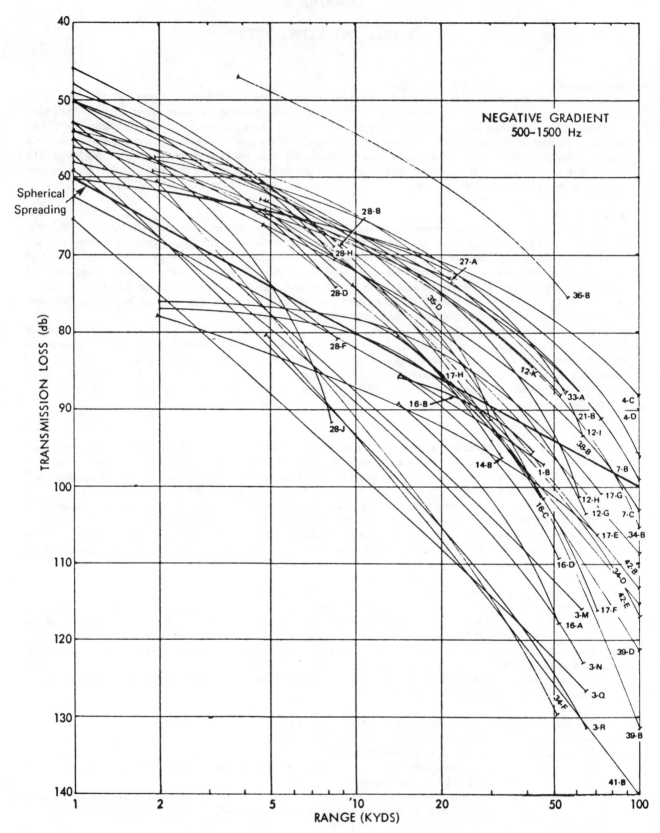

Fig. 1. A compilation of transmission runs from the literature. The run designations referred to a table of experimental conditions given in the report. (1).

A sample of the quantitative results of the wartime work at 24 kHz in seen in *Fig. 2*. This figure shows a quantity called R_{40}, plotted against d_2, the depth in the bathythermogram at which there is a 0.3°F negative change in temperature. R_{40} is the range at which the loss is 40 db higher than the loss to 100 yds.; that is, the transmission loss equals 40 + 40 = 80 db at the range denoted by R_{40}. Many of the above qualitative statements can be verified quantitatively from this data.

Low Frequency Measurements — An Example

A more recent field study emphasizing lower frequencies and the longer ranges of interest to passive sonars in shallow water was made off the West Coast of Florida (4). In this study, explosive sound signals were air-dropped out to 50 miles from a research vessel anchored in 200 feet of water in directions parallel to and at right angles to the gentle bottom slope. Recordings of shot signals were made at hydrophone depths of 80 and 180 feet, in and below a 100-foot mixed layer. *Fig. 3* illustrates the findings in octave bands between 25 and 6400 Hz, while Appendix 3 repeats the conclusions drawn from this series of field measurements.

Model Studies

As analogs of real-world shallow water conditions, and as validation of theory, work has been done in the laboratory and in very shallow natural waters. Several laboratory scale models have verified many of the qualitative predictions of simple theory. Knudsen (5) used a rectangular tank (100 x 160 cm) having a layer of oil over a layer of salt solution, and measured the sound field with a tiny hydrophone. A study of the effects of slope, roughness and bottom rigidity was done by Eby et al (6). Wood (7) used a large tank and optical means to display the complexities of the real world. Natural models have also been studied; for example, Scrimger (8) worked in a 10 foot lagoon over a 300 ft distance; Tonakonov (9) studied the transmission in a reservoir 2 to 8 meters deep over a 1.5 km distance, and Urick and Moore (10) made measurements in 4 feet of water off Panama City, Florida. These studies have served as a bridge between theory and real-world transmission runs.

Theory

Normal mode theory for the simplest shallow water model was worked out long ago by Pekeris (11) and Ide, Post and Fry (12). It appears in books by Officer (13), Brekhovskikh (14) and Tolstoy and Clay (15). This most simple two-layer case has the following characteristics:

Surface:	smooth
Water:	constant depth
	homogeneous (no gradient)
Bottom:	smooth
	non-layered (semi-infinite)
	fluid (no shear waves, i.e. no rigidity)
	homogeneous (no density or velocity gradients)
	non-absorbent

This simple model is thus the crudest approximation to reality. In subsequent years, numerous theoreticians have treated other models that are closer to the complications of the real world, for example, an absorbing bottom (16), a viscoelastic bottom (17) a layered bottom (18) (19), a sloping bottom (20) and a velocity gradient in the liquid layer (21).

Ray theory is illustrated in *Fig 4a*. Between the source S and receiver R, various ray paths are possible. Of the infinity of rays leaving S, only certain discrete rays reach R. These are called *eigenrays*, in analog with the normal modes of mode theory. These eigenrays may be designated by a pair of numbers, such as 2,2, denoting the number of surface and bottom bounces. The sound field is the sum of all the ray contributions when spreading, boundary losses (= loss per bounce times the number of bounces) and phase (including phase changes at the boundaries) have been allowed for. The pressure at R may be written

$$P_R = Po \sum_{n,m} \frac{R_S^m R_B^n \exp{(i(kr - m\varphi_S - n\varphi_B))}}{r_{n,m}}$$

where R_S, φ_S, R_B, φ_B are the (real) reflection coefficients and phase shifts at the surface and bottom. In a practical case, the summation is readily, though tediously, done on a computer. The difficult part in the ray trace computation is to sort out the eigenrays from the many rays that are traced in the computation. Depending on the computer program, a wide variety of complications can be included, such as a bottom loss that varies with angle, variable water depth, and variable velocity profile.

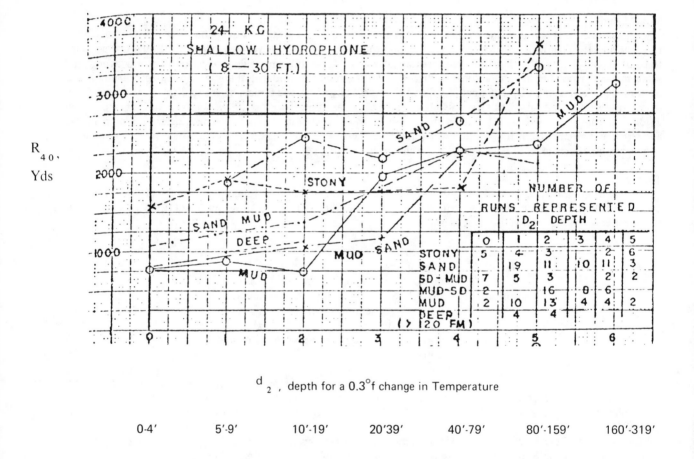

d$_2$, depth for a 0.3°f change in Temperature

| 0-4' | 5'-9' | 10'-19' | 20'39' | 40'-79' | 80'-159' | 160'-319' |

Fig. 2.   The range R$_{40}$ plotted against temperature gradient. Frequency 24 kHz, hydrophone depth 8 to 30 feet. World War II data, Reference 2.

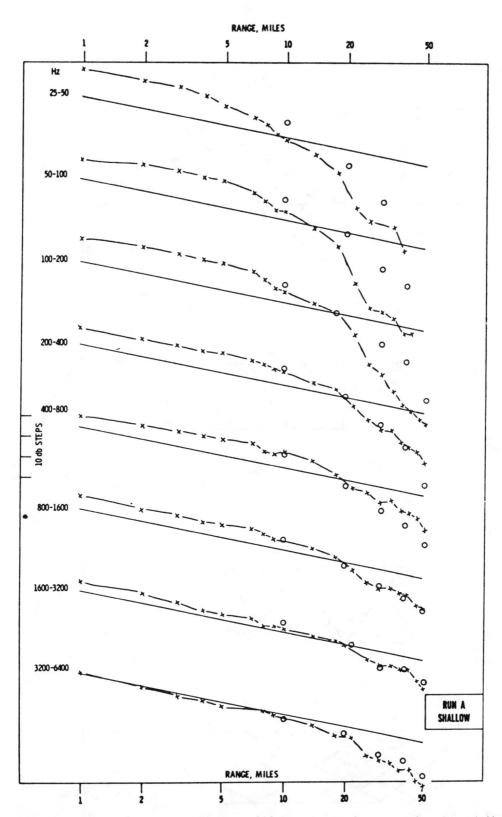

Fig. 3. Transmission along a contour out to 50 miles in 200 feet of water from an anchored vessel. Hydrophone depth 80 feet, shot depth 60 feet. The sloping straight lines show spherical spreading (20 log r). Steps of 10 db are shown at the left. Crosses are outbound data points, circles inbound of the shot-dropping aircraft. Sea calm; bottom, coral, sand and mud. (4).

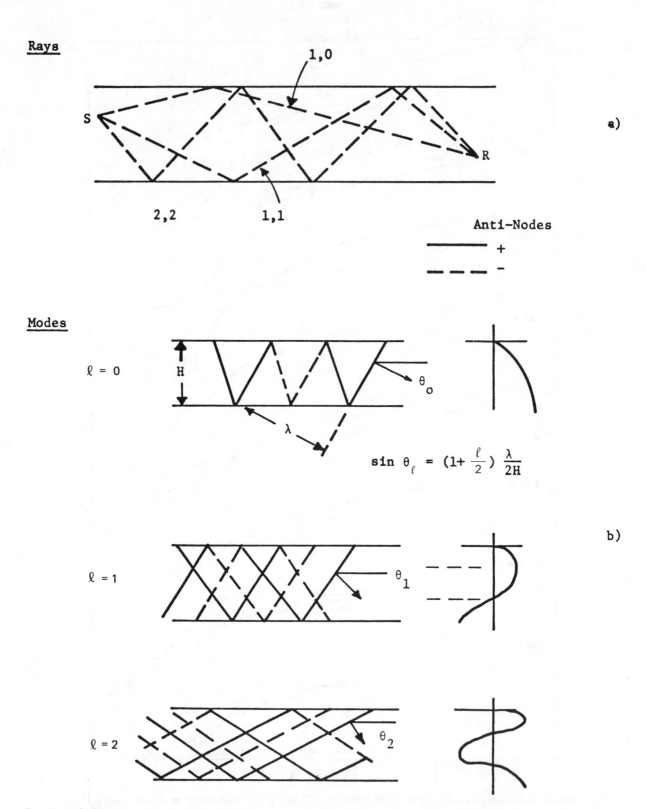

Rays

1,0

S

R

2,2   1,1

Anti-Nodes
——— +
- - - - -

a)

Modes

$\ell = 0$

H

λ

θ_o

$$\sin \theta_\ell = \left(1 + \frac{\ell}{2}\right) \frac{\lambda}{2H}$$

$\ell = 1$

θ_1

b)

$\ell = 2$

θ_2

Fig. 4.   a) Eigenrays of ray theory between a source at S and a receiver at R. b) Plane wave representation of
normal modes of the first three orders. The two waves are inclined at angle so as to satisfy the conditions of
a pressure-release (soft) surface and a pressure-reinforcement (hard) bottom.

By contrast, only relatively simple conditions can be treated by normal mode theory. For the simplest case outlined above, Brekhovskikh (14, p.338) gives for a free (pressure-release) surface and a *hard* (pressure-doubled) bottom the expressions

$$\psi = \frac{2\pi i}{H} \sum_{\ell=0}^{\infty} (\cosh b_\ell z_0)(\cosh b_\ell z) H_o^1(x_\ell r)$$

$$b_\ell = i\,(\ell + \tfrac{1}{2})\,\pi/H \quad \text{and subscript } \ell = \text{mode number}$$

$$H_o^1(x_\ell r) = \text{Hankel function of the first kind}$$

$$= (2/\pi x_\ell r)^{1/2} e^{(ix_\ell r - \pi/4)}, \, r \gg \lambda$$

$$x_\ell = [(kh)^2 - (\ell + \tfrac{1}{2})^2 \pi^2]/H; k = 2\pi/\lambda$$

ψ is the velocity potential, proportional to acoustic pressure; $|\psi|^2$ is the equivalent of intensity. The two cosh **terms** are the excitation function for a source at depth z_0 and the reception function for a receiver at z.

This is one form of solution of the wave equation for the stated boundary conditions. Other, though equivalent, forms are given by Ide, Post and Fry (12) and Pekeris (11). Each of the terms in the summation are called *normal modes* and, as shown in Chapter 2, may be represented by a pair of plane waves — one upgoing, the other downgoing — travelling outward in range, and "standing" in depth, so as to give a particular amplitude variation in depth that depends on the particular mode. These waves are shown in Fig. 4b for $\ell = 0$, 1 and 2. Here $\ell = 0$ is the "first" mode, following Brekhovskikh's numbering. For a given water depth, there is a value of $k = 2\pi/\lambda$ such that $x_\ell = 0$ for $\ell = 0$. Wavelengths longer than this (= smaller k) will make x_ℓ imaginary, even for $\ell = 0$, and damping will set in. The wavelength which makes $x_\ell = 0$ is the *cut-off wavelength* that begins to be too long to "fit" in the duct. The corresponding frequency is the *cut-off frequency* for the first mode. The condition is:

$$k_c H = (0 + \tfrac{1}{2})\,\pi$$
$$\frac{2H}{\lambda_c} = \tfrac{1}{2}$$
$$\frac{H}{\lambda_c} = \tfrac{1}{4}$$

where λ_c is the cut-off wavelength of the first mode and H is the water depth. When the bottom is not completely "hard" ($c_2 < \infty$), the cut-off relation is

$$\frac{H}{\lambda_c} = \tfrac{1}{4}\left(1 - \left(\frac{c_1}{c_2}\right)^2\right)^{1/2}$$

where c_1/c_2 is the velocity ratio of water to bottom. A nomogram facilitating the calculation of the first mode cut-off frequency $f_c = c_1/\lambda_c$ is given in *Fig. 5*.

The above summation of modes for the simplest case is readily done on a computer. But for more complicated conditions, the theoretical solutions soon become almost intractable. For example, the mathematics for the 3-layer case may be seen in the book by Brekhovskikh (14, p. 387) and has been computed by Bucker and Morris (19). Mode theory and calculations for many natural conditions occurring in real-world shallow water have not yet been worked out.

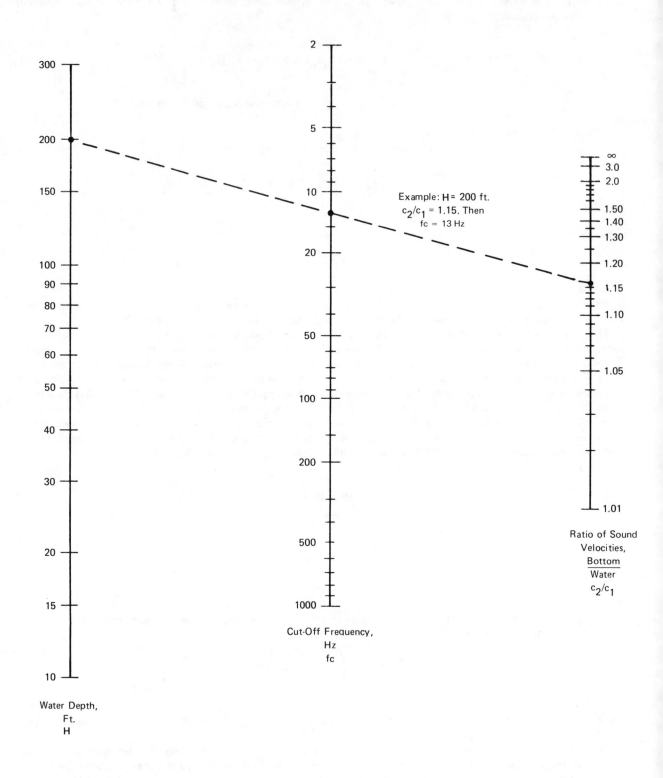

Fig. 5.   Nomogram for finding the first-mode cut-off frequency in shallow water.

Dispersion and Distortion of a Short Pulse in Shallow Water

Pekeris (11) first described the distortion produced by shallow water transmission of a short pulse, such as that from an explosion. For two fluids separated by a plane interface, the signal is received as two waves: a *ground wave* and a *water wave*. According to theory, the ground wave **begins first** and increases in *both* amplitude and frequency; the water wave begins later while the ground wave is coming in, and increases in amplitude and decreases in frequency. An example of these waves is shown in *Fig. 6a*. Both waves terminate with the same amplitude at a common frequency, called the *Airy-phase*, which is the minimum frequency on a plot of group velocity vs. frequency such as that of *Fig. 6b*.

The superposition of the two waves represents the signal when only one mode is effectively present, as is the case at long ranges when there is boundary attenuation. A slightly different dispersion pattern exists for the second and higher modes. The result is apt to be a complicated signal. A sorting out of frequency and time can be done with a sound spectrograph, which yields a record (22) like that of *Fig. 6c*. The water wave often dominates the ground wave, which occurs as a low-amplitude, low-frequency precursor to the water wave.

The result is a long drawn-out blob whose duration increases with range. Brekhovskikh (14, Fig. 141) gives a plot of the ratio of the Airy-phase velocity to the water velocity. As an example, when the ratio of bottom density to water density is 2, and the ratio of sound velocities in the two media is also 2, the velocity of the Airy-phase is 0.81 times the water velocity. One field experiment (4) using explosive sources gave pulse durations that increased with range at the rate of .01 sec per mile, a rate identical — perhaps by chance — to that of propagation in the Deep Sound Channel.

Approximation Methods

Approximations to the exact theory are useful for a number of reasons:

1) the boundary and medium conditions for a particular transmission run are never known exactly.

2) the details of the sound field are of no practical significance, and only the "average" field is of interest.

3) there is always some uncertainty in measured data, or in other parameters if a range prediction is to be made.

4) the effects predicted by theory, such as the dispersion phenomena described above, are not always of practical interest.

5) a quick handy formula is useful when a computer calculation cannot be made.

For these reasons, a number of relatively simple expressions for the transmission loss in shallow water have appeared in the literature. Examples are those of Marsh and Schulkin (23), Macpherson and Daintith (24) and Urick for the isovelocity (25) and downward-refraction cases (26). The latter two will be briefly described by way of illustration.

The first report for isovelocity conditions (25) concerns the summation of the rays of ray theory and the modes of mode theory on an intensity basis, without regard to phase. Because of reasons 1, 2 and 4 above, we are justified in ignoring phase and summing rays or modes on a power basis. When this is done, both computer summation of discrete images and modes and mathematical integration of continuously distributed images and modes give simple results. For the *loss-less case* (no boundary losses), it is found that the transmission anomaly* becomes

$$TA \equiv 10 \log \frac{I_1}{r^2 I_r} = -10 \log (r/H) - 10 \log \pi$$

where I_1 is the intensity at unit range and I_r the intensity at range r. For the *lossy case* (with boundary losses), when the loss coefficient in decibels is taken to be proportional to the grazing angle at the boundaries, the result of *image summation* is

$$TA = 5 \log L - 5 \log (r/H) + 2.0$$

where L is the slope of the boundary reflection loss coefficient in db per degree of grazing angle. This expression has been found to be valid at ranges such that $13.2Lr/H \gg 1$. It is identical to a more complicated expression given by Macpherson and Daintith (23). The term $-5 \log r/H$ means that the intensity falls off as the $-3/2$ power of the range. *Mode summation* gives an answer identical to this when many modes are trapped ($2H/\lambda \to \infty$). When the number of trapped modes is *not* large ($2H/\lambda = 10, 20$, etc.) an additional loss exists due to *mode stripping*. *Fig 7* is an example of the end-product of the theory. This is a series of curves for discrete values of the loss coefficient, giving TA as a function of normalized range r/H with $2H/\lambda$ as a parameter. Such cases are alleged to be useful for making a quick estimate of TA under isovelocity conditions.

*The transmission anomaly is the difference between the observed loss and that due to spherical spreading. Thus, TA = TL – 20 log r. A negative TA means that the received level is higher than it would be with spherical spreading.

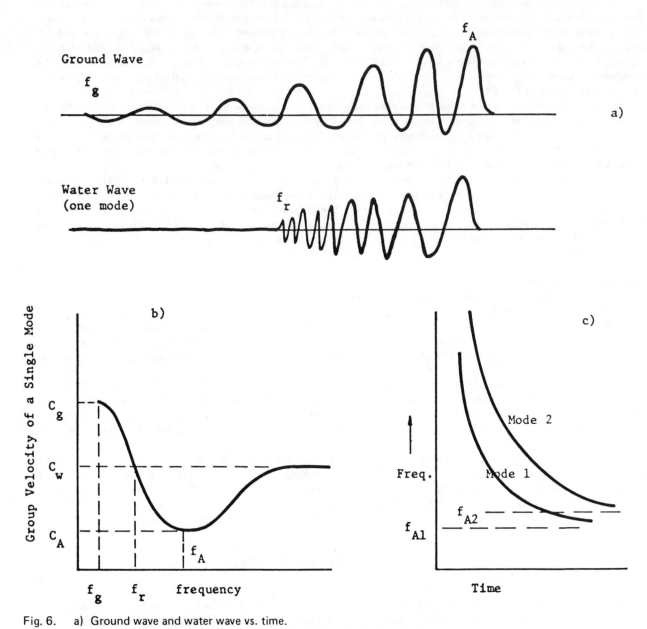

Fig. 6.   a) Ground wave and water wave vs. time.
          b) Dispersion curve of group velocity vs. frequency. f_A is the airy frequency.
          c) Diagrammatic sound spectrogram showing mode arrivals.   (11); (22),

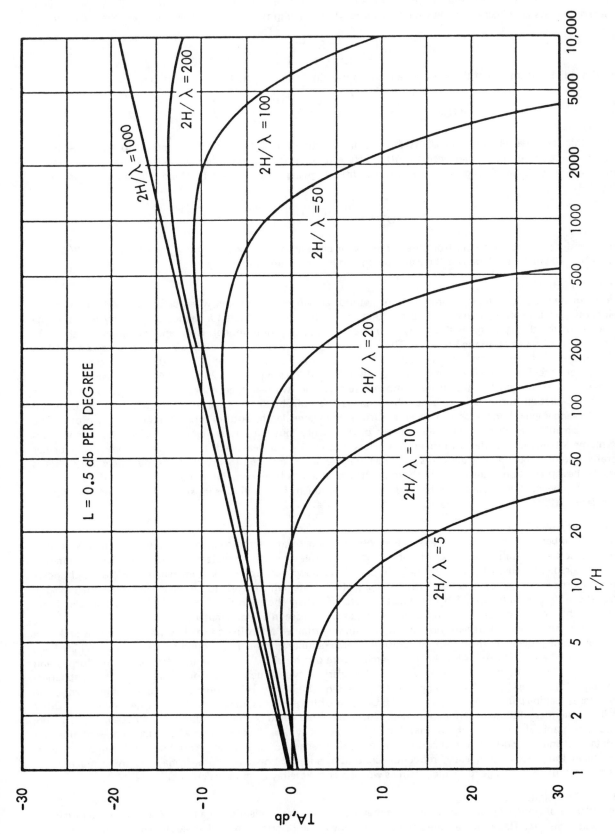

Fig. 7.   Theoretical curves of transmission anomaly vs. range for isovelocity shallow water. Loss coefficient L = 0.5 db per degree of grazing angle.   (25).

The second report (26), for negative velocity gradients, deals with the summation of rays in the linear gradient case where the rays are concave-downward circular arcs. A ray taking m bounces to range r will have the intensity

$$I_m = \frac{I_o}{r^2} R^{r/x_m}$$

where R_m is the bottom loss of the m-th ray and x_m is its skip distance. The total intensity becomes

$$I_{TOT} = \sum_{m=o}^{n} I_m = \frac{I_o}{r^2} \left(R_o^{r/x_o} + R_1^{r/x_1} + \dots R_n^{r/x_n} \right)$$

To sum this series we observe that all its terms will be equal if (r/x_o) 10 log R_o = (r/x_1) 10 log R_1 = (r/x_2) 10 log R_2 = etc., a condition that occurs if 10 log $R_k = m\theta_k$. Furthermore, only rays taking an integral number of bounces will reach a given range (the eigenray condition), giving $r/x_n = r/x_o + n$. These relationships lead to the final result:

$$I_{TOT} = \frac{I_o}{r^2} (n + 1) R^{r/x_o}$$

where n and x_o are readily found from the geometry of circular rays to be given by $x_o = 4H/\theta_o = 4H/(2\Delta V/V)^{1/2}$ and $n = (r/x_o)((H/h)^{1/2} - 1)$ where H is the water depth and h is the source depth.

Comparison with Reality

Unfortunately none of these approximation methods appear to do too well when compared with actual transmission runs on a rigorous, non-ad-hoc, basis (that is, when a "fit" to the data cannot be done by adjusting the parameters of the theory). This is shown by a comparison (27) of various models with random samples of about 60 transmission runs taken from the literature. The errors of the models averaged 7 db in 50% of the samples and 10 db in 20% of the measurement samples at ranges of 2, 5 and 10 kyds. At ranges of 20 and 50 kyds, the average model error (between prediction and measurement) was 7db in 50% of the samples and 20 db in 20% of the samples.

These errors of the existing transmission models, such as the two described above, are too great for them to be useful for prediction purposes in an area where no data is available, and where the prediction must be based on existing oceanographic knowledge in that area, such as the water depth, bottom type, and the velocity profile. The reason is not only the inherent over-simplications of the theory, but our current ignorance of the boundary losses and volume attenuation coefficient in natural shallow waters. A great deal needs to be done, not perhaps in further theoretical studies, but in measurements of parameters to insert into the theory that already exists. Until that is done, the best prediction technique is likely to be the use of a data bank containing the vast amount of transmission data already collected, wherein transmission data would be sought for conditions most like those for which a prediction is desired (28).

Seasonal and Other Effects

It has long been known that the transmission loss in shallow water tends to be higher in summer than in winter. In winter, isothermal water, well-mixed by the wind, is the rule in northern waters like the North Sea. In summer, a negative gradient, caused by solar heating, forces sound downward to the bottom where it is lost, and poorer transmission develops. A complication exists because of sea state, which tends to be higher in winter than in summer, and can reverse matters at high frequencies. These effects are shown in *Fig. 8*, taken from Reference 29. There are many other sources of variability in shallow water, as we will see in a later chapter.

German scientists have in recent years given persistent, sustained attention to shallow water problems and have made significant progress in them (30). In addition, a large number of broadband sound propagation trials have been conducted by the NATO SACLANT ASW Research Centre off the island of Elba in the Mediterranean. Murphy and Olesen (31) tried to fit the data by decay "laws" of various types, such as cylindrical spreading (r^{-1}), spherical spreading (r^{-2}), "three-halves" spreading ($r^{-3/2}$), expected where only one propagation mode is significant, and cylindrical spreading plus attenuation ($r^{-1} e^{-\alpha r}$). On plots of frequency vs. range, the regions where one or the other best fitted the measured data were determined. Not much sense could be made of the results. Indeed, quoting from the last paragraph of the paper, it was said that "while the decay laws themselves may be simple representations for the data, it is most important to realize that the transition ranges for changeover from one law to another may be complicated functions of frequency, refraction conditions and location. Therefore, it may require as much effort and environmental knowledge to predict them as would a complete ray or mode calculation".

Fast Field Technique

In order to obviate the prediction problem, a method for fast data collection in a remote area has been developed (32). It uses an aircraft, explosive sound signals, sonobuoys, and portable recording equipment. In this method, a sonobuoy is dropped by the aircraft at the center of the area of interest, and explosive sound signals are dropped

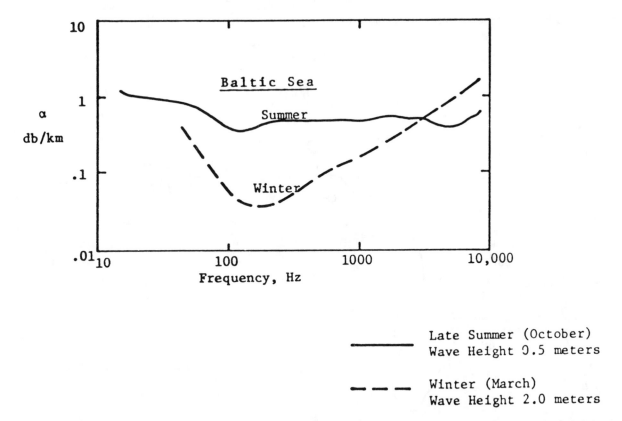

Fig. 8. Shallow water attenuation coefficient in the Baltic Sea in the summer and winter. Based on measured data. (29).

along flight radials in different directions from the sonobuoy. Recording is done aboard the aircraft. In a demonstration of feasibility (32), the eight locations shown in *Fig. 9* were measured during four flight days. At each location, the flight pattern of *Fig. 10* was executed, and, after data analysis in the laboratory, transmission loss contour charts such as the one shown in *Fig. 11* were drawn. Such charts graphically describe the transmission environment over a large area about a site in a given frequency band. Considerable differences were found among the various sites shown in *Fig. 9,* and even from season to season at one site, again confirming the irrationality of long-range shallow water transmission. One interesting characteristic, generally found at all the sites, is the non-circularity of the contours: there is better transmission in the directions of constant water depth than up or down the bottom slope. In the up-slope direction the poor transmission is likely to be the result of an increasing number of bottom encounters, while, in the downslope direction, the poor transmission is probably the effect of downward refraction in carrying sound away from a near-surface receiver.

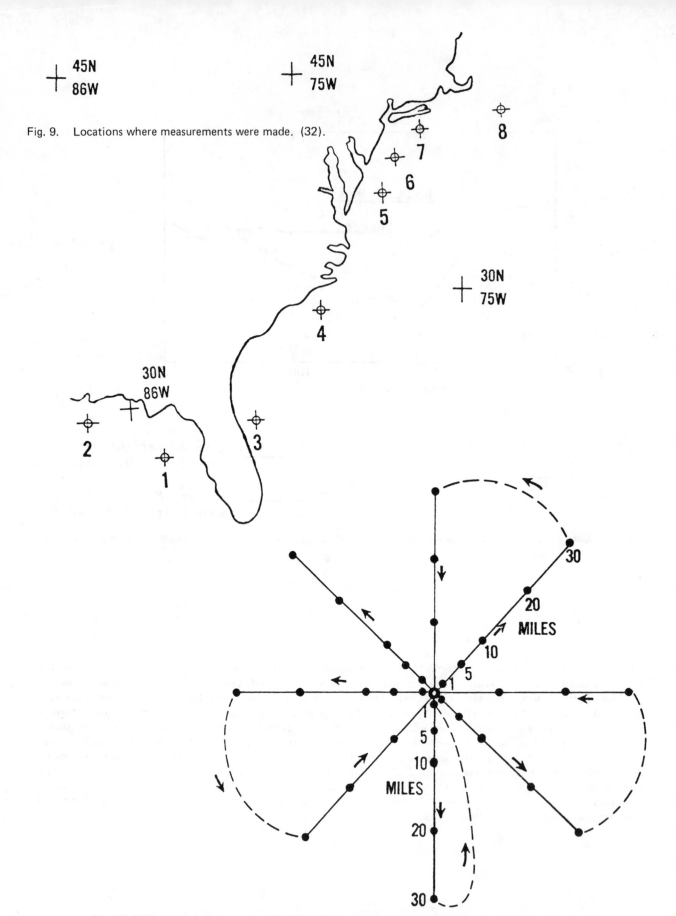

Fig. 9. Locations where measurements were made. (32).

Fig. 10. Flight pattern flown at each location of Fig. 9. A sonobuoy was dropped at the center and the radial legs were flown as indicated. Explosive sound signals were dropped at the points shown.

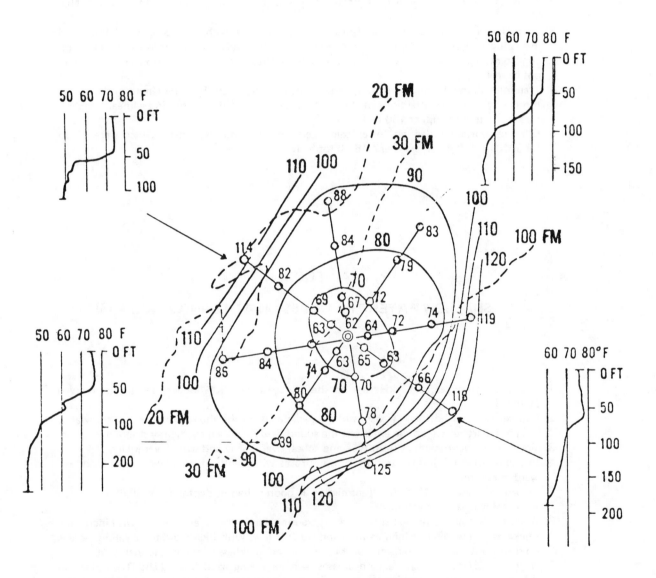

Fig. 11. Acoustic and environmental results at one location. Frequency band 100-200 Hz. Airborne bathythermo-grams were obtained at the ends of four of the legs. Loss contours shown by the solid curves were drawn from the measured loss at each point.

APPENDIX I

SHALLOW WATER TRANSMISSION AT 24 KHZ. (2)

1. Transmission loss increases with: (a) increase of average negative thermal gradient between the surface and bottom; (b) decrease of grain size when the bottom is composed of sediment; (c) decrease of bottom depth.
2. Transmission loss over ROCK is greater than that over SAND, but less than over SAND-MUD.
3. There is some evidence that transmission loss increases with increasing wind force and increasing hydrophone depth. In this connection, however, the effects were irregular, inconsistent, and considerably smaller in magnitude than those of Conclusion (1). They may not be real.
4. Transmission loss is roughly linearly dependent on R^{-1} where R is the length of the arches formed by repeated reflections of the limiting ray calculated by assuming a linear temperature gradient in the upper 150 feet.
5. Effective bottom reflection losses calculated from this observed dependence were: 4 db for SAND, 11 db for ROCK, and 16 db for SAND-MUD.

APPENDIX II

SHALLOW WATER TRANSMISSION AT 12 AND 24 KHZ. (3)

1. Transmission ranges at 12 kHz are on the average about 50% longer than those observed at 24 kHz.
2. Over all types of bottoms, transmission is dependent on the thermal gradient in the water, but more particularly on the extent of the sound field described by the ray diagram.
3. Transmission varies with bottom type and is best over SAND and worst over MUD.
4. In depths from 60-600 ft., transmission improves with depth of water when there is downward refraction.
5. In depths from 600-1200 ft., transmission is poorer than in depths from 60-600 ft. when there is downward refraction.
6. When there is an isothermal surface layer, transmission in the layer improves with increasing thickness of the layer as long as the wind force is low. With high wind force values there is no significant change in transmission with increasing thickness of the isothermal layer.
7. Near the surface the R_{40} range decreases with increasing wind force. (The R_{40} range was defined as the range at which the transmission loss, relative to 100 yds., was 40 db. Relative to 1 yd., the loss to R_{40} would be 80 db.)

APPENDIX III

SHALLOW WATER TRANSMISSION CONTOURS (4)

The transmission plots such as those of Fig. 3, in directions parallel to and perpendicular to the bottom slope have the following noteworthy features:

(a) *Effect of Range*. The transmission tends to be better than spherical (that is, the transmission anomaly is negative) out to a range generally from 5 to 10 miles, followed by a rapid fall-off with range (when a logarithmic range scale is used).

This characteristic is typical of all range runs in shallow water, and is due to trapping at short ranges and the dominant effect of boundary **and volume attenuation at long ranges.**

(b) *Effect of Frequency*. The transmission tends to be best in the 100-200 Hz or 200-400 Hz octaves, and poorer in octaves below and above. At lower frequencies, the transmission is worse because of a lower ratio of water depth to wavelength and a lesser number of trapped modes and a greater attenuation; at higher frequencies, the transmission is worse because of a higher volume attenuation. The existence of an optimum frequency for these reasons is characteristic of all sound channels, of whatever type, in the sea.

(c) *Effect of Hydrophone Depth*. The transmission to the shallow (80 feet) hydrophone is better than to the deeper (180 feet) hydrophone at the higher frequencies, presumably because of trapping in the near-surface sound channel. At the lower frequencies, there is no great difference between the two hydrophone depths.

(d) *Effect of Direction*. In any one octave band the transmission out to a distance of about 10 miles is unaffected by the depth of the hydrophone or by the direction of the run. The transmission may therefore be said to be essentially isotropic about the receiving vessel out to 10 miles, and independent of hydrophone depth. But at longer ranges, there are great differences in transmission in the different directions. For example, and most notably, the transmission to the North is poorer than to the South at low frequencies where the bottom acoustic characteristics must play a dominant role, but not appreciably different at high frequencies where trapping in the near surface layer determines the transmission. However, in the direction toward shore, the high frequencies are transmitted to the shallow hydrophone better than in other directions, possibly because of the enhancement of the mixed-layer trap by the shallow bottom at or just below its base in this direction. Contrarywise, in the direction toward deep water the transmission is the poorest of all at all frequencies, so much so that the run was aborted at 30 miles due to weak or absent shot signals in this direction.

REFERENCES

1. W. L. Bradley and R. J. Urick, "A Compilation of Acoustic Transmission Loss Measurements in Shallow Water", Naval Ordnance Laboratory Tech. Rep. 68-180, Nov. 1968.
2. R. R. Carhart and others, "Transmission of 24 kc Sound in Shallow Water", Univ. of Calif. Div. of War Research, Rep. M-423, 1946.
3. G. P. Woolard, "Sound Transmission Measurements at 12 kc and 24 kc in Shallow Water", Woods Hole Oceanographic Institution, Memo for File, Contract NObs-2083, 1946.
4. R. J. Urick, "Acoustic Observations at a Shallow Water Location off the Coast of Florida", Naval Ordnance Laboratory Tech. Rep. 69-90, 1969.
5. W. C. Knudsen, "Propagation of a Pressure Transient in a Two-Layer Liquid Model", JASA *29*, 918, 1957.
6. R. K. Eby and others, "Study of Acoustic Propagation in a Two-Layered Model", JASA *32*, 88, 1960.
7. A. B. Wood, "Model Experiments on Sound Propagation", JASA *31*, 1213, 1959.
8. J. A. Scrimger, "Signal Amplitude and Phase Fluctuations Induced by Surface Waves in Ducted Sound Propagation", JASA *33*, 239, 1961; also, "Observations of the Stability of a Normal Mode Sound Field on an Intermediate Scale Model", JASA *33*, 1329, 1961.
9. O. S. Tonakanov, "Sound Fluctuations During Propagation in a Shallow Layer of Water", Soviet Physics-Acoustics *7*, 185, 1961.
10. R. J. Urick and R. T. Moore, Low Frequency Sound Transmission in Very Shallow Water, Navy Mine Defense Laboratory Tech. Paper 117, Dec. 1958.
11. C. L. Pekeris, "Theory of Propagation of Explosive Sound in Shallow Water", Geol. Soc. Am. Mem. 27, 1948.
12. J. M. Ide, R. F. Post, and W. J. Fry, "Propagation of Underwater Sound at Low Frequencies as a Function of the Acoustic Properties of the Bottom", Naval Research Laboratory Report S-2113, 1943.
13. C. B. Officer, *Introduction to the Theory of Sound Transmission*, McGraw-Hill Book Co., New York, 1958, Chap. 3.
14. L. N. Brekhovskikh, *Waves in Layer Media*, Academic Press, New York, 1960, Chaps. 5 & 6.
15. I. Tolstoy and C. S. Clay, *Ocean Acoustics*, McGraw-Hill Book Co., New York, 1966, Chap. 4.
16. E. T. Kornhauser and W. P. Raney, "Attenuation in Shallow Water Propagation Due to an Absorbing Bottom", JASA *27*, 689, 1955.
17. A. O. Williams, Jr. and R. K. Eby, "Acoustic Attenuation in a Liquid Layer over a Slow Viscoelastic Solid", JASA *34*, 1836, 1962.
18. C. L. Pekeris, and I. M. Longman, "Ray Theory Solutions of the Problem of Propagation of Explosive Sound in a Layered Liquid", JASA *30*, 323, 1958.
19. H. P. Bucker and H. E. Morris, "Normal Mode Intensity Calculations for a Constant-Depth Shallow Water Channel", JASA *38*, 1010, 1965.
20. R. N. Denham, "Intensity-Decay Laws for Sound Propagation in Shallow Water of Variable Depth", JASA *39*, 1170, 1966.
21. A. O. Williams, Jr., "Some Effects of Velocity Structure on Low-Frequency Propagation in Shallow Water", JASA *32*, 363, 1960.
22. P. A. Barakos, "Review of the Shallow Water Propagation Problem," USL Rep. 531, 1962.
23. H. W. Marsh and M. Schulkin, "Shallow Water Transmission", JASA *34*, 863, 1962.
24. J. D. Macpherson and M. J. Daintith, "Practical Model of Shallow-Water Acoustic Propagation", JASA *41*, 850, 1967.
25. R. J. Urick, "Intensity Summation of Modes and Images in Shallow Water Sound Transmission", JASA *46*, 780, 1969.
26. R. J. Urick, "A Prediction Model for Shallow Water Sound Transmission", Naval Ordnance Lab. Tech. Report 67-12, Feb. 1967.
27. R. J. Urick and D. L. Bradley, "Comparison of Various Prediction Models with a Random Selection of Field Observations of Sound Transmission in Shallow Water," Naval Ordnance Lab. Tech. Report 69-109, 1969.
28. R. J. Urick, "Some Perspective and Recent Findings in Shallow Water Acoustics," Naval Ordnance Lab. Tech. Report 71-204, 1971.
29. G. S. Schellstede and P. Wille, "Measurements of Sound Attenuation in Standard Areas of the North Sea and Baltic", Proceedings of a SACLANTCEN Conference on Shallow Water Sound Propagation, Sept. 1974.
30. P. Wille, R. Thiele and E. Schunk, "Shallow Water Sound Attenuation in a Standard Area", JASA *54*, 1708, 1973.
31. E. Murphy and O. V. Olesen, "Intensity-Range Relations for Shallow Water Sound Propagation," JASA *59*, 305, 1976.
32. R. J. Urick, A Summary of the NOL Shallow Water Acoustics Research Program, Naval Ordnance Laboratory Tech. Rep. 70-146, 1970.

CHAPTER 10

REFLECTION AND SCATTERING
BY THE SEA SURFACE

Introduction

The surface of the sea affects underwater sound in a number of ways. The sea surface
1) produces a *reflection loss* for sound incident upon it. This loss, though small, is a major contributor to the total loss for RSR paths in the Deep Sound Channel at long ranges.
2) produces *back-scattering*, causing sea surface reverberation.
3) produces *forward-scattering*, the dominant loss process in propagation in the mixed layer.
4) produces *interference effects* with the direct path in the sound field from a shallow source.
5) produces a *doppler shift* in narrow-band reflected and scattered sound, due to its wind-driven motion.
6) has a *bubbly layer* of air just beneath it when it is rough, that often acoustically hides the surface itself.
7) casts a *shadow* in a negative gradient extending all the way up to the surface.
8) is the source of *ambient noise* in the deep sea at kilohertz frequencies (0.5 to 50 kHz).
9) *reduces the power radiated* by a sound source located a quarter-wavelength or less below it.

Of these various effects, Numbers 1 to 7 are included in what follows, leaving others to remain as topics other than propagation.

Reflection and Scattering

When a plane sound wave in water strikes *an infinite plane boundary* (a perfectly smooth sea surface), nearly all of its energy is reflected at the boundary. At normal incidence, the ratio of the intensity of the sound crossing the boundary to the incident intensity is only 0.0002. Nearly all of the sound remains in the water, and goes into the *specular direction* as a plane wave *(Fig 1a)* that is perfectly coherent, i.e. with unity correlation coefficient, with the incident wave.

When the surface begins to get rough, some sound goes into other directions, and each small surface area acquires a directional pattern *(Fig 1b)*. The correlation coefficient between the returned sound from the surface and the incident sound is less than unity, and the intensity in the vicinity of the specular direction is reduced. Finally, when the surface is very rough, the returned sound is entirely scattered sound having no trace of a maximum in the specular direction and with no coherence with the incident sound.

A measure of the acoustic roughness of a surface is the *Rayleigh parameter* R defined by the relation

$$R = 2kh \sin \theta$$

where k is the acoustic wave number = $2\pi/\lambda$, h is the rms roughness height (2h is the rms "waveheight", crest-trough) and θ is the grazing angle. R may be considered to be the rms phase difference between a reflection from a crest or trough at a distance h from the mean surface and that from the mean surface, as illustrated heuristically in *Fig 2*. It is found empirically that when $R \ll 1$ the surface may be considered to be *smooth*; when $R \gg 1$, the surface is *rough*.

The reflected field occurs in certain discrete directions at angles θ_m to the vertical, given by the *grating formula*

$$\sin \theta_m = \sin \theta + m\frac{\lambda}{\Lambda}; m = 0, \pm 1, \pm 2 \ldots$$

$$= \sin \frac{mK}{k}$$

where K and k are the two wave numbers $2\pi/\Lambda$ and $2\pi/\lambda$, respectively. The directions θ_m are shown in *Fig 3b*. The total number m_{max} of directions ("modes" or "orders") is limited by the condition that

$$|\sin \theta_m| \leqslant 1$$

The Rayleigh method has led to a certain amount of controversy. Rayleigh assumed that the sound field *everywhere* is given by the sum of the direct wave and the various contributing modal waves in the directions θ_m. The validity of this assumption at points close to the corrugated surface has been theoretically questioned by several theoreticians and has led to different alternative answers to the problem of reflection from a sinusoidal surface (4) (5) (6) (7). The different theoretical treatments result in differences in the amplitudes of the reflected modes. For example, in Eckart's theory (7), the amplitude coefficients are given by

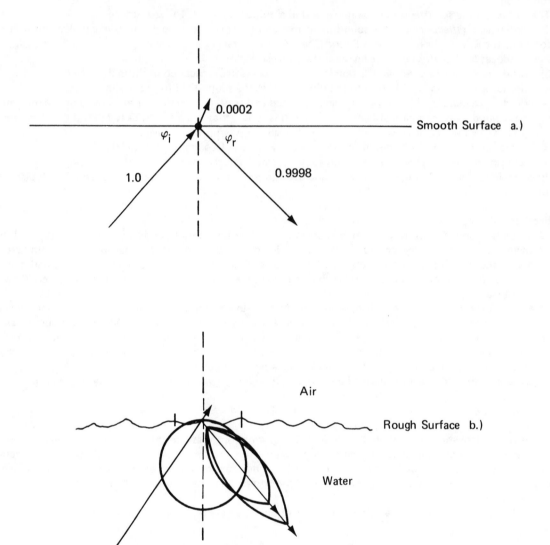

Fig.1.   a) Reflection from a smooth sea surface; nearly all the incident intensity is reflected at the specular angle at which $\varphi_r = \varphi_i$ b) Directional patterns of the return from a rough sea surface for three sea states or degrees of roughness.

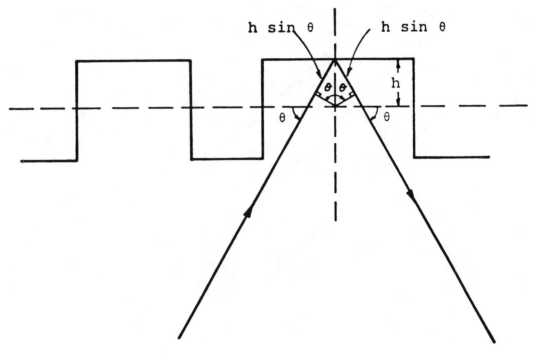

$$R = \text{rms phase difference} = \frac{2\pi}{\lambda} \cdot 2\,h\,\sin\,\theta = 2kh\,\sin\,\theta$$

Fig. 2.   The rectangular wave is an idealized rough surface of roughness height, h.
Conceptual view of the Rayleigh coefficient R. The reflection from the root-mean-square wave crest differs
in phase by R radians from the reflection from the mean surface. The difference in path length is $2h\,\sin\,\theta$.

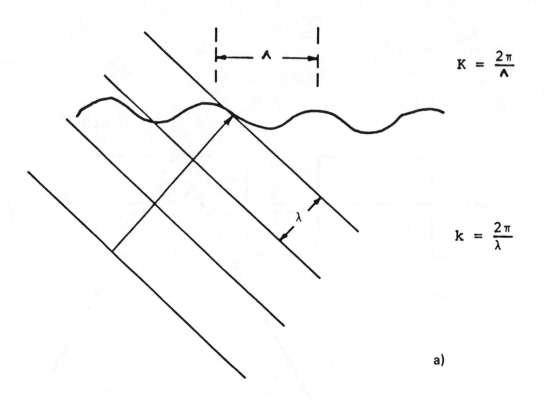

$$K = \frac{2\pi}{\Lambda}$$

$$k = \frac{2\pi}{\lambda}$$

a)

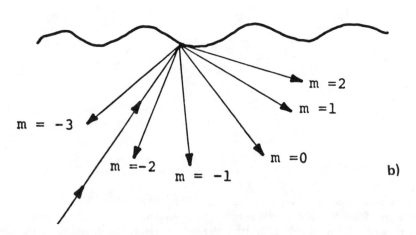

b)

Fig. 3. Reflection from a one dimensional sinusoidal surface. In a) a plane wave of wavelength λ is incident upon the surface of wavelength Λ. In b) the reflection occurs in certain discrete directions m.

$$A_m = \frac{c + c_m}{2C} \cdot J_m \left[(c + c_m)hk \right]$$

where A_m is the amplitude coefficient of the mth mode, $c = \cos\theta$, $c_m = \cos\theta_m$. In the specular direction, this reduces to

$$A_0 = J_0(2hk\cos\theta)$$

The Rayleigh method appears to be valid (1) for $kh \ll 1$. However, for many conditions of k, h, θ, the different theoretical results are not significantly different from one another.

Experimental Verification

No sea-going work has been done to relate these theories to a real quasi-sinusoidal sea surface, such as when a swell is running and a near-sinusoidal shape exists. However, two laboratory model experiments have been made. LaCasce and Tamarkin (8) used a sheet of corrugated cork floating on water to give the sinusoidal pressure release surface. Several surfaces were used, over a frequency range 80 to 300 kHz at 10 kHz intervals and at various angles of incidence. The data was compared with some 13 theoretical models (9). In this comparison, all of the models, including the Rayleigh model, were found to fit the data fairly well, with nothing to suggest that any one is better than the others. More recent measurements have been made by Barnard et al. (10) at a frequency of 100 kHz using pieces of styrofoam cut on a milling machine so as to have $\lambda = 4.5$ cm and $h = 1.5$ cm. Satisfactory agreement was found with one (Uretsky's (5)) theoretical model.

Surface Reflection Interference (Lloyd Mirror Effect)

When the sea surface is smooth enough to be a reflector ($R \ll 1$), an interference pattern is produced between direct-path sound and sound reflected from the sea surface *(Fig 4)*. This sound field may be divided into three parts, 1) a *near-field* close to the source in which the image source is too far away, and the reflected sound is too weak, to produce appreciable interference, 2) an *interference field* in which there are strong loops and nulls in the signal received by a receiver moving outward in range, and 3) a *far-field*, in which there is an increasingly out-of-phase condition between source and image and the intensity falls off as the inverse fourth-power of the range (TL increases as 40 log r). Fig. 4 c) shows the transmission anomaly (transmission loss minus spherical spreading) drawn against a normalized range in these three parts of the sound field from a source and its surface image.

The image interference or Lloyd Mirror effect was first worked out during World War II (11). Strange to say, it has not been systematically studied through at-sea measurements.

The effect of surface scattering and of bandwidth is to fill up the crests and troughs in the interference region. Simple theory assumes straight-line propagation paths; refraction shifts the interference pattern in range — a subject investigated in one of the earliest papers (12) on underwater sound published in JASA.

The Random Surface

By "random" surface is meant an irregular stochastic surface describable only in statistical terms. Referring to *Fig 5a*, the two parameters required for this description are (1) the *roughness height* h, or root mean square deviation of the surface from a plane, defined as: $h^2 = \overline{y^2(x)}$, where $y(x)$ is the height of the surface at a point x relative to the mean surface and the bar represents an average of $y(x)$ over many points and (2) a *correlation distance* determined by

$$\rho(\zeta) = \frac{\overline{y(x)\ y(x + \zeta)}}{h^2}$$

For theoretical tractibility, $\rho(\zeta)$ is commonly taken to be of the form $\rho(\zeta) = \exp(-\zeta^2/T^2)$, where T is a constant, called the *correlation length*. Other functions like $\exp(-\zeta/T)$ appear in the literature, but the normal form just given occurs most often. Both T and h are, in general, functions of direction in the plane of the surface.

For random surfaces, the scattering is quantitatively described by a scattering coefficient s; the quantity $S = 10 \log s$ is called the *scattering strength* of the surface. If a plane wave of intensity I_i is incident on a small area A of a rough surface at angle of incidence θ_1 *(Fig 5b)*, the scattered intensity at distance r at angle θ_2 is

$$I_s = \frac{sA}{r^2} I_i$$

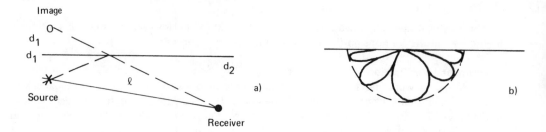

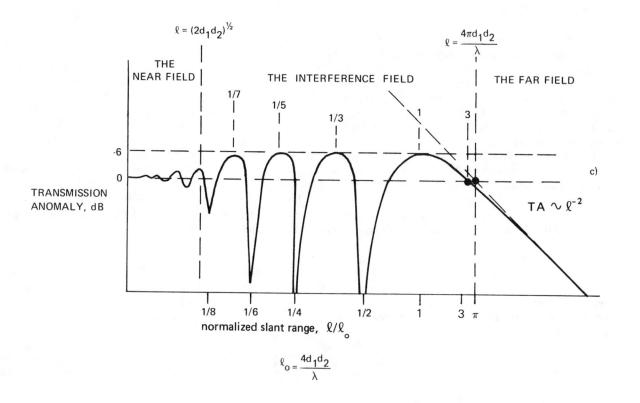

Figure 4. The Lloyd Mirror sound field. In a), a receiver at depth d_2 receives sound from the real source at depth d_1 and slant distance ℓ plus sound from an out-of-phase image. b) shows the resulting directional pattern in the interference region. c) shows the transmission anomaly (TL-20 log r) plotted against normalized range in the three regions described in the text.

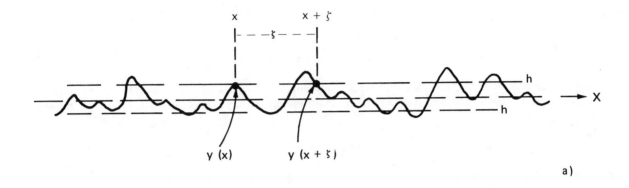

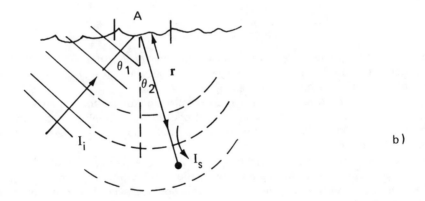

Fig . 5.   a) Cross-section in the x direction of a random surface. b) a plane wave is incident on a small area of the surface. The scattering coefficient s and the scattering strength 10 log s relate I_s to I_i.

In terms of the angles θ_1 and θ_2, Beckmann and Spizzichino (1) derived a theoretical expression for x that was made more useful to sonar by Clay and Medwin (13) as

$$s(\theta_1, \theta_2, \beta) = \frac{F^2 \cos^2\theta_1 \cot^2\beta}{\pi(\cos\theta_1 + \cos\theta_2)^2} \cdot \exp\left[-\frac{(\sin\theta_1 - \sin\theta_2)^2}{(\cos\theta_1 + \cos\theta_2)^2} \cot^2\beta \right] \tag{1}$$

where

$$F = \frac{1 + \cos\theta_1\cos\theta_2 - \sin\theta_1\sin\theta_2}{\cos\theta_1(\cos\theta_1 + \cos\theta_2)}$$

and where β is a slope angle of the surface such that the rms slope is $\frac{1}{2}\tan^2\beta$. Cox and Munk (14) made studies of the glitter pattern of the sun on the sea surface and found that the slope angle β is approximately related to the wind speed by

$$\tfrac{1}{2}\tan^2\beta = 0.003 + 5.12W \times 10^{-3}$$

where W is the wind speed in meters per second.

For *back-scattering*, $\theta = \pi - \theta_1$, and Equation (1) reduces to

$$s(\varphi) = \frac{\cot^2\beta}{4\pi\sin^4\varphi} \exp(-\cot^2\varphi/\cot^2\beta)$$

where φ is the angle of the incident wave with the horizontal. We may note that there is no dependence on frequency; the formulas apply only for a *very rough surface* such that

$$\frac{2\pi h}{\lambda}(\cos\theta_1 + \cos\theta_2) \gg 1$$

and so are restricted to *high* frequencies, *high* grazing angles and *very rough* surfaces.

At the other extreme, for low frequencies, low angles, and slightly rough surfaces, a result given by Eckart (7) predicts a variation of s with the fourth power of frequency.

The scattering of sound by rough surfaces is a vast and challenging subject to theoreticians. As long ago as 1954, a paper by Miles (15) on rough surface scattering was introduced by references to as many as 15 earlier papers; many more could have been added and many more have appeared in subsequent years. Existing summaries of the subject are references (9) and (16).

Fig 6 gives the back scattering strength s for three wind speeds at angles of $0°$ and $60°$. Notice from the curves of *Fig 7* that, as the wind speed increases, the amount of sound going into angles near the specular direction decreases, while that going into other angles increases, as one would expect. This behavior is consistent with the view that, at angles near the specular direction, the sea surface behaves as if it consisted of numerous small mirrors or wave facets which become smaller and more inclined to the horizontal with increasing wind speed.

Frequency Effects

In addition to distributing an incident plan wave in space, the *vertical* motion of the rough sea surface modulates the amplitude of the incident wave, and superposes its own spectrum as upper and lower sidebands on the spectrum of the incident sound. This is shown in *Fig 8*. Any *horizontal* motion of the surface, such as would be caused by wind or currents, also will appear in the sound scattered from the surface and cause a Doppler-shifted and Doppler-smeared spectrum. Such spectra were observed in surface back-scattering at 60kHz by Igarashi and Stern (17) and are illustrated in *Fig 9* for the downwave and upwave directions.

Another observation of real-sea back scattering at 85 kHz showed a frequency *shift* that indicated a surface velocity of 0.6 knot in a 20 knot wind (18). A frequency *spread* was also observed, due to the fact that the surface scatterers do not all have the same velocity. A frequency spread has also been measured for shallow water transmission (19) due probably to the same cause, as well as turbulent water motion of the whole water column; over 5-15 miles, the spreading amounted to ± 0.5Hz for signals in the range 350-2400 Hz. Frequency effects caused by surface

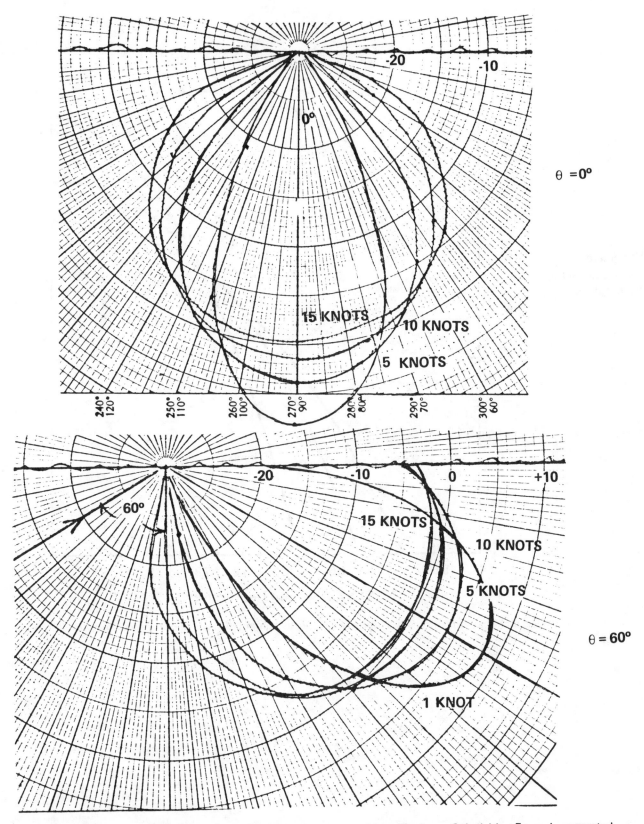

Fig. 6. Sea-Surface Scattering Patterns at 3 Wind Speeds, computed from Beckman-Spiccichino Formula as quoted by Clay & Medwin (13).

10-9

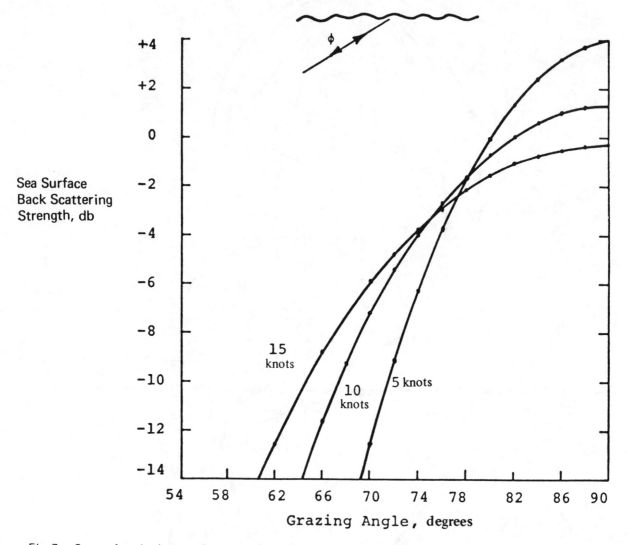

Fig. 7.   Sea surface back-scattering strength at three wind speeds computed from the Clay-Medwin formula (13).

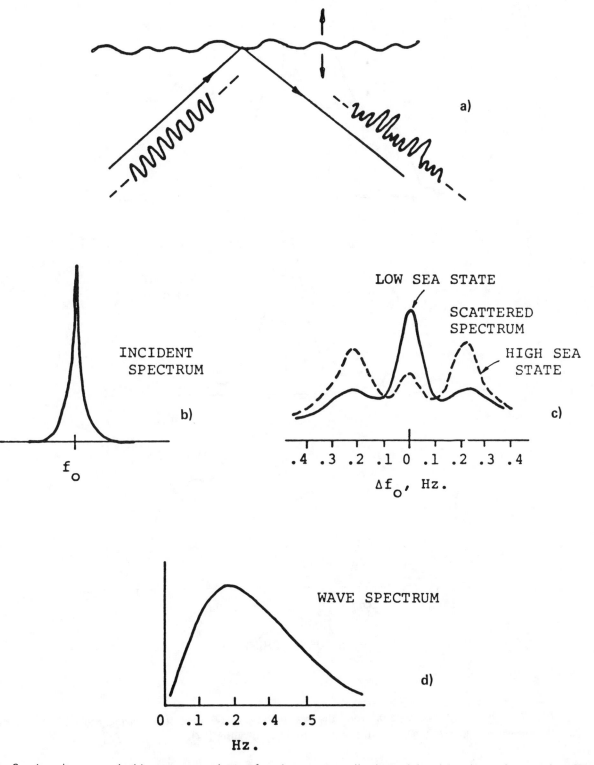

Fig. 8. In a), a wave incident on a moving surface becomes amplitude-modulated by the surface motion. The narrow-band incident spectrum shown in b) acquires sidebands as shown in c), which have the same shape as the motional wave spectrum d). With increasing sea state, the sidebands increase at the expense of the spectral peak at the center frequency f_O.

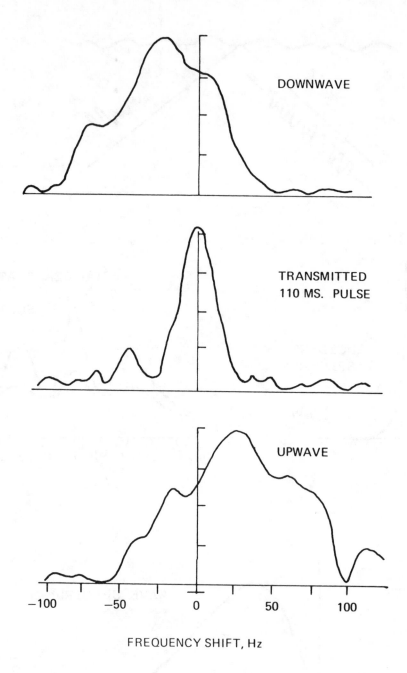

FREQUENCY SHIFT, Hz

Fig . 9.   Backscattering spectra from the sea surface at 60 kHz at a grazing angle of 30° in the downwave and upwave directions of the incident 110 ms pulse. (17).

motion were predicted from theory and observed in a laboratory tank by Roderick and Cron (20). They have been repeatedly observed in at-sea experiments, such as by Brown and Fisk (21), Williams in shallow water (22), Urick (23) and Shooter and Williams (24). Three examples of motional spectra are shown in *Fig 10*. In short, the motion of the sea surface produces amplitude fluctuations of a steady signal, with upper and lower sidebands having the same spectrum as the motion of the surface.

Surface Loss (Forward Scattering)

The loss suffered by sound after encountering the sea surface and being reflected and/or scattered in the specular direction has been investigated at sea over the years by many different investigators using different methods. Unfortunately, the results are made ambiguous in many cases by a mixture of reflected (coherent) and scattered (incoherent) sound in the surface return. Three methods have been used:

I. Comparing the amplitude or energy of pulses returned from the surface with that of the direct arrival.
II. Using the Lloyd-Mirror effect and observing the depth of the minima as the frequency is varied.
III. Measuring the attenuation in the surface duct.

Table I is a tabulation of surface loss measurements taken from the literature. From this compilation it appears that the surface loss is less than 1 db at frequencies less than 1 kHz and rises to about 3 db at 25 and 30 kHz. For long-range propagation over RSR paths at frequencies of a few hundred Hz and less, the surface loss in computer models is commonly taken to be zero.

Scattering Strength (Back-Scattering)

The other direction for which measurements have been made is *back* toward the source. The methods for determining the scattering strength of the sea surface are:

I. Using a directional source/receiver and short pulses, beamed up to the surface at different angles.
II. Using explosive sound sources and a non-directional receiver.

An example of Method I is the use by Urick and Hoover (25) of 60 kHz pulses sent and received by a tiltable narrow-beam transducer. Method II is the only method feasible for low-frequencies, and depends on the geometry to sort out the various grazing angles. A good example is the work of Chapman and Harris (26).

The measured data tend to show a strong variation with frequency at low frequencies and low grazing angles ($R \ll 1$), and no variation with frequency at high frequencies and high grazing angles ($R \gg 1$).

Several attempts to summarize existing data have been made. One, by Chapman and Scott (27), gave an expression based on Eckart's theory:

$$S = 10 \log s = -10 \log 8\pi\beta^2 - 2.17\beta^{-2} \cot^2 \varphi$$

which is said to fit their own data at grazing angles greater than $60°$. Here β is the mean square surface slope and φ is the grazing angle.

Another summary by Schulkin and Shaffer (28), relates s to the Rayleigh parameter R according to

$$s = (aR)^b$$

where a and b are empirical constants determined by the data. Individual series of measurements were fitted by values of b between 1.03 and 2.03. The data as a whole (several series by different workers) gave

$$s = \left[\frac{fh \sin \theta}{3.65 \times 10^4} \right]^{0.99}$$

The data to which this relation applies extended from fh sin θ = 0.5 to fh sin θ = 200 kHz-ft., corresponding to R between 0.6 and 250. The expression for S was said to fit all the data of a series of four measurements with a standard deviation of 5.4 db.

A third expression, given by Chapman and Harris (26) is

$$S = 3.3A \log_{10} \frac{\varphi}{30} - 4.24 \log_{10} A + 2.6$$

$$A = 158(\upsilon f)^{1/3}$$

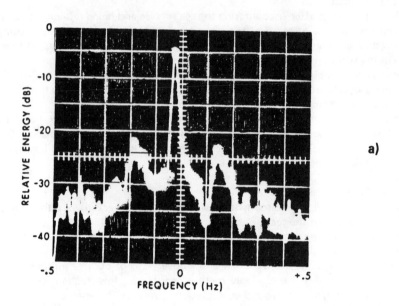

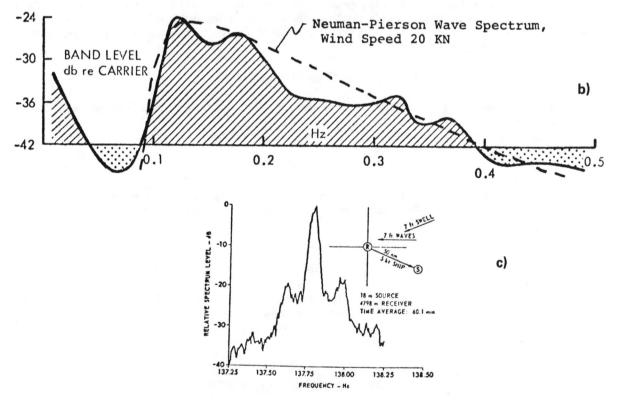

Fig. 10. Three examples of sea surface motion-induced spectra.
    a) range 19 mi., shallow water, frequency 1702 Hz, **(30)**.
    b) range 45 kyd., bottom-reflected paths, 275 Hz, **(32)**.
    c) range 50 mi., RSR paths, freq. 138 Hz, **(33)**.

where φ is the grazing angle in degrees, υ is the wind speed in knots and f is the frequency in Hz. This empirical expression was based on octave band analyses of explosive shot returns from the sea surface (Method II) over the range 0.4 and 6.4 kHz and wind speeds zero to 30 knots. *Fig 11* shows curves computed from this expression for several frequencies.

The Bubbly Layer

At wind speeds of 10 knots or so, a layer of scattering has been observed to exist (29) just below the surface. Oscilloscope photos of returns using a vertical transducer showed a return blob extending 25 feet below the surface that appeared suddenly at a wind speed of 9 knots. This return was likely to have been caused by air bubbles whipped into the sea by the waves and carried by wind mixing to a depth below the surface.

Physical Processes of Back-Scattering

The peculiar measured variation of s with angle at 60 kHz suggest three processes in different regions of angle to account for the return *(Fig 12)*. At low grazing angles (Region I) the scattering is due to the bubbly layer just mentioned, causing the curves to be flat. At high angles (Region III), the reflection from small flat wave facets ($R \geqslant 1$) was said to be effective, while at intermediate angles roughness-caused scattering was postulated to occur. There is approximate quantitative agreement between the measurements in Region III and the Beckmann-Spicci-chino formula (Eq. 1).

TABLE 1

Compilation of
Measurements of Loss
At The Sea Surface

Measured Loss db	Conditions			Ref.	METHOD
	Freq. kHz	Wave Height ft	Grazing Angle degrees		
3	25	———	4-19	30	I
3	30	0.2-0.8	8	31	II
(interdecile range −10 to +3 db)					
0	0.4-6.4	Wind Speeds 5-20 knots	10-55	32	I
3* 1*	5 1	2 5	1-5 "	33	III
1 3	3.5 "	3 "	17 35	34	I
0-1	{ .53 1.03	———	0-45±	35	II
0-1	8	Sea State 2	22-52	36	I

*Calculated from Loss = 0.1(fh)$^{3/2}$. Applies to surface duct propagation only.

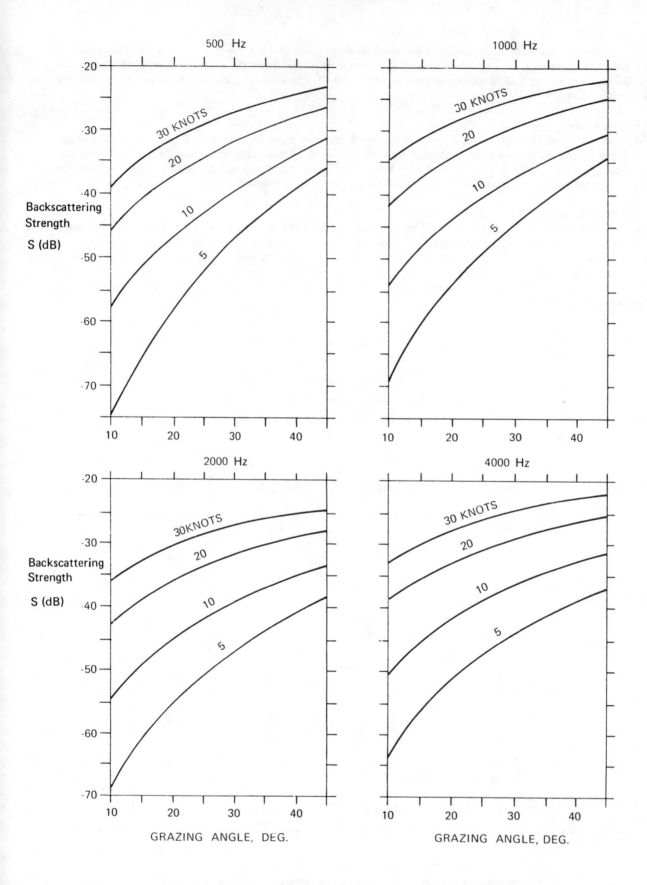

Fig. 11.   Sea surface backscattering strengths vs. grazing angle computed from Chapman-Harris formula.

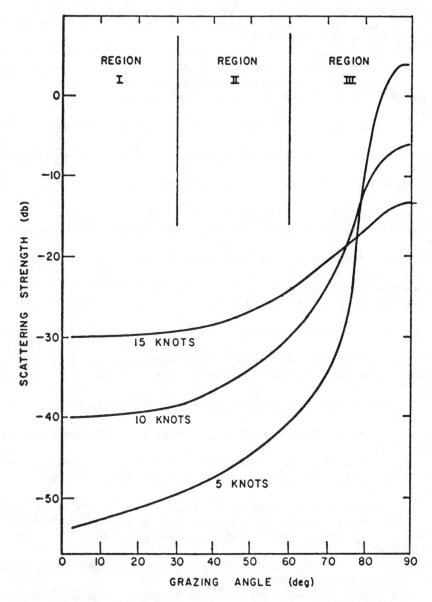

Fig. 12. Measured sea surface back scattering strengths vs. grazing angle at 60 kHz. Different processes of scattering are suggested in three regions of grazing angle.

REFERENCES

1. P. Beckmann and A. Spizzichino, Scattering of Electromagnetic Waves from Rough Surfaces, Pergamon Press, 1963, Chaps. 2, 3, 4.
2. J. L. Jones, C. B. Leslie and L. E. Barton, Acoustic Characteristics of Underwater Bottoms, JASA *36*, 154, 1964.
3. Lord Rayleigh, *Theory of Sound*, Dover Publications, New York, 1945, Vol. II, pp 89-94.
4. W. C. Meechan, Variational Method for the Calculation of the Distribution of Energy Reflected from a Periodic Surface, Jour. Appl. Phys. *27*, 361, 1956.
5. J. L. Uretsky, Scattering of Plane Waves from Periodic Surfaces, Annals of Physics *33*, 400, 1965.
6. H. S. Heaps, Reflection of Plane Waves of Sound from a Sinusoidal Surface, Jour. Appl. Phys. *28*, 815, 1957.
7. C. Eckart, Scattering of Sound from the Sea Surface, JASA *25*, 566, 1953.
8. E. O. LaCasce and P. Tamarkin, Underwater Sound Reflection from a Corrugated Surface, Jour. Appl. Phys. *27*, 138, 1956.
9. R. F. Meyer and B. Romberg, Acoustic Scattering in the Ocean Project Trident Report 1360863, A. D. Little Co., 1963.
10. G. R. Barnard and others, Underwater Sound Reflections from a Pressure Release Sinusoidal Surface, JASA *39*, 1162, 1966.
11. Physics of Sound in the Sea, National Defense Research Committee Div. 6 Summary Technical Report 8, 1946, p. 32 and p. 95.
12. R. W. Young, Image Interference in the Presence of Refraction, JASA *19*, 1, 1947.
13. C. S. Clay and H. Medwin, High Frequency Acoustical Reverberation from a Rough Sea Surface, JASA *36*, 2131, 1964.
14. C. Cox and W. Munk, Measurements of the Roughness of Sea Surface from Photographs of the Sun's Glitter, J. Opt. Soc. Am. *44*, 838, 1954.
15. J. W. Miles, Non-specular Reflection at a Rough Surface, JASA *26*, 191, 1954.
16. L. Fortuin, A Survey of Literature on Reflection and Scattering of Sound at the Sea Surface, JASA *47*, 1209, 1970.
17. Y. Igarashi and R. Stern, Wind-Wave Generated Doppler Shifts in Surface Reverberation, JASA *49*, 802, 1971.
18. R. H. Mellen, Doppler Shift of Sonar Backscatter from the Surface, JASA *36*, 1395, 1964.
19. K. V. Mackenzie, Long Range Shallow Water Signal Level Fluctuations and Frequency Spreading, JASA *34*, 67, 1962.
20. W. J. Roderick and B. F. Cron, Frequency Spectra of Forward Scattered Sound from the Ocean Surface, JASA *48*, 759, 1970.
21. M. V. Brown and G. V. Fisk, Frequency Smearing of Sound Forward-Scattered from the Ocean Surface, JASA *55*, 744, 1974.
22. R. Williams, Estimating Ocean Wind Wave Spectra by Means of Underwater Sound, JASA *53*, 910, 1973.
23. R. J. Urick, Amplitude Fluctuations of the Sound from a Low-Frequency Moving Source in the Deep Sea, NOLTR 74-43, 1974.
24. J. Shooter and S. Mitchell, "Acoustic Sidebands in CW Tones Received at Long Ranges" JASA *60*, 829, 1976.
25. R. J. Urick and R. M. Hoover, Backscattering of Sound from the Sea Surface, etc., JASA *28*, 1038, 1956.
26. R. P. Chapman and H. H. Harris, Surface Backscattering Strengths Measured with Explosive Sound Sources, JASA *34*, 1592, 1962.
27. R. P. Chapman and H. D. Scott, Backscattering Strengths Measured over an Extended Range of Frequencies and Grazing Angles, JASA *36*, 1735, 1964.
28. M. Schulkin and R. Shaffer, Backscattering of Sound from the Sea Surface, JASA *36*, 1699, 1964.
29. R. J. Urick, Processes of Sound Scattering at the Ocean Surface and Bottom, Jour. Mar. Res. *15*, 134, 1956.
30. R. J. Urick and H. L. Saxton, Surface Reflection of Short Supersonic Pulses in the Ocean, JASA *19*, 8, 1947.
31. L. N. Liebermann, Reflection of Underwater Sound from the Sea Surface, JASA *20*, 498, 1948.
32. R. H. Addlington, Acoustic Reflection Losses at the Sea Surface Measured with Explosive Sources, JASA *35*, 1834, 1962.
33. H. W. Marsh, Sound Reflection and Scattering from the Sea Surface, JASA *35*, 240, 1963.
34. R. H. Ferris and W. Kuperman, An Experiment on Acoustic Reflection from the Sea Surface, NRL Rept. 7075, 1970.
35. M. A. Pedersen, Comparison of Experimental and Theoretical Image Interference in Deep-Water Acoustics, JASA, *34*, 1197, 1963.
36. R. B. Patterson, Intensity Fluctuation of Direct and Surface Reflected Signals from a Deep Source, Jour. Underwater Acoust. *12*, 41, 1962.

CHAPTER 11

REFLECTION AND SCATTERING BY THE SEA BOTTOM

Introduction

The sea bottom has many of the same effects on sound propagation as does the sea surface. It reflects and scatters sound, making bottom-bounce sonars possible, as well as producing bottom reverberation. It casts a shadow in the positive gradient water overlying it, when the water is deep. It produces an interference pattern in the radiation from a source; image-interference directivity patterns caused by bottom reflection have been computed by Mackenzie (1) for rock, sand and silt bottoms.

But the return of sound from the sea bed is vastly more complex than from the sea surface for several reasons. *First*, the bottom is more variable in its acoustic properties, inasmuch as it may vary in composition from hard rock to a soft mud. *Second*, it is often layered, with a density and sound velocity that change gradually or abruptly with depth. *Third*, it is more likely to be laterally inhomogeneous, with different characteristics over relatively short distances. *Fourth*, sound can readily enter a sedimentary bottom and be reflected back into the sea by sub-bottom layers, or be refracted back by the steep velocity gradient in sediments. For these reasons, the loss of intensity suffered by sound encountering the sea bed is less easily predictable than the loss at the sea surface.

Reflection versus Scattering from the Sea Bottom

The ratio of the intensity of the returned sound from a rough bottom to the intensity of an incident plane wave is

$$\mu = \mu_0 \exp - \left(\frac{4\pi h \sin\theta}{\lambda} \right)^2 = \mu_0 e^{-R^2}$$

where μ_0 is the reflection coefficient that would exist if the surface were smooth, and the exponential factor is the effect of the surface roughness, where R is the Rayleigh parameter. This expression is quoted by Clay (2) and appears in a paper by Lysanov (3). The reflection coefficient μ_0 depends upon the density, compressibility, rigidity, absorption, and layering of the bottom materials, while the exponential term depends on its roughness characteristics, which, incidentally, for real world bottoms, are almost totally unknown. In other words, the exponential term expresses the reduction in the intensity of the reflected wave caused by scattering at the rough water bottom interface.

The sound received at a point Q above the sea bottom consists of the following contributions, shown diagrammatically in *Fig 1*:
1. a reflection from P spreading as if originating from the image O^1 in the bottom of the real source O.
2. *scattered sound* from the bottom in the vicinity of P.
3. *scattered sound* from other portions of the bottom such as A_1 and A_2, each such small area radiating spherical waves to the receiver at Q.
4. *reflection* and *scattering* from sub-bottom layers.
5. *refracted sound*, entering the bottom at R, turned upward back into the water by the velocity gradient in the bottom.

The result is that, when a short pulse strikes a rough bottom, it becomes, after reflection and scattering, a long drawn-out blob, often with a sharp high amplitude beginning followed by a decaying tail of scattering.

The scattered and reflected components are affected differently by the distance of source and receiver above the bottom, as illustrated in *Fig 2*. When the bottom is a *reflector*, the component of the transmission loss due to spreading is 20 log(2r) in the absence of refraction; but, when it is a scatterer, each portion of the bottom radiates spherical waves, and the spreading loss becomes 20 log r^2 = 40 log r. The difference between these two losses can be very great.

The partition between reflection and scattering is important for bottom-bounce sonars. The partition
a) determines the fall-off of the bottom return with distance from the bottom and
b) determines the *correlation loss* of correlation sonars.

Reflection Models

Various theoretical models have been used to relate μ_0 to the physical properties of natural bottoms. The models range from the single two-fluid Rayleigh model (4) to models that include bottom absorption, rigidity (i.e. shear waves) and layering. The theory and the resulting expressions for μ_0 will not be repeated here, but may be found

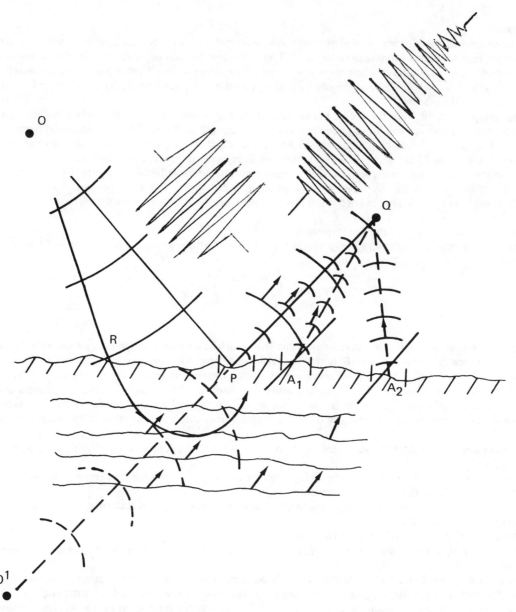

Fig. 1. A receiver at Q receives reflected and scattered sound from a variety of sources on and in a sedimentary bottom. A square-topped incident pulse becomes a long-tailed blob at Q if the initial source O and the receiver at Q are non-directional.

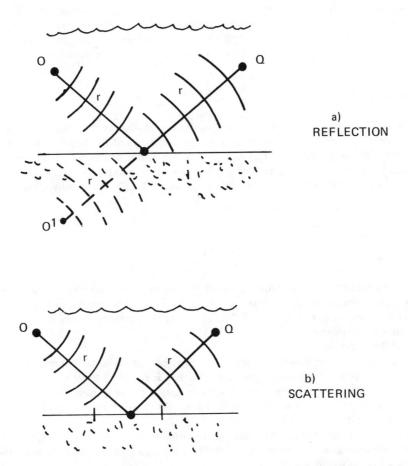

a)
REFLECTION

b)
SCATTERING

Fig. 2.   In a) the bottom is a reflector and the spreading loss from the source O to Q via the bottom is 20 log (2r). In b) the bottom is a scatterer and the spreading loss is 20 log r^2.

in Brekhovskikh's book (5), and are listed in Appendix I. The theoretical expressions have appeared in the U.S. literature in various forms and they are always computerized for computation.

For two fluids separated by a plane boundary, the reflection loss depends on the density and sound velocity in the two media. *Fig 3* shows diagrammatically how the loss varies with grazing angle for different combinations of density ratio, $m = \rho_2/\rho_1$ and $n = c_1/c_2$, where ρ_1 and c_1 are the density and sound velocity of the upper medium (water) and ρ_2 and C_2 are the density and sound velocity of the lower medium (bottom). Of the four combinations shown, a) and c) are most characteristic of sedimentary bottoms. In combination c) there exists a *critical angle*, while in a) and d) there is an *angle of intromission* where the loss reaches a maximum. When attenuation exists in the lower medium, as it always does for the real ocean bottom, these angles become smeared out and obscured, as shown by the dashed curves in the figure.

Some specific examples showing the reflection loss $10 \log \mu$, in dB, computed using Brekhovskikh's equation 3.25 (Appendix I), as a function of grazing angle for different values of the two ratios and a dimensionless attenuation coefficient, are given in *Fig 4*. The parameter of the curves in this figure is the dimensionless quantity $\alpha = \alpha^1 \lambda / 2\pi$ where α^1 is the amplitude attenuation coefficient in units of reciprocal length and λ is the wavelength.

Acoustics of Sediments
1) Density

In a simple additive mixture of two components, such as a sediment, which is a suspension of mineral particles in water, any property of the mixture equals the sum of the properties of the two components separately, weighted by the proportion of each in the mixture. For example, in a mixture of medium 1 and medium 2, let medium 1 have density ρ_1 and let it occupy a faction β of the volume of the mixture (β is the volume concentration). Let medium 2 have density ρ_2 with a volume concentration equal to $(1 - \beta)$. The *additive "law"* states that the density of the mixture is

$$\rho_{mix} = \beta\rho_1 + (1 - \beta)\,\rho_2$$

This "law" has been found to hold closely for sediments and sedimentary rocks by Nafe and Drake (35), who found from numerous measurements on sediments that $\rho_{mix} = 2.68 - 1.65\beta$, where medium 1 is taken to be water ($\rho_1 = 1$) and medium 2, the sedimentary particles ($\rho_2 = 2.68$). Here β is the *porosity* of the sediment, equal to the volume concentration of water in the mixture.

2) Compressional-Wave Velocity

Hamilton, et al. (6), reported measurements on a variety of shallow-water sediments off San Diego using both an in-situ probe method and a laboratory resonant chamber method. Additional measurements were made by Shumway (7). Sutton, et al. (8) investigated the velocity in core samples of deep ocean sediments by placing a pair of transducers on the sides of the core and measuring the travel time of short pulses diametrically through the core. This same method was described later by Winokur (9).

A compilation (10) of data has shown that the mixture formula, cited by Wood (11) and verified experimentally in the lab on kaolin-water mixtures by Urick (12), is not a bad approximation to the measured data. The mixture formula gives for the sound velocity

$$\nu = (\rho_{mix}\,k_{mix})^{-1/2} = [(\rho_w\beta + \rho_s(1 - \beta))\,(k_w\beta + k_s(1 - \beta))]^{-1/2}$$

where ρ_w, k_w and ρ_s, k_s are the density and compressibility of the water and solid particles, respectively. Measured velocities are somewhat higher than those given by this formula for low-porosity partly-indurated sediments, where grain-to-grain contact of the sediment particles exists.

The mixture formula predicts that the sound velocity in high porosity sediments should be slightly *less* than that of water. The reason for this is that as sediment is added to water, the *increase* of density of the mixture is more rapid than the *decrease* of compressibility, resulting in an initial *decrease* in sound velocity. The existence of low velocity bottoms, at least for the top few feet of the bottom material, have been repeatedly inferred (13) (14) from an observed phase reversal of the bottom reflection. Also, in stagnant in-shore waters, a low velocity condition in the bottom can be caused by gas (methane) in the bottom produced by organic decomposition (15).

3) Compressional-Wave Attenuation

A number of investigations have been made of the attenuation of compressional waves in natural (7) (16) (17) and artificial (18) sediments by methods involving (a), a resonant cylinder of the materials, and (b), a source

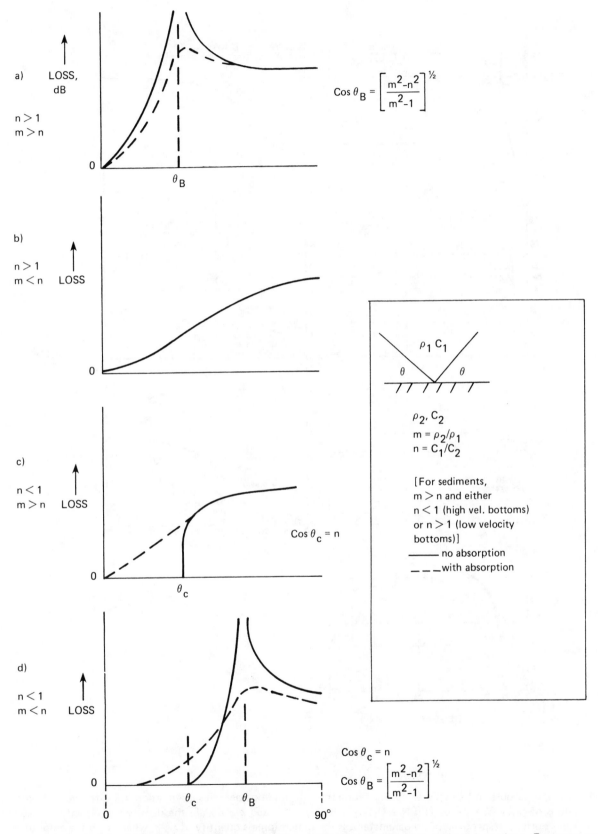

a) $n > 1$, $m > n$

$$\cos \theta_B = \left[\frac{m^2 - n^2}{m^2 - 1} \right]^{1/2}$$

b) $n > 1$, $m < n$

c) $n < 1$, $m > n$

$$\cos \theta_C = n$$

$\rho_1 C_1$

$\theta \qquad \theta$

ρ_2, C_2
$m = \rho_2/\rho_1$
$n = C_1/C_2$

[For sediments,
$m > n$ and either
$n < 1$ (high vel. bottoms)
or $n > 1$ (low velocity
bottoms)]

——— no absorption
- - - - with absorption

d) $n < 1$, $m < n$

$$\cos \theta_C = n$$
$$\cos \theta_B = \left[\frac{m^2 - n^2}{m^2 - 1} \right]^{1/2}$$

Fig. 3.   Curves of reflection loss vs. grazing angle for two fluids separated by a plane boundary. For most real bottoms only cases a) and c) apply. The dashed curves show the effect of attenuation in the bottom.

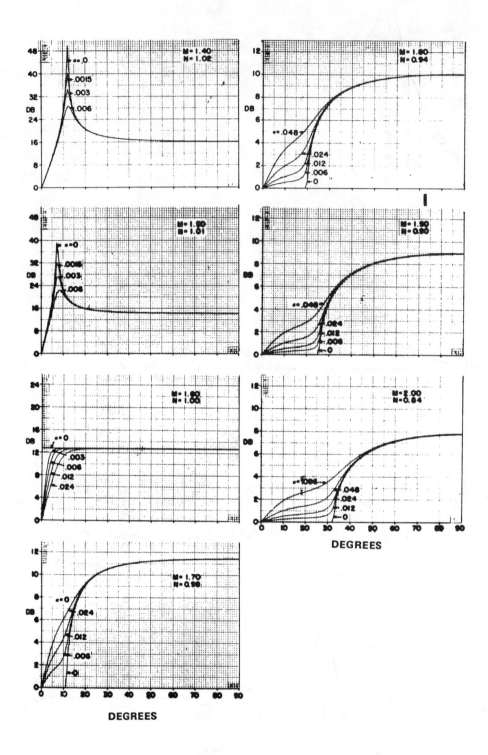

Fig. 4. Computed bottom loss vs. grazing angle for a smooth fluid bottom with attenuation, for different combinations of ratios $M = \rho_2/\rho_1$ and $N = C_1/C_2$, where ρ_1, C_1 and ρ_2, C_2 are the density and velocity of water and bottom, respectively. The parameter α is the dimensionless quantity $\alpha^1\lambda/2\pi$, where α^1 is the amplitude attenuation coefficient in units of $(\text{length})^{-1}$. Computed from Brekhovskikh's equation 3.25, Appendix I.

and receiver located in the material at different distances. A compilation made by Hamilton (19) over a wide frequency range shows that at frequency f kHz the attenuation coefficient in natural, saturated sediments, in db per meter, is approximately equal to 0.25 f. The measurements fell within the cross-hatched band in *Fig 5*, with a tendency in the data for the more dense sediments, such as compact sands, to have a higher attenuation than less dense higher porosity sediments, such as muds. In sediments the attenuation is several orders of magnitude higher than in pure water (β = 1.0) at the same frequency, as shown by the dashed curve in Fig 5.

4) Summary

The most important single physical property that determines the acoustic characteristics of sediments is their *porosity*. The importance of porosity has been verified by all workers on the subject (20); indeed, a fair estimate of velocity, density, and attenuation of sediments can be made from a knowledge of porosity alone. While porosity is not the sole determinant of the acoustic behavior of sediments — (Sutton (8) found that grain size and carbonate content have a small effect on velocity) — porosity does serve as a rough estimator of reflectivity of many sediments that are smooth enough for rough surface scattering to be insignificant. For example, a rough correlation between reflection loss and porosity using Marine Geophysical Survey data has been found (21) at oblique as well as at normal incidence. Another study (22) resulted in an expression μ_0 = 0.65 − 0.65β for the pressure reflection coefficient at normal incidence, with, it was claimed, a correlation coefficient of 0.97.

A more complete summary of the acoustic properties of the sea bottom, with attention to shear waves and deep depths, is given in Appendix II.

Measured Reflection Losses

The standard method of measurement is to use pings or explosive pulses and to compare the amplitude, intensity, or energy density (integrated intensity) of the reflected pulse with that of the observed or computed pulse travelling via a non-reflected path.

Most published papers describing field data include an attempt (always sucessful!) to match the measured reflection losses to a theoretical model. For example, Mackenzie (1) reported results at 1 kHz between grazing angles of 12° to 84° for three bottom types — sand, silt and clayey silt; the two-layer model with attenuation (Table I) was used for comparison. Bucker, et al., (23) got data in two areas off California and one in the Bering Sea; a layered model with attenuation and rigidity was employed. Menotti, et al., (24) used data from a bottomed vertical array at Bermuda and a 1 kHz CW source, and claimed agreement with a model having liquid layers resting on a semi-infinite solid. A similar model was invoked by Winokur and Bohn (25) for data in 2400 fm water off Yucatan. Barnard, et al. (26), did work in a laboratory tank and compared with theory for a single fluid layer on a semi-infinite solid. Cole (27) was able to fit 4.5 kHz data on the abyssal plain off Newfoundland with theory for an attenuating fluid bottom.

Much of the data show a loss rising with angle at low angles, followed by a nearly constant loss extending over a wide range of higher angles. High porosity bottoms, having a sound velocity less than that of water, tend to have maximum loss at an angle of 10° to 20°, where an *angle of intromission* would be expected to occur in the absence of attenuation in the bottom. However, when narrow-band pulses are used, measured losses often are irregular and variable, and show peaks and troughs due to the interference effects of layering in the bottom. Measured data rarely show a sharp *critical angle* — as would be inferred from the Rayleigh reflection model, because of the existence of attenuation in the bottom.

The Prediction Problem

As a practical matter in making performance predictions of bottom-bounce sonars, the end-product of bottom loss research is to be able to predict the bottom loss for regions of the world for which no measured data exist. The prediction must be based on the available, often fragmentary, knowledge (plus conjecture) of the geology and bathymetry of the bottom in the area where a prediction is required.

When bottom cores exist, a prediction of loss can be made from measured core properties, using one of the theoretical models, for frequencies high enough to be acoustically governed by the upper few meters of the bottom. However, bottom cores obtained at sea reveal that the sea bottom is remarkably complex in its structure; it contains, typically, a large number of layers of varying properties and thicknesses. Numerous such cores have been obtained as part of the Marine Geophysical Survey of the U.S. Navy Oceanographic Office and measurements of sound velocity in many of the cores have been published (28).

Many bottoms are penetrated by the low frequencies of many modern sonars to depths of tens or even perhaps hundreds of feet. Fortunately, the reflectivity of the deep ocean floor can be correlated to some extent with the physiographic "provinces" or "domains" recognized from depth sounding data. Physiographic charts showing these provinces have been published by Heezen and Tharp (29) and by Heezen and Menard (30). As examples, average bottom loss curves for two large physiographic provinces of the North Atlantic are given in *Fig 6*. Much of the difference between provinces may be due more to a difference in bottom roughness than to a difference in composition or layering. For example, a bottom known to be rough, such as the Mid-Atlantic Ridge, where little or no

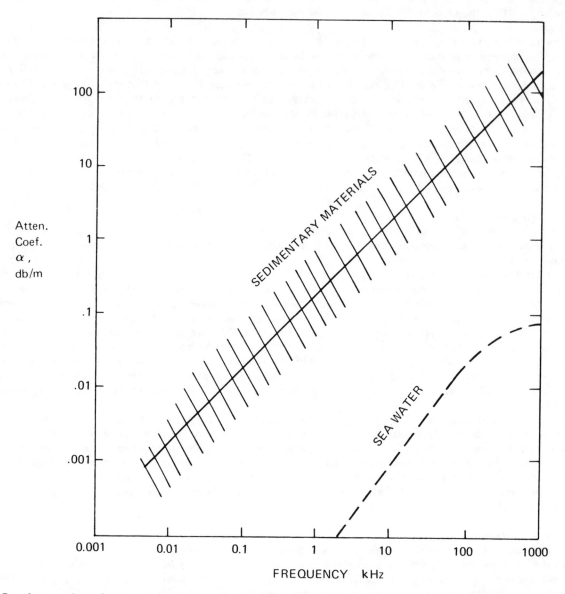

Fig. 5. Attenuation of compressional waves in natural sediments and sedimentary strata. The measurements, as compiled by Hamilton (19) fall within the cross-hatched area. The straight line through this area represent $\alpha = 0.25f$, where α is in dB/m and f is the frequency in kHz. The dashed curve at the lower right shows the attenuation in pure sea water.

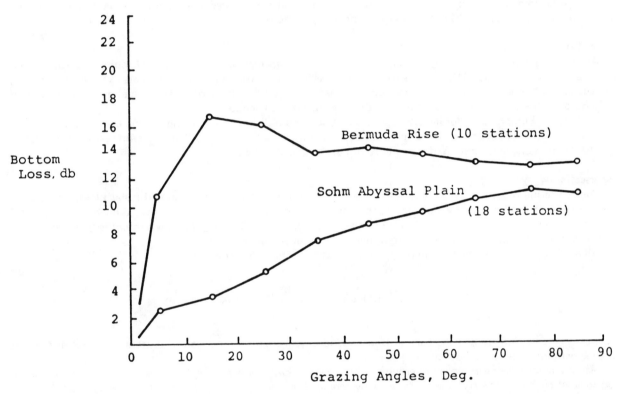

Fig. 6. Average Bottom Loss in Two Physiographic Provinces of the North Atlantic Ocean in the Frequency Band 0.5-8.0 kHz. Based on Marine Geophysical Survey data.

sedimentary cover exists, is likely to have a high loss. Generally speaking, low losses occur on the flat abyssal plains where cores show numerous sand layers (deposited by turbidity currents) that are good reflectors. All in all, a knowledge of the physiography, the depositional and erosional bottom processes and the subbottom geoloy is the key to the prediction problem in bottom-bounce echo-ranging.

Practically speaking, bottoms can be divided as a matter of convenience into a number of classes according to the magnitude of their bottom loss. Examples of loss versus angle curves for nine bottom classes are given in *Fig 7*; their shape is based on measured data, theory and conjecture. Classified bottom-class charts exist that serve to tie these curves to different ocean areas. Thus, if the bottom-loss chart indicates a Class 3 bottom, the Class 3 curve would be used to find the loss at any grazing angle in a sonar prediction problem.

At very low frequencies, such as the vicinity of 100 Hz, there is evidence that all bottoms tend to have the same loss within a standard deviation of 3 or 4 db. This is shown by *Fig 8*, taken from the work of R. E. Christensen of the Naval Oceanographic Office. The interesting negative losses at low angles are doubtless due to upward refraction within the bottom and a consequent enhancement of the sound in the water — an occurrence that has been demonstrated by field observations (32). A ray diagram showing upward bottom refraction is shown in *Fig 9*.

Other Effects

As mentioned above, scattering and layering produce *pulse distortion* (33), as does reflection at grazing angles less than the critical angle (34). This distortion is most evident for explosive pulses, which are extended into a long, drawn out blob, even at normal incidence. Layering alone distorts the shape of individual pulses and is a cause of pulse-to-pulse fluctuation in successive pings if the geometry is changing (35).

Thompson, Flowers and Hurdle (36) used a sonobuoy and a distant ship pinging off the bottom at 19 kHz to obtain the scattering pattern of the deep ocean bottom. An example of one of their scattering patterns is given in *Fig 10*. There is only a suggestion of a greater return at the specular angle.

Backscattering

The scattering of sound by the bottom in the *backward* direction has been measured many times, over a wide frequency range and for many bottom types. The measurement literature is extensive, though the theoretical literature is scanty. A compilation of measured data has been made (37). *Fig 11* shows smoothed, average curves of backscattering vs grazing angle drawn from the data in this compilation.

All modern data are expressed in terms of *back-scattering strength* S, defined as

$$S = 10 \log s = 10 \log \frac{I_{scat}}{I_{inc}} \cdot r^2 \cdot A$$

where I_{scat} is the intensity of the back-scattered sound at range r from a portion of bottom of area A and I_{inc} is the incident intensity at the bottom.

Measurements have been made either with *directional sinusoidal pulses* or with *explosives*. The relation to angle is provided by the *transducer directionality* or by *geometry* in the two cases, respectively. An early example of the former (38) and a more recent example of the latter (39) may be mentioned.

It was discovered, when the first measurements were made during World War II, that bottom reverberation was highest over coral rock bottoms, less over sand, and least over mud. In subsequent years, a correlation of back-scattering strength with the size of the sediment particles in a sedimentary bottom has been repeatedly observed; the "type" of bottom, using a terminology based on particle size, such as sand, clay, clayey-silt, silty-sand, etc, has long been used as a correlative of back-scattering. Mud bottoms tend to be smooth and have a low impedance contrast to water; coarse sand and rocky bottoms tend to be rough, with a high impedance contrast. Thus, bottom types as so defined are acoustically reasonable classifiers of bottoms for backscattering. Yet there is a large spread in measured data for apparently the same bottom type, perhaps due, in part at least, to penetration of sound into the bottom below a superficial layer.

A knowledge of S is particularly important in acoustic *minehunting* where a small object must be found when lying right on the sea bed. A more expanded treatment of bottom back-scattering and reverberation may be found in the author's book (40).

Side-Scattering

Only one study of scattering in other directions by the sea bottom appears to have been made (41). In this work, two directional transducers 1½ miles apart in shallow water were trained in angle so that their beams intersected. The intensity of the sound scattered out of one beam and received on the other was measured. It was found that at 22 kHz, the scattering was isotropic over the angular range from the backward direction around to 150° in the forward direction. This finding of isotropy is a great convenience in handling bistatic sonar prediction problems where bottom reverberation is involved.

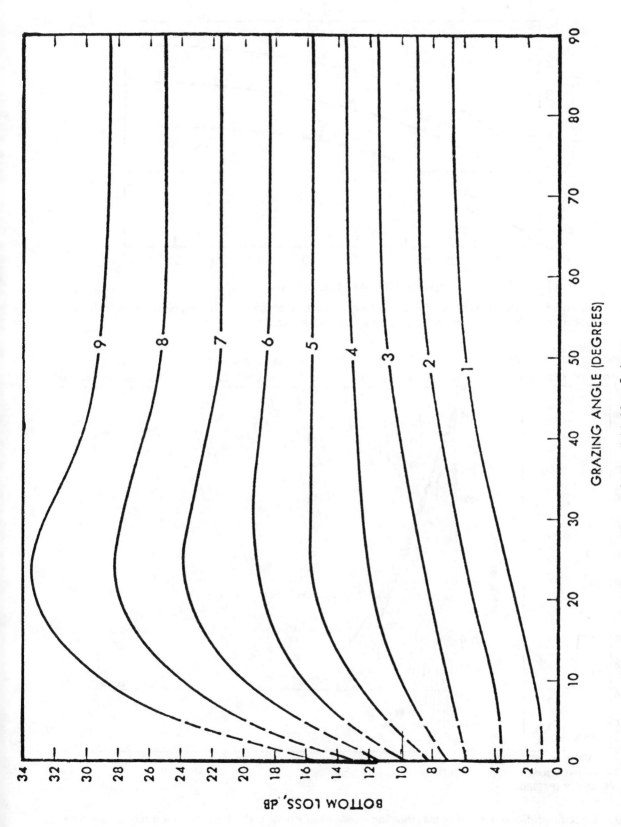

Fig. 7. Nominal Bottom Loss Curves for the Frequency Range 1-4 kHz, divided into 9 classes.

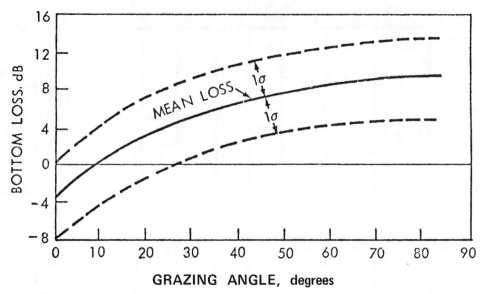

GRAZING ANGLE, degrees

Fig. 8. Results of a compilation of low frequency measurements of bottom loss. Dashed curves show limits of one standard deviation. Compiled by R. Christensen, quoted in Ref. 31.

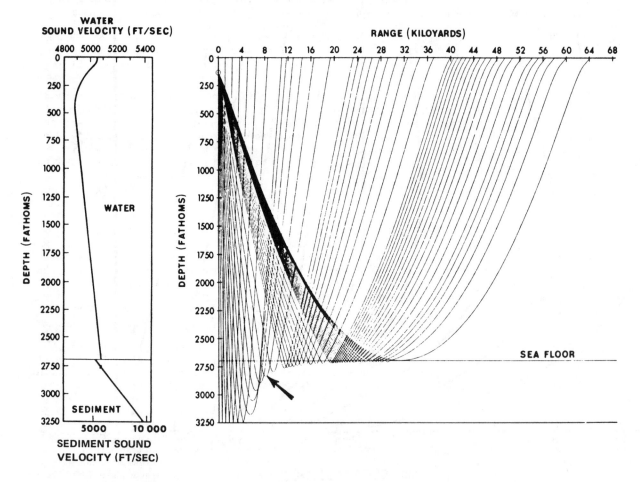

Fig. 9. Velocity profile and ray diagram, showing upward refraction in the bottom. The arrow shows where a refracted arrival from a shot was first observed on the records. (32).

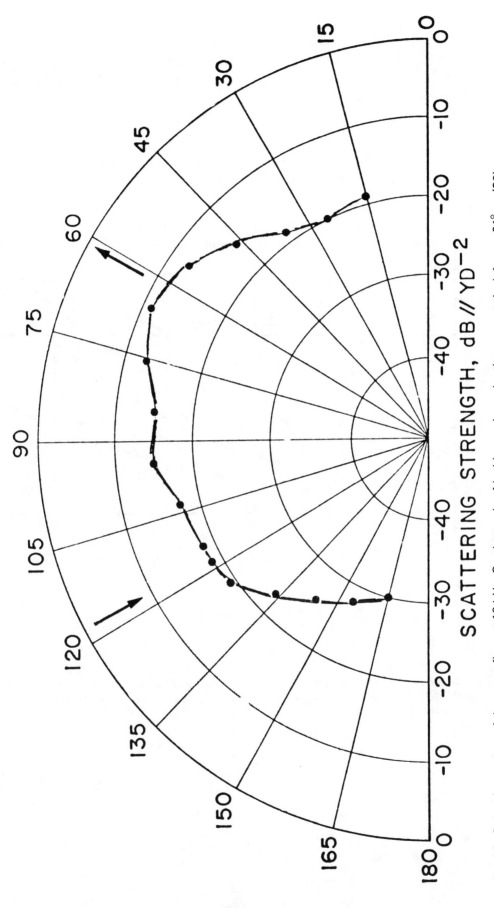

Fig. 10. Scattering pattern of the ocean floor at 19 kHz. Grazing angle of incidence, shown by the arrow at the left, was 61°. (36).

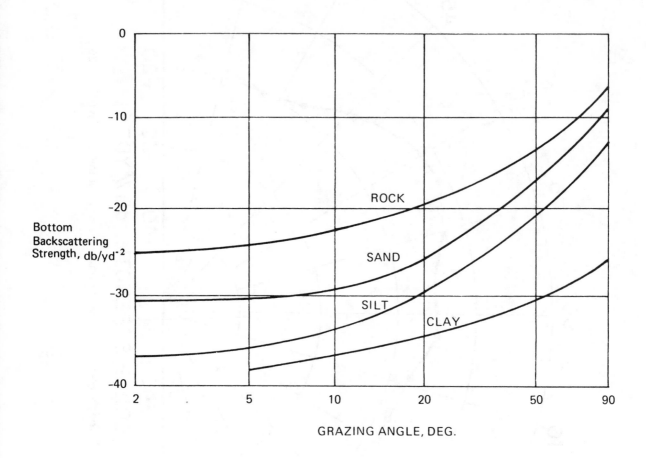

Fig. 11. Smooth curves of bottom backscattering strength vs. grazing angle for various bottom types. Frequency range 0.5-100 kHz. Individual measurements show deviations averaging about 5 db from these curves. From data compiled in (37).

APPENDIX I

REFLECTION FORMULAS given in L. N. Brekhovskikh,
Waves in Layered Media, Academic Press, New York, 1960.

APPENDIX II

ACOUSTIC PROPERTIES OF THE SEA FLOOR*

We consider in this section in greater detail the salient features of bottom acoustics, as described in the literature. This literature is extensive; many measurements have been made and many papers have appeared on the velocity, attenuation and density of sound in sediments and rocks. Here we will present only a short summary of these subjects, with references to the existing literature.

A number of summary papers on the subject have been published by E. L. Hamilton; particularly noteworthy is a review by Hamilton of the basic elastic and physical properties of marine sediments[42]. An older summary paper that may be mentioned is one by Nafe and Drake [43].

Compressional Waves

Velocity. The speed of compressional waves in sediments has been measured at shallow depths below the bottom by acoustic probes in situ and by core measurements in the laboratory. At deeper depths, a variety of geophysical techniques involving travel time measurements have been employed, including even using conventional sonobuoys and explosive shots for work over deep water [44].

The speed of sound in a sediment is closely related to its porosity and therefore to its density. At the sea bed, high porosity/low density sediments, such as muds, have compressional wave velocities only slightly less (up to 3%) than that of the overlying water; low porosity/high density sediments, such as hard sands, have a velocity 10-20% greater than that of the overlying water. For example, by means of probes placed in the bottom by divers and by measurements on core samples, Hamilton [45] found a coarse sand with a porosity of 39% to have a velocity of 1.836 km/sec, while a silty clay of porosity 76% had a velocity of 1.519 km/sec, compared to the water velocity of about 1.56 km/sec. Similarly, off San Diego, again using probes inserted into the sediments by divers, Hamilton [46] measured sediment velocities ranging from 1.463 km/sec for a "clayey fine silt" of porosity 65.6% to 1.750 km/sec for a "coarse sand" of porosity 38.3%. The bottom water alone (porosity 100%) had a velocity of 1.478 km/sec.

The many measurements made during the Marine Geophysical Survey are summarized, in terms of porosity, in *Fig 12*.

Since porosity and density are closely related, one would expect the velocity to be closely related to the density of the sediment; that such is indeed the case has been the subject of a paper by Hamilton[48]. Other correlatives between velocity and the physical characteristics of sediments, such as grain size, have been established [49].

In hard rocks, such as those of the basement beneath a sedimentary column, much higher sound speeds occur. In basalts, for example, the velocity ranges from 3.5 to 6.5 km/sec, again depending on the density of the material [48]. In the early work of Worzel and Ewing (Ref. 1 Chap. 7) refraction shooting established velocities in the range 4.62-6.63 km/sec for the crystalline basement beneath the sediments at the locations where measurements were made.

Below the sea bed, as the porosity is reduced by the increasing pressure of the overburden and as the sediment particles are forced into closer contact, the velocity increases. This increase with depth is extremely rapid compared to the velocity gradient in the overlying water; it is found[43] to lie in the range 0.5 to 2.0 sec^{-1} (meters per second per meter of depth), with a convenient average value of 1.0 sec^{-1}. (In isothermal water, the corresponding value is .017 sec^{-1}).

This steep gradient cannot continue indefinitely, but exists only for the first kilometer or two of depth. At deeper depths, a smaller gradient must exist. *Fig 13* shows velocity versus depth as found by reflection shooting at two offshore East Coast locations.

The near-surface value of 1 sec^{-1} means that sound rays for compressional waves in a sedimentary column are bent sharply upward; rays at shallow depths have a radius of curvature of only about 2 km. *Fig. 14* shows the circular rays corresponding to a 1 sec^{-1} gradient in a sedimentary column extending to a depth of 4 km.

In deep water, this steep sedimentary gradient, together with the fact that the sound velocity and density of the sediments at the sediment-water interface are nearly the same, means that sound can readily penetrate into a sedimentary bottom and quickly come back out of it by refraction. This kind of refracted sound was indeed observed by Christensen, et al. [50], in shot tests in 2700 fathoms of water; bottom refraction can account for the apparent low, or even negative, bottom reflection loss observed at low frequencies and small grazing angles.

Attenuation. The attenuation of compressional waves in sediments and rocks has been measured by a wide variety of methods, ranging from in-situ probes in sediments to resonance techniques in bars of solid rock. Such

*From R. J. Urick and H. L. Price, Seismic Sensing of Sounds in the Sea, Tracor, Inc., Contract N00173-77-C-0063, 1977, Sections 3.0 and 4.0, 1977. Also in Proc. Workshop on Seismic Propagation in Shallow Water, sponsored by Office of Naval Research, 6-7 July 1978.

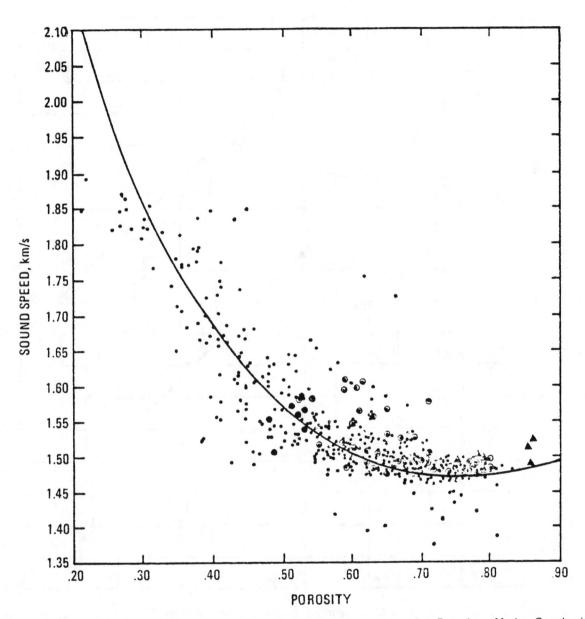

Fig. 12.   Sound speed versus porosity from measurements made on core samples. Data from Marine Geophysical Survey (47).

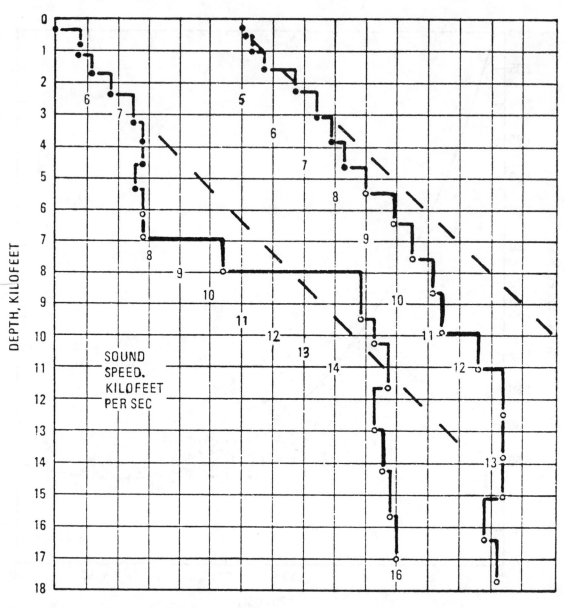

Fig. 13. Velocity profiles at two East Coast locations. Data — courtesy Shell Oil Company. Dashed lines show a velocity gradient of 1 sec^{-1}. (25).

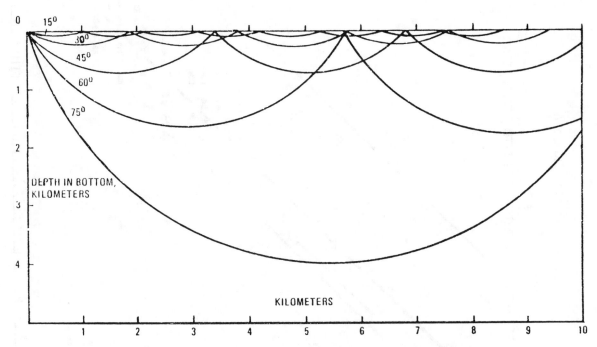

Fig. **14.** Ray diagram for a linear gradient of $1 \, \text{sec}^{-1}$. Rays are arcs of circles with centers on a line 1.676 km above zero depth.

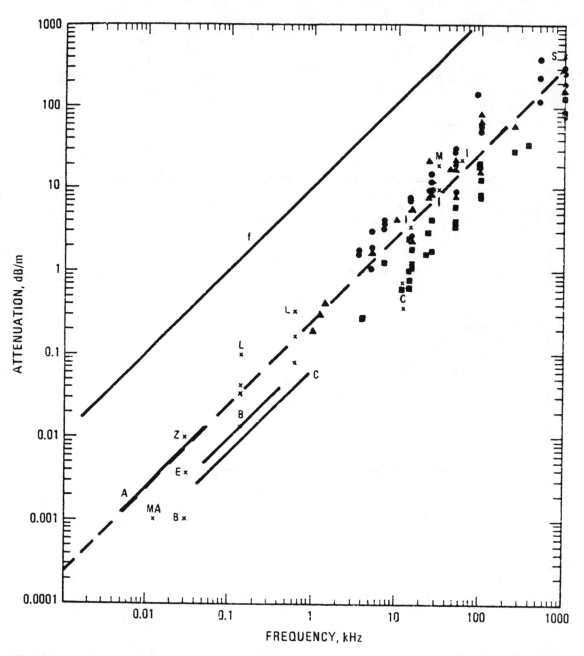

Fig. 15. Attenuation versus frequency in natural, saturated sediments and sedimentary strata. The different symbols refer to different measurements. The long solid straight line shows a first-power variation with frequency. The dashed line is drawn for k = .25 dB/km/Hz. (51).

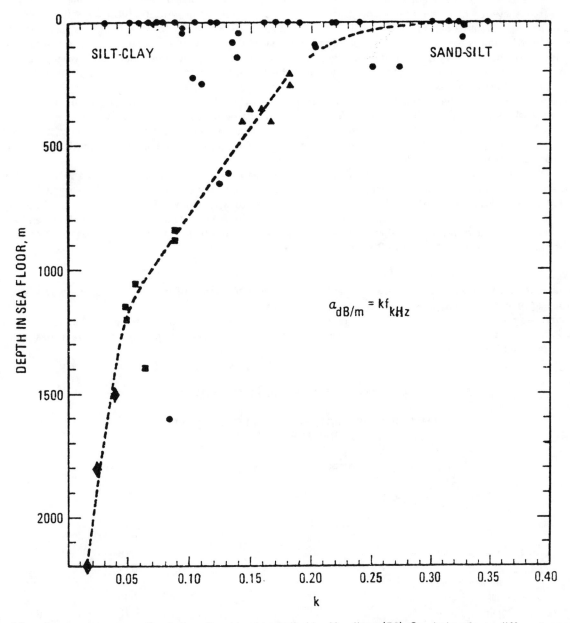

Fig. 16. Attenuation versus depth in sediments as compiled by Hamilton (53). Symbols refer to different measurements. The coefficient k is the attenuation coefficient in dB per kilometer at 1 Hz.

measurements extend over a wide frequency range. For sediments and sedimentary rocks, Hamilton (51) has compiled data from many sources over a wide range of frequency; his plot of measured values is reproduced in *Fig 15* Evidently the attenuation coefficient tends to increase approximately as the first power of the frequency; accordingly, at a frequency of f kHz, the attenuation coefficient α in dB/meter can be written α(dB/m) = kf(kHz), where k is a constant. k is the attenuation coefficient in dB per kilometer per Hz. In *Fig 15* , the dashed line is drawn for k = .25 dB/km/Hz, and is seen to give reasonable fit to the measured data. However, a recent paper by Stoll (52) casts doubt as to whether this linear variation extends downward to our very low frequency range, where another source of loss ("frame loss") may become dominant over the loss due to viscosity. Like velocity, attenuation is strongly related to porosity in sediments.

Because of compaction, the attenuation of compressional waves decreases rapidly with depth in natural sedimentary materials. *Fig 16* shows the coefficient k as plotted against depth by Hamilton (53). While there is wide variability with sediment type (i.e., porosity/density) at shallow depths where most measurements exist, the rapid decrease of k with depth is evident. At a depth of 2 km, the attenuation in a sedimentary column is only about one-tenth of its value at the surface.

Lower values of attenuation are found in hard rocks. Here too, the attenuation coefficient tends to vary as the first power of frequency; this is equivalent to a constant Q, independent of frequency, not only for rocks but for metals and other solids as well (54). *Table 1* gives some values of k, converted from data given in a book by White (55), for both compressional and shear waves. The compressional wave values average .034 dB/km and are lower by about an order of magnitude than those for sediments at the sea bed. This rate of attenuation is comparable with that for sediments at a depth of 2 km or so. Fig *16* .

Shear Waves

In sediments, shear waves have a vastly different velocity and attenuation than do compressional waves, since their propagation is governed by a vastly different elastic constant.

Velocity. At the sea bed, sediments have an extremely low shear wave velocity. A review by Hamilton of this subject (56) shows that at a depth of one meter below the sea bed, marine sands and silt-clays have a shear velocity in the range 50-150 m/sec.

TABLE 1   ATTENUATION COEFFICIENTS IN HARD ROCKS.

VALUES OF k (dB/km/Hz) DERIVED FROM TABLE 3-1
OF REFERENCE 55

	Compressional Waves	Shear Waves
Granite	.019	—
	.017	—
	.119	.146
	.062	.075
Limestone	.023	.025
	.013	.011
Sandstone	.015	—
Chalk	.004	.005
Shale	.200	1.78

However, the increase with depth or compaction is rapid, increasing to about 200 m/sec at 10 meters and to about 400 m/sec at a depth of 100 meters. Surface shear waves, traveling along the bottom interface, have comparable velocities; two independent measurements of Stonely waves gave velocities of 89-123 m/sec in one experiment (57) and 83-110 m/sec in the other (58). In still another measurement, Bucker, et. al. (59), used vertical geophones on the bottom in 60 ft. of water and, with blasting caps as sources at ranges of 2, 15, 30 and 45 ft., measured the velocity of Stonely waves to be 170 m/sec, with an attenuation of .06 dB/ft at 25Hz, corresponding to a value of k of 7.9 dB/km at 1 Hz. Such waves travel, in theory, with a speed of 0.9 that of body shear waves (60).

Shear waves are dispersive. For Rayleigh and Love waves observed in earthquakes, the average shear velocity was found to lie between 200 and 400 m/sec in the upper 0.5 km of sediments for waves of periods shorter than 5-10 seconds (0.1-0.2 Hz); for longer periods, the velocity rapidly rises to about 4000 m/sec (56).

Attenuation. The subject of the attenuation of shear waves in marine sediments has, like many aspects of the subject, been reviewed by Hamilton **(61)**. In this summary the following values for a number of materials are listed:

Material	k (dB/km per Hz)
Sand	13.2
Sand and Clay	4.8
Silt	13.4
Mud (silt, clay)	17.3
Water-saturated Clay	15.2
Tertiary Mudstone	10.1
Pierre Shale	3.4

The average of these values is 11 dB/km/Hz; thus, at a frequency of 10 Hz, the shear wave attenuation coefficient would range from 34 to 173 dB/km. An attenuation of this same magnitude would apply for waves of the Rayleigh/ Stonely type which are surface shear waves traveling near the water-bottom interface. Deeper-going body shear waves would suffer a smaller attenuation, since the shear coefficient, like the compressional wave coefficient, must decrease with depth. However, it appears that the shear wave attenuation is larger by at least an order of magnitude than the attenuation of compressional waves and is so large at sonar frequencies ($>$5 Hz) as to prohibited long-distance propagation. Although strong Rayleigh waves that have traveled long distances are commonly observed in earthquakes, they are always of a low frequency ($<$1 Hz) and have a corresondingly low attenuation.

On the other hand, in rocks such as those of a crystalline basement, the attenuation of shear waves is comparable with, or only slightly greater than, the attenuation of compressional waves.* This is indicated by the values listed in Table **1**.

Types of Seismic Waves

When a compressional sound wave in water strikes a sedimentary bottom at P *(Fig 17)*, a variety of waves is, in principle, generated.

The most familiar is the *bottom-reflected compressional wave* (R, Fig **17**) that remains in the water medium and has been much studied in connection with bottom-bounce sonars. Within the bottom itself, there appears a *compressional wave* C starting at the water-bottom boundary at nearly the same angle as that of the incident wave (since the bottom velocity there is not greatly different from the water velocity) and propagating outward in range with upward refraction. Another generated wave is the *body shear wave*, S, originating at a smaller angle. It is similarly upward refracted by the gradient of shear velocity in the bottom and is more highly attenuated than the compressional wave C. The third wave is a surface shear wave ST propagating along the bottom with a still higher attenuation, since the rate of attenuation in a sedimentary column is highest at its top. ST is a guided polarized surface wave; it is called the *Stonely wave* when the medium on top of the solid boundary is a fluid, or a *Rayleigh wave* when the upper medium is a vacuum or air. Its particle motion is in the vertical plane in the retrograde direction if the propagation is to the right. In the literature, this wave is variously called the *SV wave*, the *modified-Rayleigh wave* or the *Scholte wave*.

When a shear wave impinges on a solid boundary, a *Love wave* or *SH wave* can be generated; like the Stonely wave, the Love wave is a polarized surface wave, but its particle motion is in the horizontal plane. Finally, when solid layers exist, flexural waves in the layer can be excited and propagated, and are termed *Lamb waves*.

All of these waves in the bottom, with the exception of the compressional wave, have a shear component and in sediments suffer the high attenuation characteristic of shear waves.

The partition of energy between these various waves is a classic problem in seismology. For two uniform solid media separated by a plane boundary, the problem was solved long ago in a classic paper by Knott **(62)**, who derived the equations that satisfy the boundary conditions in this idealized case. For our simpler problem of an incident compressional wave, the solution was later given by Zoeppritz, and may be found in a seismology text by Macelwane and Sohon **(63)** as well as in a short readable book by Bullen **(64)**. But for our real world conditions, this idealized model would seem to have little value; the energy partition for a realistic water-bottom model appears to be a yet-unsolved problem.

---

*A recent paper **(65)** describes earthquake observations in the Pacific Ocean, made with a high frequency seismograph, of strong shear waves at frequencies up to 15 Hz, travelling over paths several thousand miles long, that apparently had an attenuation *less* by a factor of two or three than the accompaning compressional waves.

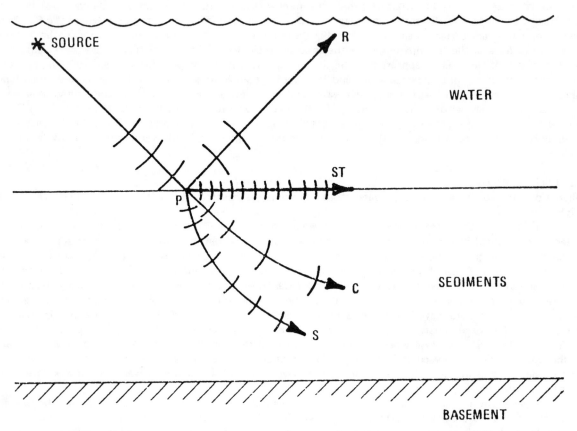

Fig. 17. Waves generated by a wave in water striking the bottom. The symbolic wave fronts indicate the wave-length of the various waves.

REFERENCES

1. K. V. Mackenzie, Reflection of Sound from Coastal Bottoms, JASA *32*, 221, 1960.
2. C. S. Clay, Coherent Reflection of Sound from the Ocean Bottom, J. Geoph. Res. *71*, 2037, 1966.
3. Y. Lysanov, Average Decay Law in a Surface Sound Channel with an Uneven Boundary, Soviet Physics Acoustics *12*, 425, 1967.
4. Lord Raleigh, Theory of Sound, Dover Publications, New York 1945, vol II, pp 78-82.
5. L. N. Brekhovskikh, *Waves in Layered Media*, Academic Press, New York, 1960.
6. E. L. Hamilton and others, Acoustic and Other Physical Properties of Shallow Water Sediments off San Diego, JASA *28*, 1, 1956.
7. G. Shumway, Sound Speed and Absorption Studies of Marine Sediments by a Resonance Method, Pt. I, Geophysics *25*, 451, 1960; Pt. II, Geophysics *25*, 659, 1960.
8. G. H. Sutton, H. Berckhemer and J. E. Nafe, Physical Analysis of Deep Sea Sediments, Geophysics *22*, 779, 1957.
9. R. Winokur, Sediment Sound Speed Using a Pulse Technique, Proc. Third Symp. on Military Oceanography, p. 181, 1966.
10. J. E. Nafe and C. L. Drake, Physical Properties of Marine Sediments, Lamont Geol. Obser., Columbia Univ., Report 2, Contract NObsr 85077, 1961.
11. A. B. Wood, *A Textbook of Sound*, Macmillan Co., New York, 1941, pp 360-363.
12. R. J. Urick, A Sound Velocity Method for Determining the Compressibility of Finely Divided Substances, Jour. Appl. Phys. *18*, 983, 1947.
13. E. L. Hamilton, Low Sound Velocities in High Porosity Sediments, JASA *28*, 16, 1956.
14. J. C. Fry and R. W. Raitt, Sound Velocities at the Surface of Deep Sea Sediments, Jour. Geophys. Res. *66*, no. 2, 1961.
15. R. Bobber, Acoustic Characteristics of a Florida Lake Bottom, JASA *31*, 250, 1959.
16. E. G. McLeroy and A. DeLoach, Sound Speed and Attenuation from 15-1500 kHz Measured in Natural Sea Floor Sediments, JASA *44*, 1148, 1968.
17. A. B. Wood and D. E. Weston, Propagation of Sound in Mud, Acustica *14*, 156, 1964.
18. L. D. Hampton, Acoustic Properties of Sediments, JASA *42*, 882, 1967.
19. E. L. Hamilton, Compressional Wave Attenuation in Marine Sediments, Geophysics *37*, 620, 1972.
20. H. Brandt, Factors Affecting Compressional Wave Velocity in Unconsolidated Marine Sand Sediments, JASA *32*, 171, 1960.
21. R. J. Urick and D. E. Bradley, Prediction of Bottom Reflection Loss from a Single Sediment Parameter, Naval Ordnance Laboratory Tech. Rep. 68-127, 1968.
22. R. W. Faas, Analysis of the Relationship Between Acoustic Reflectivity and Sediment Porosity, General Dynamics EB Div Tech. Rep. U417-67-036, 1967.
23. H. P. Bucker and others, Reflection of Low Frequency Sonar Signals from a Smooth Ocean Bottom, JASA *37*, 1037, 1965.
24. F. R. Menotti and others, Studies of Observed and Predicted Values of Bottom Reflectivity as a Function of Incident Angle, JASA *38*, 707, 1965.
25. R. S. Winokur and J. Bohn, Sound Reflection from a Low Velocity Bottom, JASA *44*, 1130, 1968.
26. G. R. Barnard and others, Underwater Sound Reflection from Layered Media, JASA *36*, 2119, 1964.
27. B. F. Cole, Marine Sediment Attenuation and Ocean Bottom Sound, JASA *38*, 291, 1965.
28. B. C. Schreiber, Sound Velocity in Deep Sea Sediments, J. Geophy. Res. *73*, 1259, 1968.
29. B. C. Heezen and H. W. Menard, Topography of the Deep Sea Floor in *The Sea*, edited by M. N. Hill, Interscience Publishers, New York, 1963.
30. B. C. Heezen and M. Tharp, Physiographic Diagram of the Atlantic Ocean, Sheet 1, Physiographic Diagram of the South Atlantic Ocean, Geological Society of America, 1961.
31. R. J. Urick, Sound Transmission Through the Ocean Floor, article in *Physics of Marine Sediments*, L. Hampton, ed Plenum Press, New York, 1974.
32. R. E. Christensen, J. A. Frank and W. H. Geddes, Low Frequency Propagation via Shallow Refracted Paths Through Deep Ocean Unconsolidated Sediments, JASA *57*, 1421, 1975.
33. B. F. Cron and A. H. Nuttall, Phase Distortion of a Pulse Caused by Bottom Reflection, JASA *37*, 486, 1965.
34. A. H. Nuttall and B. F. Cron, Signal Waveform Distortion Caused by Reflection off Lossy Layered Bottoms, JASA *40*, 1094, 1966.
35. M. V. Brown and J. Richard, Interference Pattern Observed in Reflections from the Ocean Bottom, JASA *37*, 1033, 1965.

36. K. P. Thompson, K. D. Flowers and B. G. Hurdle, Scattered Fields from the Ocean Bottom, JASA *38*, 932(A), 1965.

37. H. Wong and W. Chesterman, Bottom Backscattering Strengths Near Grazing Incidence in Shallow Water, JASA *44*, 1713, 1968.

38. R. J. Urick, Backscattering of Sound from a Harbor Bottom, JASA *26*, 231, 1954.

39. J. P. Buckley and R. J. Urick, Backscattering from the Deep Sea Bed at Small Grazing Angles, JASA *44*, 648, 1968.

40. R. J. Urick, *Principles of Underwater Sound*, 2ed, McGraw-Hill, N. Y. 1975, pp 243-251.

41. R. J. Urick, Side Scattering of Sound in Shallow Water, JASA *32*, 351, 1960.

42. E. L. Hamilton, Elastic Properties of Marine Sediments, Jour. Geophys. Res *76*, 579, 1971.

43. J. E. Nafe and C. L. Drake, Physical Properties of Marine Sediments, *The Sea*, Interscience Publishers, New York, 1963.

44. E. L. Hamilton and others, Sediment Velocities from Sonobuoys, Jour. Geophys. Res *79*, 2653, 1974.

45. E. L. Hamilton, Sound Velocity and Related Properties of Marine Sediments, North Pacific, Jour. Geophys. Res *75*, 4423, 1970.

46. E. L. Hamilton, Acoustic and Other Physical Properties of Shallow Water Sediments Off San Diego, Jour. Acous. Soc. Am. *28*, 1, 1956.

47. B. C. Schreiber, Sound Velocity in Deep Sea Sediments, Jour. Mar. Res. *73*, 1259, 1968.

48. E. L. Hamilton, Sound Velocity — Desnity Relations in Sea-Floor Sediments and Rocks, Jour. Acous. Soc. Am. 63, 366, 1978.

49. R. S. Anderson, Statistical Correlation of Physical Properties and Sound Velocity in Sediments, paper in Physics of Sound in Marine Sediments (L. Hampton, ed.), Academic Press, New York, 1974.

50. R. E. Christensen, J. A. Frank, and W. H. Geddes, Low Frequency Propagation via Shallow Refracted Paths Through Deep Ocean Unconsolidated Sediments, Jour. Acous. Soc. Am. *57*, 1421, 1975.

51. E. L. Hamilton, Geoacoustic Models of the Sea Floor, paper in *Physics of Sound in Marine Sediments*, Plenum Press, New York, 1974.

52. R. D. Stoll, Acoustic Waves in Ocean Sediments, Geophysics, *42*, 715, 1977.

53. E. L. Hamilton, Sound Attenuation as a Function of Depth in the Sea Floor, Jour. Acoust. Soc. Am. *59*, 528, 1976.

54. L. Knopoff, Attenuation of Elastic Waves in the Earth, *Physical Acoustics*, Vol. III, Part B, (W. P. Mason, ed.) Academic Press, New York, 1965.

55. J. E. White, *Seismic Waves*, McGraw-Hill, New York, 1965.

56. E. L. Hamilton, Shear Wave Velocity Versus Depth in Marine Sediments: A Review, Geophysics *41*, 985, 1976.

57. E. L. Hamilton and others, Velocities of Pressional and Shear Waves in Marine Sediments Determined In-Situ from a Research Submarine, Jour. Geophy. Res. *75*, 4039, 1970.

58. E. G. McLeroy, and A. Deloach, Measurements of Sea Bottom Elastic Waves form Underwater Explosions, Mine Defense Laboratory Report U2727, 1968.

59. H. P. Bucker and others, Use of Stoneley Waves to Determine the Shear Velocity in Ocean Sediments, Jour. Acoust. Soc. Am. *36*, 1595, 1964.

60. L. Knopoff, On Rayleigh Wave Velocities, Bull. Seism. Soc. Am. *42*, 307, 1952.

61. E. L. Hamilton, Attenuation of Shear Waves in Marine Sediments, Jour. Acoust. Soc. Am. *60*, 334, 1976.

62. E. G. Knott, Reflection (sic) and Refraction of Elastic Waves with Seismological Applications, Phil. Mag. *48*, 64, 1899. See a summary in L. D. Leet Earth Waves, John Wiley & Sons, New York, 1950, Chapt III.

63. J. B. Macelwane and F. W. Sohon, *Theoretical Seismology*, John Siley & Sons, New York, 1936, Sect. 79.

64. K. E. Bullen, An Introduction to the *Theory of Seismology*, Cambridge University Press, 1953.

65. D. A. Walker et al, Spectral Analyses of High Frequency Pn and Sn Phases Observed at Great Distances in the Western Pacific, Science *199*, 1333, 1978.

66. R. J. Urick, Underwater Sound Transmission Through the Ocean Floor, *Physics of Sound in Marine Sediments*, L. Hampton, ed., Plenum Press, New York, 1974.

CHAPTER 12

TEMPORAL COHERENCE (FLUCTUATION)

Introduction

A CW signal or a series of pulses from a steady source is always received by a distant hydrophone as a fluctuating signal or series of pulses. The reason for this is that the sea and its boundaries contain inhomogeneities of various kinds, and these inhomogeneities are constantly moving in an irregular manner relative to the source or receiver. The result is to produce scattering and multi-path transmission of constantly varying phase and amplitude, and the various contributions add up to give a fluctuating signal at a distant point. Fluctuation may be said to be caused by the *moving inhomogeneities* of the sea. Completely "frozen" inhomogeneities, as in a completely solid ocean, would not cause fluctuation between a fixed source and a fixed receiver.

Fluctuation, or "temporal" coherence, refers to the changes in the signal received by a single hydrophone, relative to a steady source, over a period of time. The changes occurring between spatially separated hydrophones constitute "spatial" coherence and are the subject of the following chapter.

Fluctuations have been a topic of continued interest in underwater sound ever since World War II, when they attracted interest because of their scientific implications as well as because of their importance in sonar detection and maintenance of contact. An early — and still a most excellent — summary of the subject was written by C. Eckart and R. R. Carhart (1) in 1950, while an indication of its continued popularity over the years is a recent bibliography (2) that lists a total of 132 literature references devoted to fluctuations in underwater sound transmission.

Causes of Fluctuation

At the beginning of reference (1) it is said that "if sound of constant intensity and frequency is transmitted through the sea from one ship and received on another at some fixed distance, the intensity of the signal received from one second to the next will not be constant; it fluctuates, often by a factor of ten. Indeed, the presence of fluctuation is perhaps the most constant characteristic of sound in the sea!"

A number of causes, or physical processes, producing fluctuation may be mentioned. An obvious source of change in a received signal is *motion of the platform* on which source or receiver is mounted, such as the roll, pitch and yaw of an unstabilized sonar transducer, causing a wandering-about of the sonar beam. A less obvious cause is the presence of *thermal microstructure* in the body of the sea, resulting in a twinkling of a distant source in basically the same way that the microstructure of the optical index of refraction in the atmosphere causes the twinkling of stars. The *sea surface*, through its motion when rough and its image interference when smooth, is a cause of fluctuation when sound travelling via surface paths is allowed to contribute to a received signal. *Scatterers* in the body of the sea, such as fish, air bubbles and turbulence patches are contributors to fluctuation in received sound. Finally, *internal waves* are a form of oceanic inhomogeneity that are believed to produce fluctuations of long range transmission where near-surface refracted (RSR) paths are involved in the transmission.

Basic to all of the above is multipath propagation in the presence of *moving inhomogeneities,* which cause propagation multipaths, together with *scattered contributions* to a received signal, to interfere with one another.

In summary, the presence of inhomogeneities in the sea, of the kinds mentioned above, as well as others, together with the motion of the sea, the source and/or the receiver, are the underlying causes for the fluctuation of the signal from a distant, steady source of sound.

Long-period fluctuations with time scales measured in hours, weeks and months, are associated with changes in the ocean medium itself. The tides, for example, produce changes in water depth and current flow, while diurnal and seasonal changes in the velocity profile produce marked changes in transmission.

Measures of Fluctuation

In the literature, *amplitude fluctuation* is described quantitatively by the *coefficient of variation V* equal to the standard deviation of a series of pressure amplitudes divided by the mean. In symbols, if P is the absolute magnitude of the acoustic pressure of a received pulse or of a time sample of a continuous received signal, then V is defined by

$$V = \left[\frac{\overline{(p - \overline{p})^2}}{(\overline{p})^2} \right]^{\frac{1}{2}}$$

$$= \left[\frac{\overline{p^2} - (\overline{p})^2}{(\overline{p})^2} \right]^{\frac{1}{2}}$$

where the bars denote an average of a large number of pulses or signal samples. V thus expresses the normalized *magnitude* of the fluctuation. *Fig 1* shows how V would be determined from a series of rectified short-pulse transmissions.

The other parameter describing fluctuation is its *time scale*. This is given by the *auto-correlation function* of the fluctuation, defined by

$$\rho(\tau) = \frac{\overline{p(t) \cdot p(t + \tau)}}{\overline{p^2(t)}}$$

where p(t) is the pressure amplitude of the fluctuating signal, τ is a delay time and $\overline{p^2(t)}$ is the mean square pressure amplitude. The normalization term in the denominator serves to make $\rho(0) = 1$. Thus, $\rho(\tau)$ is the normalized time-displaced time-averaged product of the time function, or series of amplitudes, denoted by p(t). As a function of the time delay τ, the result is an *auto-correlogram*, as illustrated in *Fig 2*. It can be characterized for practical purposes by a single, arbitrary number called the *correlation time* of the fluctuation. Different definitions of correlation time have been used by different workers as, for example, the time for the correlogram to fall to 0.5, to e^{-1}, or to zero (A, B + D of Fig. 2c), or as the equal-area time C in Fig. 2c, given by

$$C = \int_0^\infty \rho(\tau) d\tau.$$

More meaningful for an understanding of physical processes, but less useful for prediction purposes, is the *spectrum* of the fluctuations, giving the fluctuation power per unit band-width as a function of fluctuation period or frequency. Since the spectrum is the cosine-transform of the auto-correlation function, they are equivalent ways of describing the fluctuation time scale. The fluctuation spectrum is particularly useful for theoretical studies involving the causes of fluctuation, while the auto-correlation function, with its parameter the correlation time (however defined), is useful as in input quantity in operational and detection models.

Phase changes of a received single-frequency signal may also be described by a correlation coefficient. Let the source signal be $p_s = \sin \omega\tau$ and the received signal be $p_r = \sin(\omega\tau + \varphi)$ where φ is the fluctuating phase angle, and where amplitude fluctuations have been eliminated by, say, a clipper amplifier. Then the correlation coefficient of phase is

$$\rho(\varphi) = \frac{\overline{\sin \omega t \cdot \sin(\omega t + \varphi)}}{\overline{\sin^2 \omega t}}$$

$$= \frac{\frac{1}{2} \cos[\omega t - (\omega t + \varphi)] - \frac{1}{2} \cos[\omega t + (\omega t + \varphi)]}{\frac{1}{2}}$$

$$= \cos \varphi$$

Thus, *the correlation coefficient for phase in the absence of amplitude fluctuations is equal to the mean value of the cosine of the fluctuating phase angle*. Such phase changes are equivalent to fluctuations in travel time over the existing propagation path or paths.

Short-Range Ping-to-Ping Fluctuations

These have been much studied. The initial work was done by Sheehy (3) in World War II, and interest has continued up to the present time, principally in connection with their effects on acoustic homing torpedoes. In field studies, the rectified amplitudes of a succession of short pulses transmitted between a source and a receiver are

Fig . 1.   A series of rectified pulses as they might appear on a line or paper playout. The coefficient of variation V is the standard deviation σ divided by the square of the mean amplitude $|\overline{P}|$ of the series of pulses.

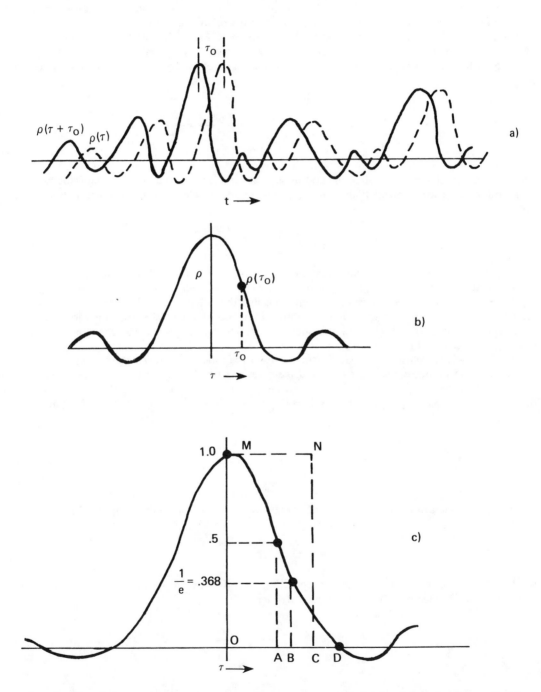

Fig. 2.   (a) a time function p(t) and the time-displaced function p(t + τ). (b) the autocorrelogram of p(t). (c) different measures of the fluctuation time scale based on the autocorrelogram. The equal-area time is such that the area of the rectangle MNCO is equal to the positive area of the correlogram.

12-3

observed (Fig. 1). Fig. 3 shows the results of three different series of measurements giving V as a function of range for the direct transmission from source to receiver. In these studies, short pulses from 10 to 100 ms in length at kilohertz frequencies and ranges up to a few kiloyards were used. They agree in showing that, for the direct path, *V increases as the square-root of the distance between source and receiver.*

The theory for this kind of fluctuation has been worked out in some detail. Bergmann (4) first used ray theory, and found the $r^{3/2}$ variation of V. Mintzer, in a series of papers (5), reconciled the field data of Sheehy with wave theory, and correctly deduced an $r^{1/2}$ variation of V. Later, Skudryzk (6) unified the theory so as to include both theoretical domains, and provided a physical insight into the processes producing the fluctuation. Chernov's book (7) is a fine exposition of this and other aspects of propagation in a random medium.

The physical theory may be summed up by reference to *Fig 4.* The medium is assumed to consist of patches of thermal (more generally, index of refraction) inhomogeneity (Fig. 4a). These patches have a *patch size "a"* determined by the spatial coherence of changes in the index of refraction or sound velocity. Define a spatial variable

$$\mu = n - 1 = \frac{c_0}{c} - 1 = \frac{c_0 - c}{c} = \frac{\Delta c}{c} \approx \frac{\Delta c}{c_0}$$

where n and c are the index of refraction and velocity at some point and c_0 is the mean velocity in its vicinity.

Then the auto correlation coefficient of the changes in sound velocity in the x direction is given by

$$\rho_\mu(x) = \frac{\overline{\mu(x_0) \cdot \mu(x_0 + x)}}{\overline{\mu^2}}$$

where $\mu(x_0)$ and $\mu(x_0 + x)$ are the values of μ at two points separated by distance x, and the bars represent a space average. In the theory, (x) is approximated by one of two convenient functions: $\rho_\mu(x) = \exp(-x/a)$ or $\rho_\mu(x) = \exp(-x^2/a^2)$. In either case, "a" may be called the patch size of the inhomogeneities and both functions reduce to unity at x = o, as they should. While "a" denotes the spatial size of the inhomogeneities, the thermal or index-of-refraction size is given by the quantitiy $\overline{\mu^2}$. The two are related by the Kolmogorov Law of turbulent mixing, which says that $\overline{\mu^2}$ is proportional to $a^{2/3}$.

The fluctuation behavior of a patch depends upon the range from it. At short ranges (Fig. 4c), the patch acts like a lens, and produces *focussing* and *defocussing* as described by *ray theory*; at long ranges, it acts like a scatterer of sound according to *wave theory*. The two regions correspond crudely to the Fresnel and Fraunhofer regions of optics. In the *focussing region* (7, p. 34), taking $\rho_\mu(x) = e^{-x^2/a^2}$, the coefficient of variation is related theoretically to the range r by

$$V^2 = \frac{8}{3} \pi^{1/2} \frac{\overline{\mu^2}}{a^3} r^3$$

meaning that V increases as the 3/2 power of r, while in the scattering region (7, pp 75-77)

$$V^2 = \pi^{1/2} \overline{\mu^2} k^2 \, ar$$

so that V varies as the square-root of the range (Fig. 4d). The two regions correspond, respectively, to small ($\ll 1$) and to large ($\gg 1$) values of a "wave parameter" defined by

$$D = \frac{4r}{ka^2}$$

The "transition range" between the two regions occurs in the vicinity of D = 1, or at a range equal to

$$r_0 = \frac{ka^2}{4}$$

12-4

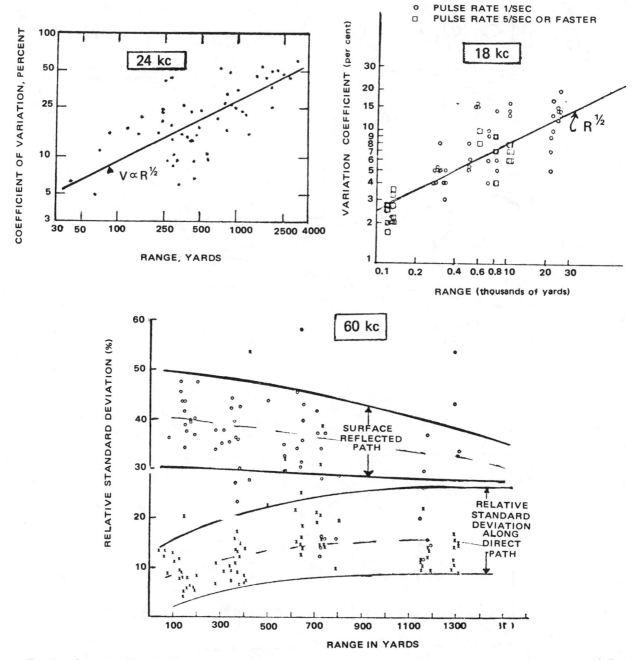

Fig. 3.   Observed fluctuation as a function of range at kilohertz frequencies as reported in the literature.   a) Reference 3;   b) Reference 43;   c) Reference 16.

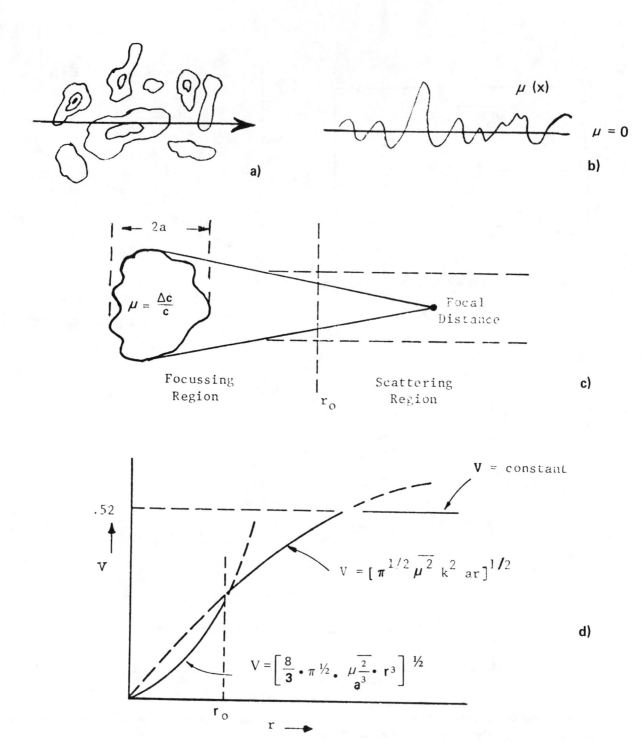

Fig. 4.   a): patches of inhomogeneity in the sea indicated by contours of equal index of refraction. b): u(x) as it might be traced out by a probe moving along the line in (a). c): the two regions of interference. d): theoretical variation of V with range in the two regions.

Concerning the two regions, Chernov (7, p. 82) says that "it is easy to give a qualitative explanation for the difference in the distance dependence of the mean square amplitude fluctuations in the regions of small and large values of the wave parameter. In the first case, the dimensions of the first Fresnel zone are small compared to the scale of the inhomogeneities. The deviations of the refractive index from its mean value within the zone all have the same sign. Therefore, all the waves scattered by the different elements of the first zone arrive at the observation point in phase, and the fluctuations increase rapidly with distance (like r^3). In the second case, the dimensions of the first Fresnel zone are large compared to the scale of the inhomogeneities. The deviations of the refractive index μ from its mean value have different signs at different points of the zone. Therefore, all of the elementary waves do not arrive in phase at the observation point. They partially interfere, and, as a result, the fluctuations grow more slowly with distance (like r)."

All of the above applies to spherical patches, which are likely to occur in a well-mixed surface layer. But below the layer in the thermocline the patches are known to be lenticular rather than spherical in shape. By means of sensitive thermal probes, the thermocline has been found to have a stepped structure consisting of a regular series of homogeneous layers. For example, in the Sargasso Sea off Bermuda, the layers have been found (9) to be a few meters thick and to have a horizontal extent of several hundred meters. For lenticular patches the fluctuation is said (16) to be increased by the factor

$$\frac{V(\text{lenticular})}{V(\text{spherical})} = \frac{1}{16}\left(\frac{4}{y^2} + \frac{6}{y^4} + 6\right)$$

where y is the ratio of vertical to horizontal patch size.

Such structure has a significant effect only on sound travelling horizontally, or more generally, on ray paths that vertex within the layers (10). For example, in one experiment (11), a rapid fluctuation of 10, 20 and 40 kHz pulses between a sinking source and a sinking receiver a few kiloyards away was attributed to differential refraction (focussing) produced by irregularities in the velocity profile between the two.

In underwater sound the patch sizes in the sea and the wavelengths employed cause r_0 to be relatively small. For example, if a = 1 meter, then even at 150 kHz, r_0 is only 156 meters and is less at lower frequencies. Nearly always a sonar receiver lies in the scattering region of the microstructure where V varies as $r^{1/2}$. On the other hand, in the transmission of light through the atmosphere, r_0 is large, so that V varies as $r^{3/2}$, as verified by observations of the twinkling of stars (7, p. 121).

Within the scattering region, the sound field is given as the sum of a direct unscattered term plus a scattered term. But at long ranges, the unscattered contribution becomes small and eventually disappears altogether. The sound field then becomes completely scattered and broken up, and there is no further increase of V with range. The amplitudes then are Rayleigh-distributed and V becomes equal to 52%. However, this far-region appears never to have been reached in underwater experiments on transmission through microstructure, probably because of weak signals (relative to noise) at the long ranges required.

The theory of wave propagation in a random medium has a vast literature. One recent review article (12), for example, has some 196 references, all on the theory and applications of radio and sound propagation in a variety of random media.

Microthermal Data

Observations of temperature microstructure of the sea have been described a number of times in the literature. In 1944 Holter (13) put a thermopile on a submarine and carried it through the sea at a speed of 3 knots at a constant depth. Three scales of thermal structure were identified: 1) *large scale changes* occurring over distances of the order of 200 yards with temperature differences of the order of 0.5°F; 2) *medium scale changes* occurring over distances of the order of 50 yards with differences of 0.1°F; 3) *"a microstructure"* of the order of 10 yards with differences of .02°F. Finer structure could not be observed due to slow response of the thermopile. Later, Urick and Searfoss (14) repeated this experiment using a faster thermopile having a time constant 0.4 sec. This work revealed marked differences in the microstructure in the mixed layer and in the thermocline; within the layer the patch size was found to be about 6 yards with an rms temperature deviation of 0.05°C ($\mu^2 \approx 10^{-8}$); below the layer the patch size was about 100 yards, with $|\overline{\Delta T}|$ of 0.4°. Still later, Liebermann (15) used a thermocouple of time constant 0.02 sec, and found a = 60 cm and $|\overline{\Delta T}| = 0.5$°C at depths from 100-200 feet, without correlation with the bathythermogram. Whitmarsh et al. (16), made simultaneous measurements of temperature along a horizontal bar 10 ft long, and found $|\overline{\Delta T}|$ about .05°C and a=2.5 yds. More recently, and on a larger scale, Piip (17) reported variations in velocity profiles taken repeatedly over a period of time at the same spot; these show changes in velocity of several meters per second in a few hours time at the same depth near the axis of the Deep Sound Channel.

There is therefore a broad spectrum of inhomogeneity in the body of the sea requiring different instruments and methods for its measurement. An admirable way to determine the microstructure of the sea would be to measure the fluctuation of acoustic pulses, since a body of valid theory apparently exists. Two papers (16)(18) report fair agreement between observed acoustic fluctuations and those computed from simultaneous microthermal measurements.

Some examples of recorded microstructure may be seen in *Fig 5*.

Fluctuation of the Surface Reflection

The irregular moving surface also causes fluctuation of sound reflected from it. An early study (19) of ½ ms 25 kHz pulses emitted by a submarine-mounted source at 200 feet and received by a surface ship at 12 feet showed that surface-reflected pulses were highly and rapidly variable in amplitude, being sometimes larger and sometimes smaller than the direct pulse, with an average amplitude ratio of 0.8. Often the reflection was multiple and showed more than one reflected pulse. These pecularities were ascribed to reflection from curved portions of the sea surface in the region not far from the reflection point for a smooth surface. Interference between the direct arrival of a short-range sonar echo and the fluctuating surface reflection causes the apparent vertical direction of arrival in the echo to fluctuate and so to prevent a determination of target depth by a surface ship sonar.

The coefficient of variation V for the surface reflection is greater than for the direct path, and *decreases* with range, so as to have eventually the same value as that of the direct path at long ranges. The reason is that the sea surface becomes sensibly smooth at long ranges, where the Rayleigh parameter $R = 2kh \sin \theta$ becomes less than unity. When this occurs, the fluctuation caused by the moving sea surface becomes less than the fluctuation caused by the microstructure. This was also observed (20) for reflections of 168 Hz pulses from the surface between a deep (2880') source and a deep (3000') receiver separated by ranges from 1 to 5.5 kyd. In tank experiments with short pulses, Russian scientists have found V to increase with the Rayleigh parameter $R = 2kh \sin \theta$ until R was about unity and to remain nearly constant between 0.25 and 0.40 for R greater than unity. Similarly, in a deep water experiment, Nichols and Senko (23) in 2400 fathoms of water at frequencies from 400 to 1500 Hz and at grazing angles of 18, 31 and 85°, found V for surface-reflected pulses to increase with R to a value of about 0.35 near R = 1 and to rise only slowly with R thereafter. In an experiment in the Severn River off Annapolis (24), V for the surface reflection ranged from 0.40 to 0.51 while V for the direct path, 100 ft long, ranged from 0.03 to 0.21; other differences were that the surface reflection had a Rayleigh amplitude distribution compared to a Gaussian distribution for the direct transmission, together with a more rapid rate of fluctuation. In one final experiment that may be mentioned (25), done at 750 and 1500 Hz over a 24-mile path south of Bermuda and involving a surface reflection, V for a series of pulses over a period of 90 minutes had median values of 0.23 at 750 Hz and 0.32 at 1500 Hz for wind speeds between 2.5 kts and 25 kts, with no dependence on wind speed; V was greater (.31 and .46) at seasons when this path failed to reach the surface but became horizontal at a shallow depth.

Fluctuation Time Scale

The many forms of inhomogeneity in the sea, and the variety of propagation paths result in a wide range of fluctuation time scales.

At the short period end of the scale are the high frequency fluctuations produced by the *turbulent microstructure* and the motion of source and/or receiver through it. In World War II (26), the correlation coefficent of the amplitude of short 24 kHz pulses travelling via a direct path a distance of 965 yards fell to zero in about 2 seconds; inside a shadow zone, where the low-level sound is due to scattering, CW signals were observed to be uncorrelated over 0.05 seconds. Next higher on the time scale come fluctuations of sound reflected and scattered by the *moving sea surface*, which imposes its own motion on an impinging sound wave. Amplitude and phase fluctuations having the periodicity of ocean waves are regularly observed in CW and pulse propagation where the sea surface is involved. An example is given in *Fig 6a*, where the fluctuation spectrum* is seen to be essentially identical to the spectrum of ocean waves. *Internal waves* have been suspected of causing fluctuations with periodicities measured in minutes. They are observed in long-range propagation experiments where the available propagation paths are refracted paths that become horizontal at shallow depths. An example of a spectrum thought to be of this type may be seen in *Fig 6b*. This cause was originally postulated by Nichols and Young (27) to account for transmission fluctuations observed between a fixed source at Eleuthera and a fixed receiver at Bermuda 720 miles away, and has been subsequently postulated for other data in this same area by Stanford (28) and Baxter and Yang (29).

The *tides* cause fluctuations at the tidal periods in shallow water where a small change in water depth can produce a large change in received signal level by causing interference between the normal modes of the propagation. *Fig 7* shows the fluctuations of 10-15 db over a distance of 5000 ft in 60 ft of water that occurred simultaneously with a two-foot range of the tide.

---

*obtained by narrow-band analysis of the envelope of the received signal.

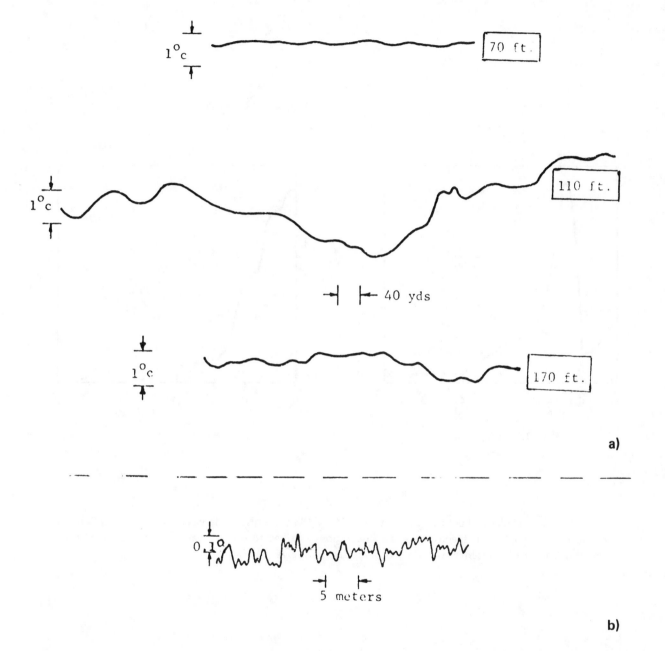

Fig. 5. Thermal microstructure as recorded by a thermopile moved horizontally through the sea. a) thermal traces at three depths with a 100 ft. mixed layer; the temperature changes in the layer are less than below it. (14). b) a trace in the layer made with a fast-response thermopile, showing fine-grained micro-structure. (15).

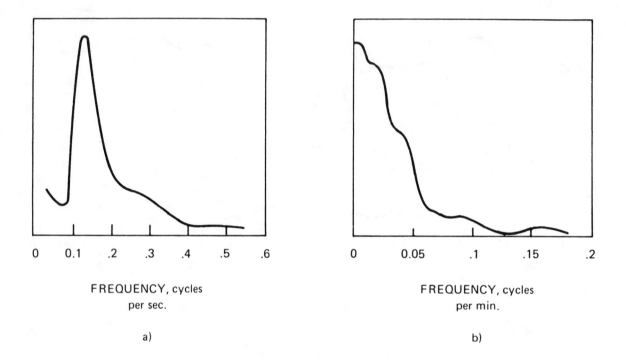

0   0.1   .2   .3   .4   .5   .6   0   0.05   .1   .15   .2

FREQUENCY, cycles   FREQUENCY, cycles
per sec.   per min.

a)   b)

Fig. 6.   Two examples of fluctutation spectra of 270 Hz CW transmission between **Eleuthera and Bermuda,** a distance of 700 miles. a) spectrum of fast fluctuations ascribed to surface waves. b) spectrum of slow fluctuations ascribed to internal waves. Vertical scale was not given. **(27).**

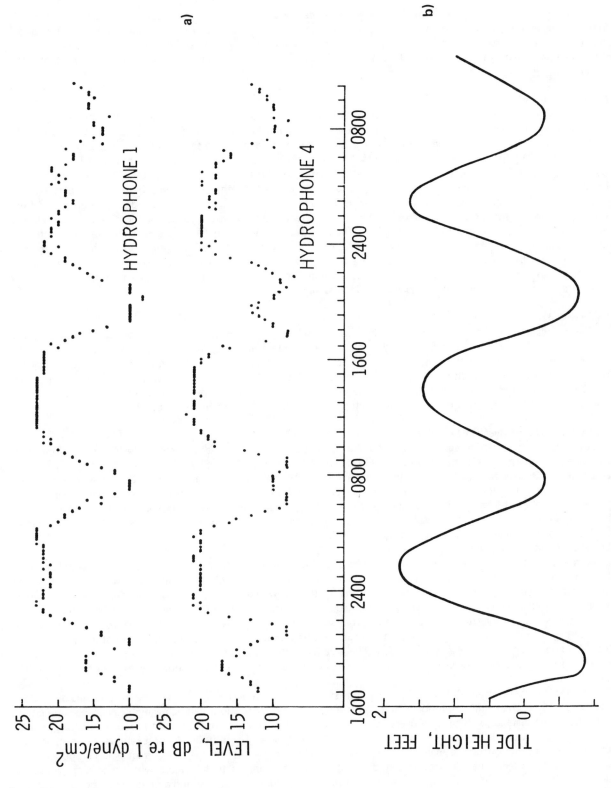

Fig. 7.   a) Level of 1120 Hz CW transmission over a distance of 5000 feet to two hydrophones 100 feet apart b) tidal cycle in 60 feet of water. (42).

12-11

Finally, at the long-period end of the overall time scale are the fluctuations caused by *seasonal and metero-logical changes* in the ocean medium between source and receiver. An example of phase changes in 420 Hz CW trans-mission between source and receiver over paths 41 miles long over a four-day period of time are shown in *Fig 8*. We note in this data the strong diurnal variability of phase and the effect of the passage of a cold front through the area.

Effect of Source-Receiver Motion

When the source or receiver or both are in motion, the fluctuation time scale depends on the rate at which the motion causes the multipaths to interfere. An example (30) of fluctuation that is likely to have been primarily caused by motion of the source is seen in *Fig. 9*. This shows what was received by sonobuoys at two depths (90 and 300 feet) from a steady two-frequency (142 and 275 Hz) source as it was towed at a speed of 2.7 knots out to the first convergence zone. The propagation here is by bottom-surface multipaths. There is little evident correlation of the envelope of the received signal between the two depths at the same frequency or between the two frequencies at the same depth. Also, there is a wide range of fluctuation periods, from fast unresolved fluc-tuations to slow signal surges lasting about one hour; the effect of a faster towing speed would doubtless be to speed up the fluctuations. For the 142 Hz CW bottom-bounce data illustrated in *Fig 9*, the auto-correlation coefficient of signal samples integrated over 16 seconds was found (30) to fall to 1/e (.368) in times ranging from 0.25 minute (no correlation between successive samples) to 7.5 minutes, with a frequency of the correlation time to increase with range. In short, in this data, the many transmission multipaths interfered in a complex and constantly changing manner as the range between source and receiver increased.

Shallow Water

Shallow water is noted for its variability, both with time at a single location, and with location at a single time. *Table I*, from Weston (31), is a list of eight fluctuation mechanisms, in order of periodicity, that have been ob-served in shallow water. As an example of one shallow water fluctuation study, Mackenzie (32) has described quan-titatively the amplitude fluctuations and frequency spreading of 350 to 2400 Hz CW transmissions at distances of 10 to 30 miles over a 60-fathom deep sand bottom. The results of this experiment are in keeping with the view that the fluctuations were due to interferences between numerous surface-reflected multipaths.

Fixed Source-Fixed Receiver Studies

A number of papers have appeared by a number of authors on the fluctuations received at Bermuda from a CW source at Eleuthera in the Bahamas 720 miles away. Among these are papers by Nichols and Young (27), Nichols and Senko (23), Stanford (28) and Baxter and Yang (29). Another favorite transmission region has been between Miami and Bimini in the Bahamas 41 miles away (33-35), where phase changes in the received signal were found to be associated with changes in the characteristics of the Florida current between source and receiver. An example has been shown previously in *Fig 8*. Fluctuations in phase and amplitude have proven to be useful oceanographic tools in studies of large-scale time-varying water masses.

Signal Fluctuation Statistics

A model for the statistics of the amplitude of signal fluctuations can be derived (36) from some simple consid-erations. At the outset of this chapter, it was noted that the fluctuations of the signal from a steady distant source in the sea may be said to be caused by *multipath propagation in an inhomogeneous moving medium*. Some examples of the multipaths that come to mind are the refracted paths in ducts, the four paths involving one bottom encounter in bottom-bounce propagation, and the paths from scatterers in the body or on the boundaries of the sea. Some examples of *inhomogeneities* are the rough sea surface, the temperature and salinity microstructure, and the bio-logical matter existing in the body of the sea. These various inhomogeneities are always *in motion* relative to each other and to the source or receiver, or both, because of currents, turbulences, and source or receiver motion relative to the medium.

The result is that a received signal is likely to consist, in whole or in part, of a number of contributions of random and time-varying phase and amplitude. These random multipath contributions will be negligible near the source but, with increasing distance, will tend to overwhelm the steady, direct path component and produce, at a long enough range, a resultant consisting only of components of varying phase and amplitude. As an example, the propagation through random microstructure may be viewed conceptually as consisting of a steady, direct path component that decreases with range, together with scattered or diffracted components that increase with range and eventually dominate the received signal. At any range, the resultant is the sum of a steady and a random component, with an amplitude distribution that depends only on the fraction of the total average power in the random component.

In a classic paper published in 1945, S. O. Rice (37) derived the distribution function of the envelope of a sine wave plus narrow-band Gaussian random noise. This is the same as the distribution of the sum of a constant vector and a random vector whose x and y coordinates are Gaussian time-functions. In his honor, the function is called the *Rician Distribution*.

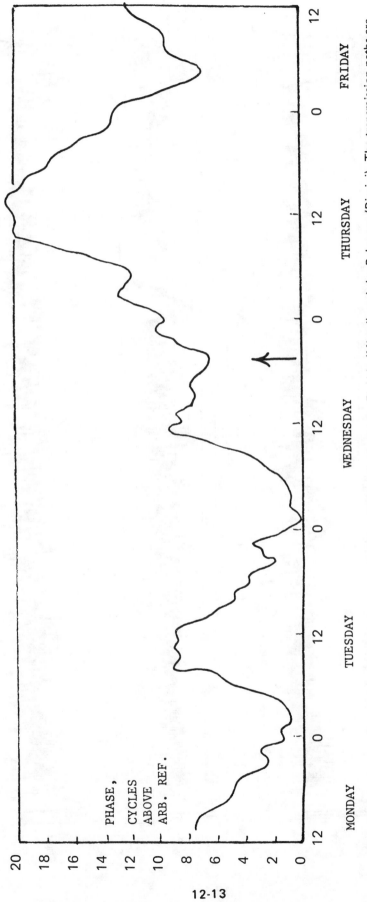

Fig. 8. Phase changes in 420 Hz transmission over a distance of 41 miles between Florida (Miami) and the Bahamas (Bimini). The transmission paths are refracted-bottom reflected (RBR). The arrow marks the passage of a cold front. (33).

12-13

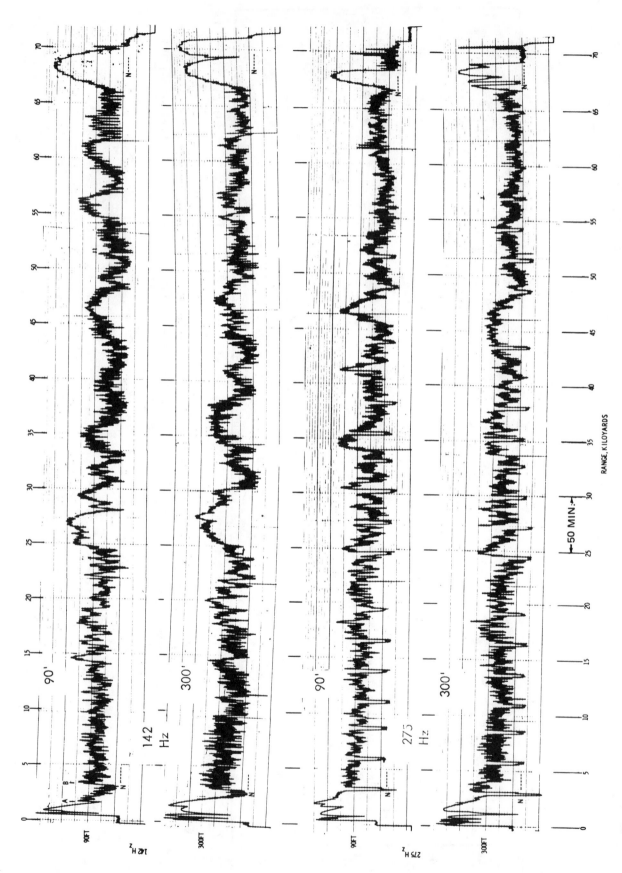

Fig. 9. Level vs. range from a two-frequency source towed outward in range to the convergence zone and received at two depths. (41).

TABLE I

Fluctuation Mechanisms in Shallow Water.
(31).

Mechanism	Predominant Period	Parameter Affected	Comment
Seasonal change in conditions — temperature structure, fish population etc.	One Year	Mainly amplitude	Transmission is best in Winter
Seasonal change in mean temperature	One Year	Mainly phase	Phase delay is greatest in Winter
Fish shoaling	One day	Amplitude	The level changes occupy only about 10 minutes near dusk and dawn
Changes in water depth	Tidal	Amplitude and phase	The changing mode interference patterns cause fluctuations at the tidal period or its harmonics
Depth-dependence of streaming velocity	Tidal	Amplitude	The mode parameters can be greatly changed (especially above 2 kc/s), causing fluctuations as just above.
Changes in mean streaming velocity	Tidal	Phase	The phase delay is a direct measure of the resolved velocity component
Storms	Order of several hours	Mainly amplitude	Transmission is reduced by the extra scattering loss, etc.
Surface waves	Many seconds	Amplitude and phase	

Let P be the magnitude of the constant vector, and let V be the magnitude of the sum of the constant vector and a random vector whose x and y coordinates have unit variance. Then Rice showed that the probability density of V is given by

$$p(V) = V \exp \left[-\left(\frac{V^2 + P^2}{2} \right) \right] \cdot I_0(PV)$$

where $I_0(PV)$ is the modified Bessel function of argument PV, for which tables are available (38).

When the constant component vanishes, the result is the Rayleigh distribution

$$p(V) = V \exp \left(\frac{-V^2}{2} \right)$$

The signal is now made up entirely of random components. At the other extreme, when the constant component is very large, or more accurately, when $PV \gg 1$, the distribution is essentially Gaussian with unit variance:

$$p(V) = \left(\frac{V}{2\pi P} \right)^{1/2} \exp \left[\frac{-(V - P)^2}{2} \right]$$

We define now a ratio T, which may be call the *randomicity* of the signal, defined as the fraction of the power of the received signal that is random, or

$$T = \frac{\text{Random Power}}{\text{Total Power}} = \frac{2}{2 + P^2}$$

where the mean power of the random vector is 1 and P^2 is the power of the constant vector. The randomicity T is small close to the source, in a convergence zone, and generally when there is a single, strong, dominant propagation path; under these conditions the amplitude distribution tends to be Gaussian. T approaches unity when the signal is composed principally of scattered contributions, as in a shadow zone at high frequencies in deep water, or generally when many multipaths exist; now the distribution will approach the Rayleigh limit.

Fig 10 gives cumulative distribution curves of the ratio 10 log I/Ī where I is the power, or amplitude squared, of a given sample of signal and Ī is the mean power, or mean squared amplitude, of an ensemble of samples. When T can be estimated from the existing propagation conditions, the corresponding cumulative distribution curves give the fraction of signal samples having an intensity equal to or less than the mean intensity of the sample population. When T is greater than about 0.5, the distribution is insensitive to T. From a prediction standpoint, *the fluctuation of a received signal about its mean intensity can often be predicted better than can be the mean intensity itself.*

The model has been validated empirically by comparison with field data observed under a wide variety of propagation conditions (36). Included in the comparison was transmission to a receiver in and below a surface duct, low frequency CW bottom-bounce transmission to ranges short of the first convergence zone, CW transmission from Eleuthera to Bermuda, and several other cases. The model applies only to fluctuations that are stochastic, rather than deterministic, in origin.

Ambient Noise Fluctuation Statistics

The ambient noise background of the sea, in the absence of wave crashes, biological noises, and ice cracking has been found (39) to have a Gaussian amplitude distribution. This is to be expected if the background received by a hydrophone is the sum of many individual noise contributions from the sea surface overhead or from ships at a distance. When Gaussian noise is fed into a conventional processor consisting of a bandpass filter of bandwidth w, a square-law detector, and a low-pass filter or integrator of integration time t, the output can be represented by 2wt independent samples of the Gaussian input. In statistical theory it is shown (40) that the sum of the squares of n independent samples of Gaussian variate has a chi-square distribution with n degrees of freedom. Thus, in our case, samples of Gaussian ambient noise at the output of the processor should be distributed according to a chi-square distribution with 2wt degrees of freedom.

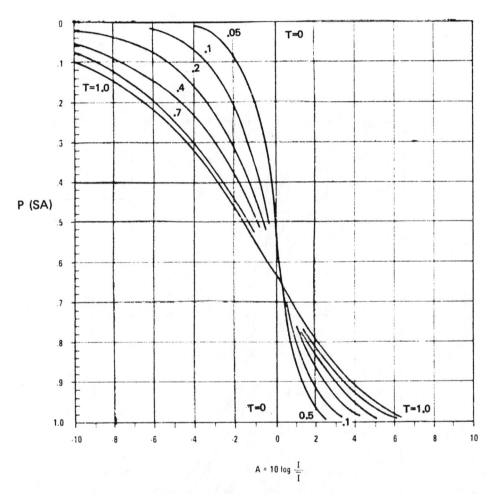

Fig. 10. Cumulative distribution curves of the level of a received sinusoidal signal. Vertical scale is the fraction of signal samples equal to or less than the number of decibels relative to the mean, as abscissa. T is the randomicity, or fraction of random power in the received signal.

Fig 11 gives curves of the cumulative chi-square distribution for values of 2wt between 2 and 128 and with 10 log I/$\overline{I}$ as abscissa. We may note how similar this family of curves is to the Rician curves of Fig. 10; mathematically, the chi-square distribution for 2wt = n = 2 is identical to the Rayleigh distribution (T = 1). At the other extreme, for large 2wt and small T, the distributions are nearly normal, with 2wt approximately equal to 1/T.

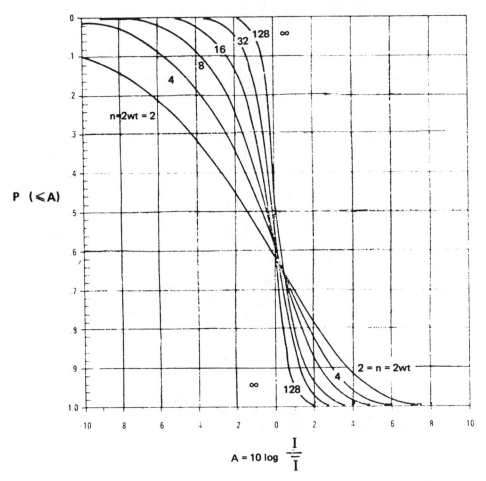

Fig. 11. Cumulative distribution curves of the level of Gaussian noise at the output of a processor of bandwidth w and the integration of time t.

REFERENCES

1. C. Eckart and R. R. Carhart, Fluctuations of Sound in the Sea in "A Survey Report on Basic Problems in Underwater Acoustics Research", National Research Council Committee on Underseas Warfare, 1950.

2. G. Gaunaurd, Categorized Bibliography on Underwater Sound Transmission Fluctuations, Naval Ordnance Laboratory Tech Report 73-176, 1976.

3. M. J. Sheehy, Transmission of 24 kc Underwater Sound from a Deep Source, JASA *22*, 24, 1950.

4. P. G. Bergmann, Propagation of Radiation in a Medium with Random Inhomogeneities, Phys. Rev. *70*, 486, 1946.

5. D. Mintzer, Wave Propagation in a Randomly Inhomogeneous Medium I, JASA *25*, 922, 1953; II: JASA *25*, 1107, 1953; III: *26*, 186, 1954.

6. E. Skudryzk, Scattering in an Inhomogeneous Medium, JASA *29*, 50, 1957.

7. L. Chernov, *Wave Propagation in a Random Medium*, McGraw Hill Book Co., New York, 1960.

8. V. I. Tatarski, *Wave Propagation in a Turbulent Medium*, McGraw Hill Book Co., New York, 1961.

9. J. W. Cooper and H. Stommel, Regularly Spaced Steps in the Main Thermocline near Bermuda, Jour. Geoph. Res. *73*, 5849, 1968.

10. L. E. Melberg and O. M. Johannessen, Layered Oceanic Microstructure — Its Effect on Sound Propagation, JASA *53*, 571, 1973.

11. D. C. Whitmarsh and W. J. Leiss, Fluctuation in Horizontal Acoustic Propagation over Short Depth Increments, JASA *43*, 1036, 1968.

12. A. Ishimaru, Theory and Application of Wave Propagation and Scattering in Random Media, PROC. IEEE, *65*, 1030, 1977.

13. N. J. Holter, Measurements of the Horizontal Thermal Structure of the Ocean, USN Radio and Sound Lab Report S-17, August 1944.

14. R. J. Urick and C. W. Searfoss, Microthermal Structure of the Ocean near Key West, Florida Part I, NRL Report S-3392; Part II, Report S-3444.

15. L. Liebermann, Effect of Temperature Inhomogeneities in the Ocean on the Propagation of Sound; JASA *23*, 563, 1951.

16. D. Whitmarsh, E. Skudryzk and R. Urick, Forward Scattering of Sound in the Sea and its Correlation with the Temperature Microstructure, JASA *29*, 1124, 1957.

17. A. T. Piip, Fine Structure and Stability of the Sound Channel in the Ocean, JASA *36*, 1948, 1964.

18. R. F. Shvachko, Sound Fluctuations in the Upper Layer of the Ocean and their Relation to the Random Inhomogeneities of the Medium, Soviet Physics-Acoustics *9*, 280, 1964.

19. R. J. Urick and H. L. Saxton, Surface Reflection of Short Supersonic Pulses in the Ocean, JASA *19*, 8, 1947.

20. M. V. Brown and J. Ricard, Fluctuations in Surface-Reflected Pulsed CW Arrivals, JASA *32*, 1551, 1960.

21. G. F. Smirnov and O. S. Tonakanov, Fluctuations in Hydroacoustic Pulse Signals on Reflections from a Water Surface in which Waves are Present, Soviet Physics-Acoustics *6*, 480, 1960.

22. E. P. Gulin and K. I. Malyshev, Statistical Characteristics of Sound Surface Reflected from the Undulating Sea Surface, Soviet Physics-Acoustics *8*, 228, 1962.

23. R. H. Nichols and A. Senko, Amplitude Fluctuations of Low Frequency Underwater Acoustic Pulses Reflected from the Ocean Surface, JASA *55*, 550, 1974.

24. J. R. Smithson, A Statistical Study of Sound Fluctuation in an Estuary, Ches. Bay. Inst. Johns Hopkins Univ. Spec. Rep 6, Dec. 1960.

25. M. R. Gerber, Seasonal Fluctuations of Propagation between a Fixed Source and a Fixed Receiving Array on the Bermuda Rise, USL Tech Memo 2135.2 — 367-69, Apr 1969.

26. Physics of Sound in the Sea, NDRC Div. 6 Summary Tech. Rept. 8, Chapt. 7, 1946.

27. R. H. Nichols and H. J. Young, Fluctuations in Low-Frequency Acoustic Propagation in the Ocean, JASA *43*, 716, 1968.

28. G. Stanford, Low-Frequency Fluctuations of a CW Signal in the Ocean, JASA *55*, 968, 1974.

29. L. Baxter and C. Yang. "Fluctuations of Narrow-Band Sound Amplitudes from Long-Range Transmissions in the Deep Atlantic Ocean, JASA *58*, 595, 1975.

30. R. J.. Urick, "The Time Scale of the Fluctuation of a Bottom-Bounce Narrow Band Signal from a Moving Source in the Sea," NSWC/WOL/TR 75-83, 1975.

31. D. E. Weston, On Shallow Water Sound Fluctuations, with Speculations upon an April Evening, NATO Advanced Study Institute on Problems in Sound Propagation, Sept. 1967.

32. K. V. Mackenzie, Long Range Shallow Water Signal Level Fluctuations and Frequency Spreading, JASA *34*, 67, 1962.

33. J. C. Steinberg and T. G. Birdsall, Underwater Sound Propagation in the Straits of Florida, JASA *39*, 301, 1966.

34. J. G. Clark, R. Dann and J. R. Yarnall, Recent Results from the Straits of Florida Underwater Sound Propation Study, JASA *40*, 1195, 1966.

35. J. C. Steinberg and others, Fixed Systems Studies of Underwater Sound Propagation, JASA *52*, 1521, 1972.

36. R. J. Urick, A Statistical Model for the Fluctuation of Sound Transmission in the Sea, Naval Surface Weapons Center, White Oak, Tech. Rept. 75-18, 1975. Also, Models for the Amplitude Fluctuation of Narrow-Band Signals and Noise in the Sea, JASA *62*, 878, 1977.

37. S. O. Rice, "Mathematical Analysis of Random Noise," Bell System Tech J. 24, 46, 1945, Art. 3.10.

38. Handbook of Mathematical Functions, M. Abramowitz and I. Stegan, eds., U.S. Dept. of Commerce Applied Math Series 55, Sec. 9, 1964.

39. M. A. Calderon, Probability Density Analyses of Ocean Ambient and Ship Noise, USN Electronics Laboratory Report 1248, 1964.

40. J. E. Freund, *Mathematical Statistics*, 2 ed., Prentice Hall, Englewood Cliffs, N.J., 1971, p.213.

41. R. J. Urick, Amplitude Fluctuations of the Sound from a Low-frequency Moving Source in the Deep Sea, Naval Ordnance Laboratory Tech. Rept. 74-43, 1974.

42. R. J. Urick, G. R. Lund and D. L. Bradley, Observations of Fluctuation of Transmitted Sound in Shallow Water, JASA *45*, 683, 1969.

43. D. C. Whitmarsh, Underwater Acoustic Transmission Measurements, JASA *35*, 2014, 1963.

CHAPTER 13

SPATIAL COHERENCE (CORRELATION BETWEEN SEPARATED RECEIVERS)

Introduction

In the preceding chapter, we considered the fluctuations of amplitude of the signal from a steady source as received at a distant point in the sea. This subject was dignified by the term *temporal coherence*, since reference was made to the time variability of the envelope of a received signal relative to that of a source (assumed constant). In this chapter, we deal with the *spatial coherence* of signals, wherein the amplitude and/or phase of a signal received on one hydrophone is compared nearly simultaneously with the signal received on another, separated from the first by a certain distance in some direction relative to the direction of propagation. The magnitude of the spatial coherence of the outputs of two hydrophones is their *cross-correlation coefficient;* as a function of a time delay inserted in one of them, the cross-correlation coefficient is expressed by a *time-delay correlogram*.

Although the subject of signal fluctuations has a large literature, as we have noted in the last chapter, the subject of spatial coherence does not. Field observations are relatively scanty and the effects of propagation on coherence, except in the case of homogeneous microstructure, are not well understood.

The subject is important for the design and performance prediction of hydrophone arrays. The array gain of an array is determined by the cross-correlation coefficient of signals and noise between all elements of the array; the coherence distance — defined as the hydrophone separation at which the coefficient for a received signal diminishes to some stated value — is the most important natural parameter involved in array design. The relationship between coherence and the gain over noise of an array is given in the author's book (1) and in a paper by Nielsen (2).

Types of Coherence

The similarity of the outputs of two hydrophones, or their *coherence*, can be measured in various ways, depending upon the particular characteristic of the output that is of interest. Let the output of one be the time function $s_1(t)$, and that of the other be $s_2(t)$. If $s_1(t)$ is simply multiplied by $s_2(t)$ and time-averaged, the correlation coefficient between them is defined by:

$$\rho_T = \frac{1}{T}\int_0^T \frac{s_1(t) \cdot s_2(t)}{[\quad]}\, dt = \frac{\overline{s_1(t)\, s_2(t)}}{[\quad]}$$

where the denominator is a factor inserted to make $\rho_T = 1$ when $s_1(t) = s_2(t)$; it amounts to the product of the rms values of $s_1(t)$ and $s_2(t)$; that is:

$$[\quad] = \left[\frac{1}{T}\int_0^T s_1^2(t)dt\right]^{1/2} \cdot \left[\frac{1}{T}\int_0^T s_2^2(t)dt\right]^{1/2}$$

$$= \left[\overline{s_1^2(t)} \cdot \overline{s_2^2(t)}\right]^{1/2}$$

This may be called the "true" or "multiplier" correlation coefficient since it involves both the amplitude and the phase of the two signals and can be obtained electronically with a multiplier correlator.

Another kind of correlation involving only phase (since amplitude changes are removed before multiplying) is called *clipped* or *polarity-coincidence correlation* and has a great deal of engineering usefulness. Here s_1 and s_2 are hard-clipped before multiplying, so as to have values proportional to either $+1$ or -1. The clipped correlation coefficient may be written

$$\rho_c = \frac{1}{T}\int_0^T \frac{\operatorname{sgn} s_1(t) \cdot \operatorname{sgn} s_2(t)}{[\quad]}\, dt = \frac{\overline{\operatorname{sgn} s_1(t)\, \operatorname{sgn} s_2(t)}}{[\quad]}$$

where "sgn" refers to the sign of the two signals whether positive or negative, and [   ] has an analogous definition as before. When the phase variation between the two signals is small and highly correlated, the clipped correlation coefficient is the same as the *phase correlation coefficient*, inasmuch as amplitude variations have been removed by clipping.

The opposite kind of correlation, wherein amplitude is preserved and carrier phase is eliminated, is *envelope correlation*, involving the smoothed magnitudes of the two signals, or

$$\rho_{env} = \frac{1}{T} \int_0^T \frac{env\ s_1(t) \cdot env\ s_2(t)}{[\quad]}\ dt = \frac{\overline{env\ s_1(t)\ env\ s_2(t)}}{[\quad]}$$

where "env" is the envelope of the two signals equivalent to

$$env\ s(t) = \frac{1}{T'} \int_0^{T'} |s(t)|dt$$

where T' is the time constant of the envelope averager.

Which kind of correlation is appropriate for particular sonar systems application, whether ρ_T, ρ_c or ρ_{env}, depends upon the processor employed. Many sonars employ clipped processing in some form or another, and in such cases ρ_c will be the one of greatest interest.

Coherence of Single-Frequency and Band-Limited Signals

If $s_1(t)$ and $s_2(t)$ are sinusoidal functions of time having random phase and random amplitude, we can write

$$s_1(t) = a_1(t) \sin(\omega t + \varphi_1(t))$$

$$s_2(t) = a_2(t) \sin(\omega t + \varphi_2(t))$$

where a_1, a_2, φ_1, φ_2, are random time variables. The true or multiplier cross correlation coefficient between $s_1(t)$ and $s_2(t)$ is

$$\rho_{12} = \frac{\overline{a_1 a_2 \cdot \sin(\omega t + \varphi_1) \cdot \sin(\omega t + \varphi_2)}}{\left[\ \overline{a_1^2}\ \overline{a_2^2}\ \right]^{\frac{1}{2}}}$$

which becomes, after some trigonometric manipulation,

$$\rho_{12} = \frac{\overline{a_1 a_2 \cos t(\varphi_1 - \varphi_2)}}{[\quad]}$$

If the amplitude and phase fluctuations are uncorrelated — an assumption not always valid in the real ocean — we can separate the amplitude and phase terms and get

$$\rho_{12} = \frac{\overline{a_1 a_2}}{[\quad]}\ \overline{\cos(\varphi_1 - \varphi_2)}$$

The first term in the above product is the "envelope" correlation coefficient; the second is the "phase" correlation coefficient. The first can be ignored, or rather considered to be unity, when clipped, or DIMUS, beam-forming is employed. This kind of processing is the rule rather than the exception in sonar, since it provides great hardware benefits at only a slight reduction in array gain. Hence, we can write

$$\rho(\varphi)_{12} = \overline{\cos(\varphi_1 - \varphi_2)}$$

In other words, the correlation coefficient for phase is equal to the mean value of the cosine of the phase difference of the signal at two receivers. The phase correlation coefficient can be measured by a phase meter or by travel time differences, and represents the magnitude of fluctuations of the phase of a signal between spatially separated receivers.

For band-limited signals lying in a band of frequencies centered around frequency f, we have

$$\varphi_1 - \varphi_2 = 2\pi f\,(\tau_1 - \tau_2)$$

where $(\tau_1 - \tau_2)$ is the difference of travel times to the two receivers. By expanding the cosine, we obtain for small phase differences (i.e., highly correlated signals) the result

$$\rho(\varphi)_{12} = 1 - \frac{(2\pi f)^2}{2}\,\sigma_{12}^2$$

where σ_{12}^2 is the variance of the travel time difference between the two receivers.

Coherence of Isotropic Noise

For isotropic noise, we can obtain the coherence function in a straight-forward way. We start with a single source of plane sinusoidal waves arriving at an angle θ to the perpendicular to the line separating the two hydrophones, as shown in *Fig. 1a*. The correlation coefficient is

$$\rho_T = \frac{\overline{\sin \omega t \cdot \sin \omega(t+\tau)}}{\left[\,\overline{\sin^2 \omega t} \cdot \overline{\sin^2 \omega(t+\tau)}\,\right]^{\frac{1}{2}}}$$

$$= \frac{\overline{\sin \omega t\,(\sin \omega t \cos \omega\tau + \cos \omega t \sin \omega\tau)}}{\frac{1}{2}}$$

$$= \frac{\overline{\sin^2 \omega t \cos \omega\tau}}{\frac{1}{2}} = \cos \omega\tau$$

$$= \cos \omega\,\left(\frac{d}{c}\sin\theta\right)$$

Here τ is the time delay between the two hydrophones, equal to $(d \sin \theta)/c$ where d is their separation distance and c is the velocity of sound.

For isotropic noise we integrate ρ_T over θ and obtain

$$\rho_T\left(\begin{array}{c}\text{isotropic}\\ \text{noise}\end{array}\right) = \int_{-\frac{\pi}{2}}^{\frac{\pi}{2}} \cos\left(\frac{\omega d}{c}\sin\theta\right)\cos\theta\,d\theta \div \int_{-\frac{\pi}{2}}^{\frac{\pi}{2}}\cos\theta\,d\theta$$

$$= \frac{1}{2}\,\frac{1}{\frac{\omega d}{c}}\,\sin\left(\frac{\omega d}{c}\sin\theta\right)\Bigg|_{-\frac{\pi}{2}}^{\frac{\pi}{2}}$$

$$= \frac{\sin \dfrac{\omega d}{c}}{\dfrac{\omega d}{c}} = \frac{\sin kd}{kd}$$

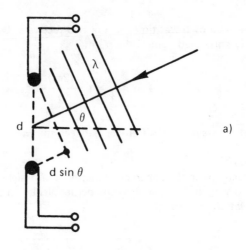

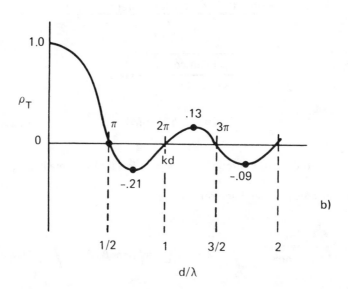

Fig. 1.   a) A plane wave incident on two hydrophones spaced a distance d apart. b) the function (sin kd)/kd, where k = $2\pi/\lambda$. The zeros occur multiples of half wavelength separation, or when d/λ = n/2, n/2, n = 1, 2, 3 . . .

where $k = 2\pi/\lambda$. The function $(\sin kd)/kd$ is plotted against d in *Fig. 1b.* The correlation coefficient goes to zero, and the noise becomes incoherent, for separations of a half-wavelength and multiples thereof. When an electrical delay τ_e is inserted into one hydrophone, the result is

$$\rho_T = \frac{\sin kd}{kd} \cos \omega \tau_e$$

For a band of frequencies, a further integration is necessary over ω. A similar procedure can be gone through for noises of arbitrary (non-isotropic) directionality, such as for monopole or dipole noise sources lying on a single plane. Correlation functions for planar and volume distribution of noise sources radiating like $\cos^m\theta$, where θ is the angle with the vertical, have been worked out (3).

Relation between Clipped and True Correlation Coefficients

If the two sine waves are hard-clipped before multiplying and time averaging, the clipped cross-correlation coefficient can be shown to be equal to the difference between the fraction of the time that they have like and unlike signs; that is, for sampling at equal time intervals, the clipped coefficient equals $(m-n)/(m+n)$ where m is the number of *agreements* of sign in a given time and n is the number of *disagreements*.

The relation between the true and the clipped correlation coefficients may be readily found for two sine waves of the same frequency differing by a time delay τ. Let the two sine waves be written $f_1(t) = A \sin\omega t$ and $f_2(t) = B \sin\omega(t + \tau)$. The time delay τ can be written $\varphi T/2\pi$ where φ is the phase angle and T is the period of the two sine functions. They will have the opposite polarity during the interval 2τ of each cycle, and the same polarity during the interval $(T - 2\tau)$ of each cycle. The clipped correlation coefficient becomes, accordingly,

$$\rho_c = \frac{m-n}{m+n} = \frac{T-2\tau}{T} - \frac{2\tau}{T} = 1 - \frac{4\tau}{T} \; ; \; \varphi = 2\pi\frac{\tau}{T}$$

$$\therefore \rho_c = 1 - \frac{2}{\pi}\varphi \; ; \; \frac{\pi}{2}\rho_c = (\frac{\pi}{2} - \varphi)$$

But, since $\rho_T = \cos \varphi$, $(\pi/2 - \varphi) = \arcsin \rho_T$, and we get the result

$$\rho_c = \frac{2}{\pi} \arcsin \rho_T$$

This simple relation between the two coefficients was established long ago for random Gaussian functions by Faran and Hills (4). ρ_c is always smaller than ρ_T except at the extremes of unity and zero, when they are equal. A plot of the above relationship is given in *Fig. 2.* In sonar applications involving clipped signals, such as in DIMUS beam-forming, the clipped coefficient is pertinent for array design considerations; in other applications where amplitude information is preserved, the true coefficient is appropriate.

The clipped correlation coefficient may be interpreted in terms of the crenulations of the wavefronts that pass by the two hydrophones. Imagine that at some instant of time a cross-section of the wavefronts in the vicinity of hydrophones A and B is as shown in *Fig. 3a.* Here the wiggly lines are wavefronts separating the positive and negative pressure regions of a quasi-plane wave propagating to the right, normal to the line joining A and B. The crenulations may be assumed to be the result of multipath and/or scattered interferences with the primary plane wave. If now the successive wavefronts are allowed to propagate toward the right without change of shape (an unlikely assumption, but a useful one for our heuristic purpose), then the outputs of A and B will be the time functions shown in *Fig. 3b.* The two outputs may be found to have a correlation coefficient of 0.36 by comparing the length of record M having the same polarity, with the length of record N having opposite polarity according to the relation $\rho_c = (m-n)/(m+n)$. This calculation is performed electronically in electronic correlators. Thus, *the value 0.36 may be taken to be a measure of the deviation from a plane wave or the wavefront crenulations*, of the wave passing by the hydrophones. A perfectly plane wave would, of course, have the value 1.0.

Spatial Coherence in a Random Medium

The theory of coherence between separated receivers in a random, isotropic, inhomogeneous medium is developed in a book by Chernov (5). It is shown that for inhomogeneities described by an auto-correlation function of the form $\rho(x) = \exp(-x/a)^2$, where "a" is the correlation distance or "patch size" of the inhomogeneities, and for

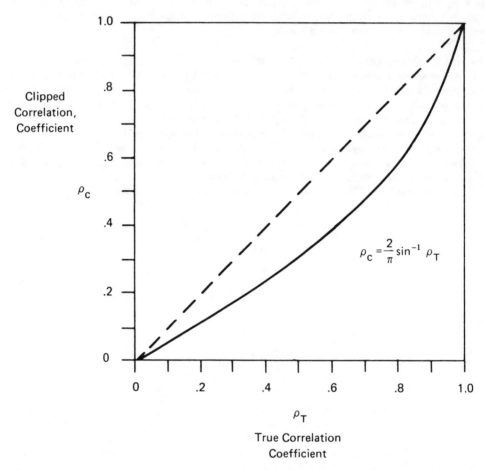

Fig. 2. Relation between the clipped and true correlation coefficient for sinusoidal and random Gaussian functions. The quantity $10 \log \rho_c/\rho_T = 10 \log 2/\pi = -2$ db for small ρ_T is the clipping loss in clipped processing.

13-6

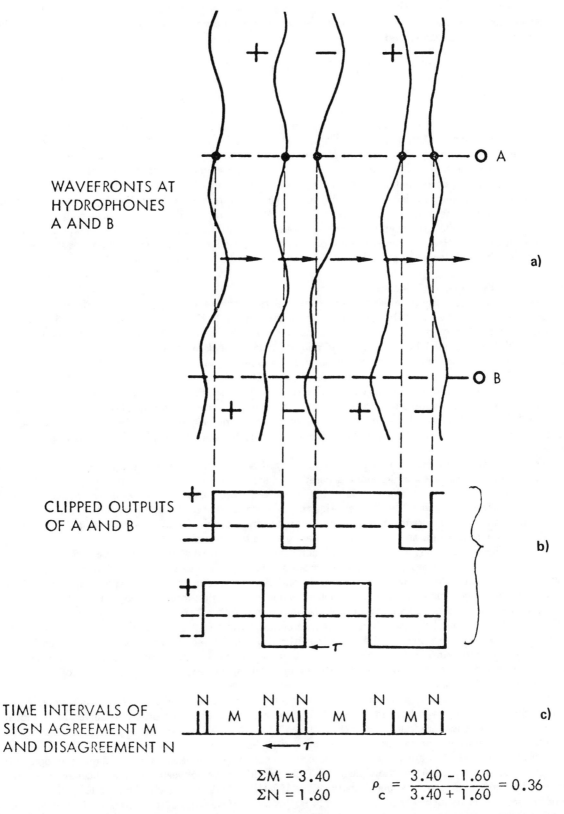

WAVEFRONTS AT
HYDROPHONES
A AND B

CLIPPED OUTPUTS
OF A AND B

TIME INTERVALS OF
SIGN AGREEMENT M
AND DISAGREEMENT N

$$\Sigma M = 3.40$$
$$\Sigma N = 1.60$$

$$\rho_c = \frac{3.40 - 1.60}{3.40 + 1.60} = 0.36$$

Fig. 3. a) a quasi-plane wave is incident from the left on hydrophones A and B. b) clipped amplitude of the output of A and B as a function of time. c) the two outputs have the same sign during the intervals M and opposite sign during the intervals N. The total time interval M was 3.4 arbitrary units and that of N, 1.6 units. The clipped correlation coefficient over the entire time shown would be 0.36.

distances long compared to the Fresnel or "transition" range of the patches (Chapt. 11) given by a^2/λ, the *correlation coefficient for amplitude* and the *correlation coefficient for phase* are both *equal to unity* for longitudinal separations d *equal to or less than a*, and equal to

$$\left(1 + \frac{2d}{ka^2} \right)^{-1}$$

for longitudinal separations *much greater than a*. For transverse separations, when $2\pi a/\lambda \gg 1$, the correlation coefficients are both equal approximately to $\exp(-d^2/a^2)$. Thus, we may say as a generality that, under the above conditions, *the correlation distance of separated hydrophones is about the same as the correlation distance of the inhomogeneities*. At shorter separations the two receivers are in an essentially homogeneous medium; at longer separations, the two receivers become decorrelated by the scattering and diffraction of the inhomogeneities.

This body of theory, while elegant, applies only to propagation through a random, isotropic microstructure. It does not apply to long-range propagation in the real ocean where multipath interferences, caused by refraction in the body of the sea and reflection from its boundaries, are often the prime reason for the decorrelation of separated receivers. The theoretical effect of microstructure on the directivity pattern and the array gain of a short line array (shorter than the coherence length or patch size of the medium) may be found in Reference 6.

Field Observations by the Naval Ordnance Laboratory

A variety of signals and noise have been observed in a series of coherence measurements under different condi- over a period of years at the Naval Ordnance Laboratory (now Naval Surface Weapons Center). In this series, the outputs of the hydrophones to be correlated were tape-recorded in the field; a string or line of separated hydrophones was used. Later, in the laboratory, selected pairs of tape channels were fed into a Deltic correlator to produce on an oscilloscope screen a time-delay correlogram that was photographed and subsequently measured.

A number of reports were written. In Reference (7), the coherence of reverberation from the Deep Scattering Layer and from the bottom in deep water was measured; in References (8) and (9), ambient noise and transmitted single frequency sound was measured using a bottom-mounted vertical array at Bermuda (TRIDENT Vertical Array); in Reference (10) the coherence of transmitted sound within and in the neighborhood of the first convergence zone was observed; while in references (11) and (12), the vertical and horizontal coherence of explosive reverberation in shallow water was studied.

For this variety of signals, noise, and reverberation, *Figs. 4 and 5* show a compilation of measured coherence data as a function of normalized hydrophone separation in the vertical in an octave band near $1 - 2$ kHz. In all cases, *the clipped correlation coefficient falls off with separation at a rate intermediate between that for uni-directional noise and isotropic noise*. Of the various kinds of noise and reverberation, the return from the bottom is most coherent, while the coherence of volume reverberation from scatterers outside of the Deep Scattering Layer is essentially like that of isotropic ambient noise originating at the sea surface.

Reverberation having a totally different spatial coherence occurs in shallow water. Observations (11) with a vertical string in shallow water show that the reverberation from an explosive source occurs within a small vertical angle about the horizontal. At 1 kHz at a time of 7 seconds after the detonation, this angle is approximately ± 5°, decreasing with increasing time and frequency. Shallow water reverberation thus becomes more vertically coherent, with a smaller vertical angle, with increasing range and frequency. With a horizontal string of hydrophones, it was found (12) that the horizontal spatial coherence of reverberation was less than in the vertical, in keeping with the fact that the reverberation from an explosive source received with a non-directional hydrophone arrives equally from all directions in the horizontal plane. Comparing horizontal and vertical in terms of array gain, this means that a horizontal array would be expected to have a far greater array gain against shallow water reverberation than would a vertical array of the same size.

The coherence of the ambient noise background in deep water has been measured (13) at a number of intermediate depths between top and bottom off St. Croix, Virgin Islands. The correlograms observed at this location were essentially the same as those found earlier (8) with the TRIDENT Vertical Array.

Examples of correlograms of the ambient background at St. Croix for hydrophones vertically separated by 21 feet at a depth of 4000 feet are shown in *Figure 6*. Each correlogram here is a sum of 25 ms correlograms integrated over a 3-second period. They show most strikingly the difference between the coherence characteristics of the ambient background in a low frequency band ($88 - 177$ Hz), where distant shipping produces the major part of the noise, and a high frequency band ($707 - 1414$ Hz), where surface noise of local origin is the principal source of noise. Similar results were found at other depths throughout in the water column.

Turning to transmitted sound, two field experiments may be mentioned. In one (10), a vertical hydrophone string was dangled from one ship *(Fig 7)*, while a second ship towed a continuous 1120 Hz source outward in range. Coherence data were obtained in and out of the first pair of convergence half-zones at ranges of 33 and 41 mi. The

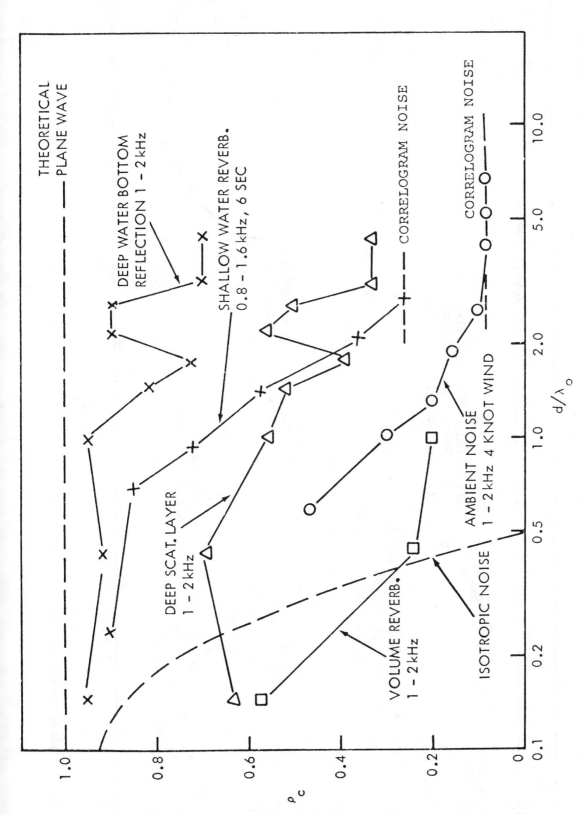

Fig. 4. Examples of clipped correlation coefficient of reverberation and noise for vertically-separated hydrophones of normalized separation d/λ_0 where λ_0 is the mid-band wavelength. Each point was measured from a correlogram based on 25 ms of input data. The dashed lines the theoretical extremes of a plane wave and an isotropic sound field.

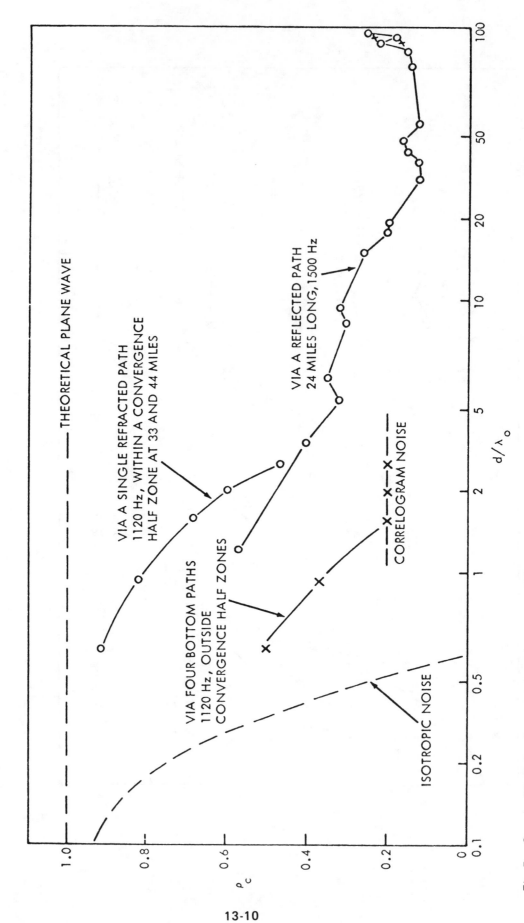

Fig. 5. Same as Fig. 4, but for transmitted cw at 1120 and 1500 Hz.

13-10

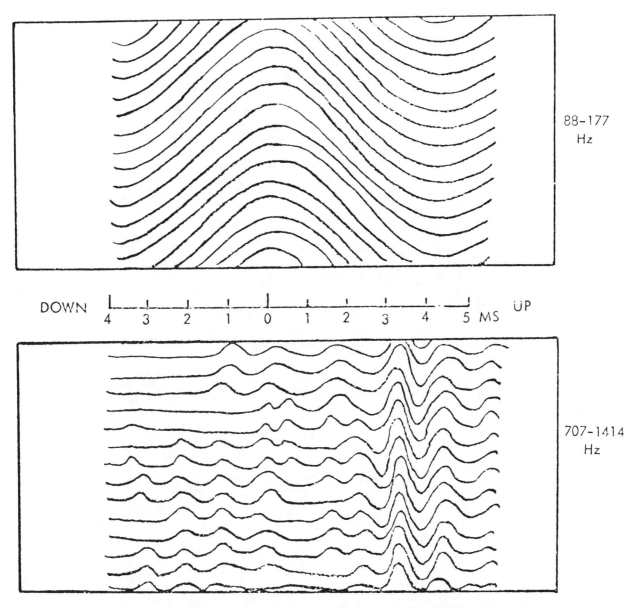

Fig. 6. Successive 3-second samples of correlograms of the two types of ambient noise observed at a depth of 4000 ft. The 3.5 millisecond delay of the high frequency correlogram peak corresponds to an apparent, or effective, arrival angle of 55°. The hydrophone separation was 21 ft. (8).

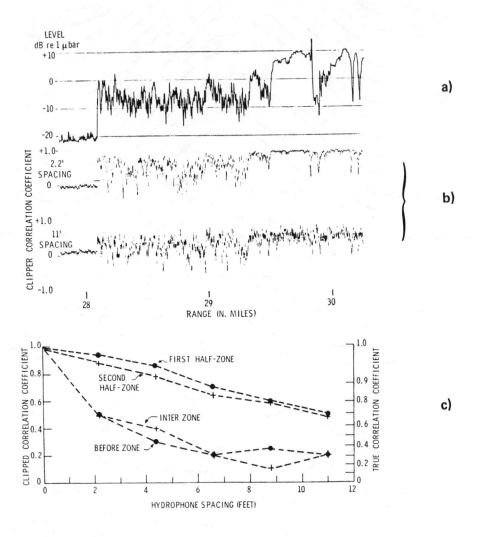

Fig. 7.   a) Intensity vs. range from a 1120 Hz CW source at ranges from 28-30 miles. The two convergence half-zones occur at the right. b) Clipped correlation of two vertically spaced hydrophones 2.2 and 11 feet apart. c) Clipped correlation coefficient vs. vertical separation at ranges short of the first half-zone, within the two half-zones and between them (inter-zone). **(10).**

spatial coherence of the received sound was found to be *greater* when the source was *inside* the zones, when only a single dominant propagation path effectively exists, than when outside the zones, where the only available paths are the four paths that involve one bottom bounce and have a nearly equal transmission loss. The other experiment (9) used the TRIDENT Vertical Array at Bermuda with transmission from a source 24 miles away. The time delay correlograms enabled the two paths, shown in *Fig. 8*, to be separated. The clipped correlation coefficient was found to fall off slowly with normalized separation d/λ and to remain appreciable (at about 0.2) for d/λ as high as 100. Reflections from the surface at a grazing angle of $4°$ appeared to play no part in the degradation of coherence, since no effect of wind speed from $5 - 25$ knots upon coherence could be detected. This is in keeping with the fact that, because of the small grazing angle at the surface, the Rayleigh parameter was never much larger than unity, so that the sea surface was always effectively smooth.

In still another field test (14), the coherence between two hydrophones 500 feet apart at depths of 4000 and 4500 feet was investigated as a ship passed overhead *(Fig 9)*. In the three one-octave bands 44-88 Hz, 177-354 Hz, and 354-707 Hz, the clipped correlation coefficient fell off to 0.5 at horizontal ranges of the ship of about 1, 1½ and 2 miles, respectively. This rapid decorrelation of ship-noise with range can be ascribed to interference between the direct-path sound and surface-bottom multipaths, which become relatively weaker with increasing frequency because of a higher bottom loss. In other words, the various surface-bottom multipaths acted as noise to the coherent direct path sound and so degraded its coherence. The effects of such interference on array gain are profound: a vertical array in a multipath environment steered in the direction of one multipath suffers a loss in array gain due to the interfering multipaths. It can be shown (14) that for a perfectly coherent signal in a background of incoherent interference, the array gain is

$$AG = 10 \log \frac{nI_s + I_i}{I_s + I_i}$$

where I_s is the intensity of the coherent signal to which the array is steered, I_i is the intensity of the interfering multipaths, and n is the number of elements in the array. When n is large enough to make $nI_s \gg I_i$, this becomes

$$AG = 10 \log \left[n \cdot \frac{I_s}{I_s + I_i} \right]$$

where the term $I_s / (I_s + I_i)$ is the loss in array gain due to the interference. In the experiment described, I_s/I_i was the ratio of the intensity carried by surface-bottom multipaths to the intensity of the direct-path sound.

Comparison with Theory

When source and receiver are shallow and the range is not too great, the meager available data suggest the validity of the Chernov formulas for coherence in a randomly inhomogeneous medium. For example, the envelope cross-correlation coefficient between vertically separated hydrophones for 25 and 60 kHz pulses at ranges of several hundred yards was found (15) to fall to $1/e$ in a vertical separation of 8 feet, equal to the patch size of the microstructure observed independently. In Russian work (16), the transverse correlation of two shallow receivers spaced horizontally from 20 meters to 3000 meters for 7.5 kHz sound over distances out to 12 km was said to agree with Chernov's theoretical work. In another Russian experiment on surface reflected sound (17), the horizontal amplitude coherence of 2.5 and 4 kHz CW sound was of the same order of magnitude as the horizontal coherence of the amplitude of the surface waves — again suggesting that the acoustic coherence is of the same scale as the inhomogeneities of the medium.

On the other hand, when the propagation paths are deep, the coherence is maintained over much greater distances, and the correlation coefficient falls only slowly to zero with increasing separation. An example is the vertical coherence of transmission over 24 mi to a deep receiver, as already plotted in Fig. 5. Another (18) is the measurement of coherence with a distributed array on the sloping bottom near Bermuda. Using 400 Hz sound transmitted over several hundred miles in the Deep Sound Channel, individual ray arrivals (making 14 to 16 loops) were found to have a transverse phase correlation coefficient falling to $1/e$ at a longitudinal separation of 700 feet and a transverse separation of 1300 feet. Various other observations show good coherence between hydrophones separated by long distances in the Deep Sound Channel, suggesting the presence of much larger patch sizes — a "macrostructure" — in the deep sea. The dominant scale of this deep macrostructure has not yet been determined, but is doubtless larger by at least an order of magnitude than that already measured near the surface.

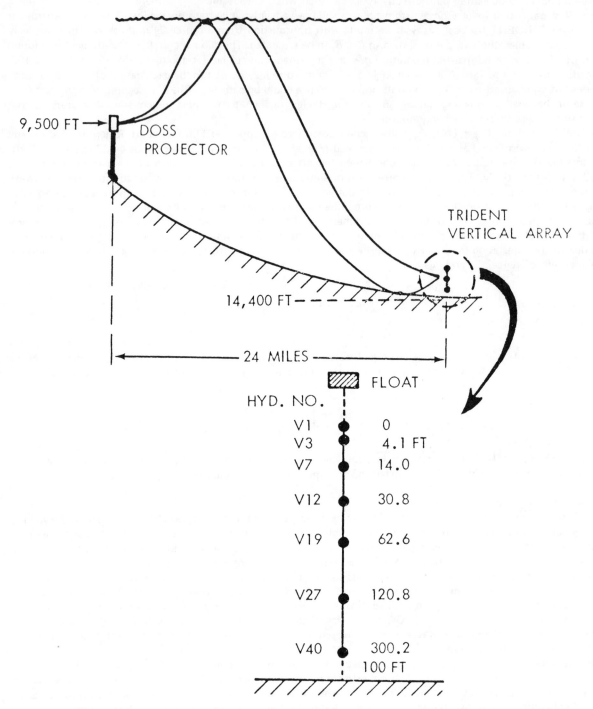

9,500 FT →

DOSS PROJECTOR

TRIDENT VERTICAL ARRAY

14,400 FT

← 24 MILES →

FLOAT

HYD. NO.	
V1	0
V3	4.1 FT
V7	14.0
V12	30.8
V19	62.6
V27	120.8
V40	300.2
	100 FT

Fig. 8. An experiment to measure coherence over a transmitted path. The two paths shown could be separated by the time delay between them and were reflected at the sea surface at a grazing angle of $4°$. **(9)**.

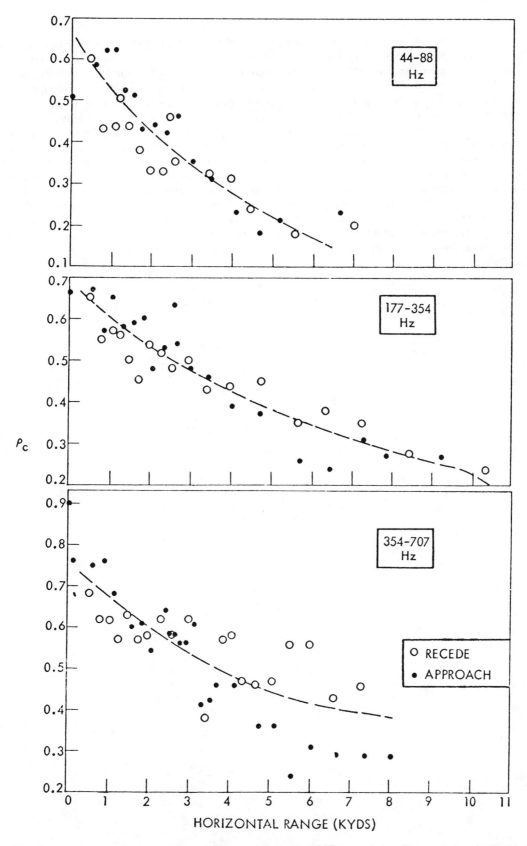

Fig. 9. Clipped correlation of ship noise vs. horizontal range in 7000 feet of water between two hydrophones 500 feet apart. The circles and dots show the measured correlation for the recession and the approach of the approach of the ship source.

Data Summary

Table 2 is a summary of measurements of coherence length r_o for transmitted signals, as reported in the unclassified literature, together with the experimental conditions under which they were obtained. The coherence length here is taken to be the length defined by $r_o = \int_0^\infty \rho(r)dr$, where r is the separation of the receivers being correlated and $\rho(r)$ is the phase, or clipped, correlation coefficient. r_o is, in effect, the area under the function $\rho(r)$; if ρ decreased linearly with r, then r_o is the separation for which ρ falls to 0.5; if ρ decreases exponentially with r, then r_o is the separation at which $\rho = e^{-1} = .37$. r_o gives a rough idea of the maximum useful length of an array for achieving array gain; arrays in incoherent noise longer than about $2r_o$ realize no further increase in array gain. Many of the entries in Table 2 are, because of brevity, not entirely meaningful; the references themselves should be consulted in cases of special interest. Most noticeable is the wide variety of conditions applying for the measured data.

A study of these coherence results, augmented by an understanding of propagation of sound in the sea, indicates that the coherence of transmitted sounds, and therefore the gain of deep-water arrays in incoherent noise, should be greatest under conditions of (a) *narrow frequency bands,* (b) *low frequencies,* (c) *short averaging times,* (d) propagation such that *a single dominant propagation path* exists, and (e) *horizontal rather than vertical separation.* In the design of receiving arrays, these conditions can never be all achieved at the same time, while others will be incompatible with system requirements, so that the usual trade-off procedure will be necessary in the search for the optimum array design.

TABLE 2
TABULAR SUMMARY OF COHERENCE MEASUREMENTS

COHERENCE LENGTH r_o	FREQUENCY	BAND WIDTH	AVERAGING TIME	PROPAGATION PATH(S)	SOURCE DEPTH	RECEIVER DEPTH	SOURCE RECEIVER RANGE	HYDROPHONE ORIENTATION	REFERENCE
>3 km (ρ=0.8, constant to 3 km)	7.5 kHz cw	Narrow	0.1 sec	Single, Near Surface	Shallow	—	0.6-12 km	Horizontal Transverse	16
6 meters 1 meter	4, 7, 15 kHz	Pulses	3 and 30 ms Pulses	Surface Reflection	Shallow Water, Depth 80 m.		600 m.	Horizontal Transverse Vertical	17
>4000 ft. 1600 ft.	400 Hz	Pulses	0.1 hr.	Single, Refracted	—	Artemis*	19 mi.	Horizontal Vertical	19
1300 ft. 700 ft.	400 Hz	Pulses	—	Single, Refracted	1200 ft	Artemis*	270 mi.	Horizontal Vertical	18
48 ft. 6 wavelengths	750 Hz cw	Narrow	106 ms	Surface Reflected	9500 ft	TVA**	24 mi.	Vertical	9
300 ft.	800 Hz Pulses	—	5 ms	Single, Refracted	9500 ft	TVA**	24 mi.	Vertical	20
8 wavelengths	50-100 Hz 100-200 Hz 200-400 Hz	Octave	Shot Duration	Multiple Refracted	800 ft.	TVA**	100-600 mi.	Vertical	21
300 ft. 1000 ft.	367 Hz	Narrow	840 sec 150 sec	Multiple Refracted (RSR)	—	Artemis*	700 mi.	—	22
2 wavelengths 8 wavelengths 10 wavelengths 30 wavelengths	3.1-3.3 kHz 1.5-1.7 kHz 0.7-0.9 kHz 0.3-0.5 kHz	200 Hz	Shot Duration	Shallow Water Paths	Shallow Water, Depth 65 m.		4 mi.	Horizontal Transverse	23
500 ft. ±	44-88 Hz 177-354 Hz 354-707 Hz	Octave	2 sec	Surface-Bottom Reflections	15 ft.	4000 ft.	1 ky 2 ky 3 ky	Vertical	14

*Hydrophone field on bottom 2000 - 4000 feet depth on channel axis near Bermuda.
**Vertical string on bottom at 14,000 feet near Bermuda (TRIDENT Vertical Array).

REFERENCES

1. R. J. Urick, *Principles of Underwater Sound*, 2 ed., McGraw-Hill, New York, 1975, pp. 33-37.
2. R. J. Nielsen, Array Gain, Correlation Coefficients and Patch Size, JASA *61*, 60, 1977.
3. B. F. Cron and C. H. Sherman, Spatial Correlation Functions for Various Noise Models, JASA *34*, 1732, 1962.
4. J. J. Faran and R. Hills, Correlators for Signal Reception, Acoustics Research Lab., Harvard Univ., Tech. Memo *27*, 1952.
5. L. A. Chernov, *Wave Propagation in a Random Medium*, McGraw-Hill Book Co., New York, 1960, Chap. VI.
6. R. Bourret, Directurly of a Linear Array in a Random Transmission Medium, JASA *33,* 1793, 1961.
7. R. J. Urick and G. R. Lund, Vertical Coherence of Explosive Reverberation, JASA *36*, 2164, 1964.
8. R. J. Urick, Correlative Properties of Ambient Noise at Bermuda, JASA *40*, 1108, 1966.
9. R. J. Urick, T. J. Tulko and I. I. Abrams, Vertical Coherence of Sound Transmitted over a 24-mile Path, JASA *46*, 1308, 1969.
10. R. J. Urick and G. R. Lund, Coherence of Convergent Zone Sound, JASA *43*, 723, 1968.
11. R. J. Urick and G. R. Lund, Vertical Coherence of Explosive Reverberation, JASA *47*, 342, 1970.
12. R. J. Urick and G. R. Lund, Horizontal Coherence of Explosive Reverberation, JASA *47*, 909, 1970.
13. R. J. Urick, Coherence of Ambient Noise and the Signal from a Steady Source at Different Depths at a Deep Sea Location, Naval Ordnance Laboratory Tech. Rep. 73-68, 1973.
14. R. J. Urick, Measurements of the Vertical Coherence of the Sound from a Near-Surface Source in the Sea, JASA *54*, 115, 1973.
15. D. C. Whitmarsh, E. Skudryzk and R. J. Urick, Forward Scattering of Sound in the Sea and its Correlation with the Temperature Microstructure, JASA *29*, 1124, 1957.
16. S. G. Gershman and Y. I. Tuzhilkin, Measurement of the Transverse Correlation of a Continuous Signal in the Sea, Soviet Physics-Acoustics *6*, 291, 1961.
17. E. P. Gulin and K. I. Malyshew, Spatial Correlation of Amplitude Fluctuations of a Continuous Tone Signal with Reflections from Ocean Surface Waves, Soviet Physics Acoustics *11*, 428, 1966. See also, same authors, SPA *10*, 365, 1964.
18. H. W. Brock, Fluctuations in Single Path Underwater Sound Transmission over a 540-mi path, Bell Telephone Labs Ocean Science Report 1, 1968.
19. R. M. Kennedy, "A Statistical Study of the Perturbation of an Acoustic Wavefront", USN Underwater Sound Lab. Report 868, (1968).
20. R. M. Kennedy, "Phase and Amplitude Fluctuations in Propagation in a Layered Ocean", JASA *46*, 737, (1969).
21. R. J. Urick and G. R. Lund, "Low Frequency Coherence of Long Range Explosive Sounds and Ambient Noise in the Deep Sea", NOLTR 70-111, (1970).
22. B. E. Parkins and G. R. Fox, "Measurement of the Coherence and Fading of Long Range Acoustic Signals", IEEE Trans. Audio and Electro. Acoust. *19*, 158, (1971)
23. P. Wille and R. Thiele, "Transverse Horizontal Coherence of Explosive Signals in Shallow Water", JASA *50*, 348, (1971).

CHAPTER 14

MULTIPATHS IN THE SEA

Introduction

This chapter is intended to give a synoptic view of the paths by which sound reaches a distant point in the sea under different conditions of depth and distance. These paths, generally speaking, become more numerous, and acquire greater differences in travel time and transmission loss, as the range from source to receiver increases. Except very near the source, multipath transmission is the rule rather than the exception in sound transmission in the sea.

Sound propagation in the sea has its above-water analog in electromagnetic propagation in the atmosphere, where many of the same propagation phenomena are found.

Deep Water — Shallow Source and Receiver

Fig 1 attempts to show in a diagrammatic way the transmission paths between a shallow source and a shallow receiver approximately in the order of increasing range from source to receiver. Starting at a short range at the upper left, *the direct path A* is a nearly straight-line path between source and receiver, over which spherical spreading, plus attenuation, determines the transmission loss. Even this path can be considered as multiple if we consider the effects of microstructure, which cause fluctuation of the transmitted sound and the decorrelation of separated receivers. When this path becomes equal in length to the geometric mean of the depths of source and receiver, *the surface reflection B* begins to be a significant contributor to the total sound field, and coherently interferes with the direct-path sound under conditions of calm seas, high frequencies and small grazing angles, such that the Rayleigh parameter is less than unity and the sea surface may therefore be said to be acoustically smooth.

When a negative velocity gradient extends upward all the way to the surface, the direct and surface paths become bent downward into arcs of circles (for a linear gradient) and a shadow is then cast by the sea surface on the waters below *(Paths C)*. A receiver within the shadow receives sound only by scattering (x), diffraction (y), and from the bottom (z); within the shadow in deep water, a short pulse is received as a weak, irregular elongated blob. During World War II, 24 kHz pulses received well within the shadow were found (1) to be some 40 db weaker than they would be if the shadow were absent, perhaps representing forward-scattered sound from the biological scatterers in the Deep Scattering Layer.

Wind-mixing often creates isothermal water on top of the negative gradient, or thermocline, so as to form a *surface duct D*. At frequencies well above cutoff, and for a thick layer with a calm sea, the surface duct becomes an effective trap, preventing the loss of sound to the abyssal depths of the sea. Under other conditions, the duct is so lossy as to be useless as a sonar trap. There is an optimum frequency for duct transmission, such that poorer transmission occurs at frequencies much higher or much lower than the optimum. A point well below a duct receives duct-transmitted sound only by diffraction near the cutoff frequency of the duct and by surface scattering at higher frequencies.

Path E is the bottom-bounce path. This is the only effective path from a shallow source to a shallow receiver, unless a strong surface duct is present. Sound travelling over this path suffers a loss at the sea bed, which may vary from near 0 db for smooth layered bottoms at low angles, to 20 db or more for rough bottoms at moderate angles. At short ranges, the high grazing angles and the longer path length make this a high-loss path. There are four paths (B, SB, BS, SBS) making one encounter with the bottom, and the loss is reduced by 10 log 4 = 6 db for non-directional sonars.

At greater ranges, the bottom reflected paths became refracted, and a *convergence zone (F)* occurs if the water is deep enough. The two half-zones formed by down- and up-going rays merge together as the source of sound nears the surface, and result in a convergence gain of 10-15 db (typically) in a zone 3-5 miles wide. In addition, a receiving array may be expected to have a higher array gain within a convergence zone than when outside it, due to the occurrence of only a single strong propagation path. Deep refracted paths, shown dashed, insonify ranges beyond the zone to a range depending on water depth. The zones are repeated at regular range intervals and have been observed out to 500 miles or so.

Beyond the first zone, *multiple bottom-bounce paths (G)* occur that involve higher losses due to the multiple bottom encounters. Few sonars have figures-of-merit high enough to exploit these paths.

Finally, if there is a depth-excess (water of higher velocity than at surface), *RSR paths* may occur *(Path H)*, which suffer only the loss at the surface, and for which the loss is only slightly greater than that for purely refracted paths. These paths reach the surface on the far side of convergence zones, and serve to extend the ranges of good transmission in the vicinity of the zones.

Fig. 2 is a diagrammatic plot of loss vs. range for the various transmission paths just described.

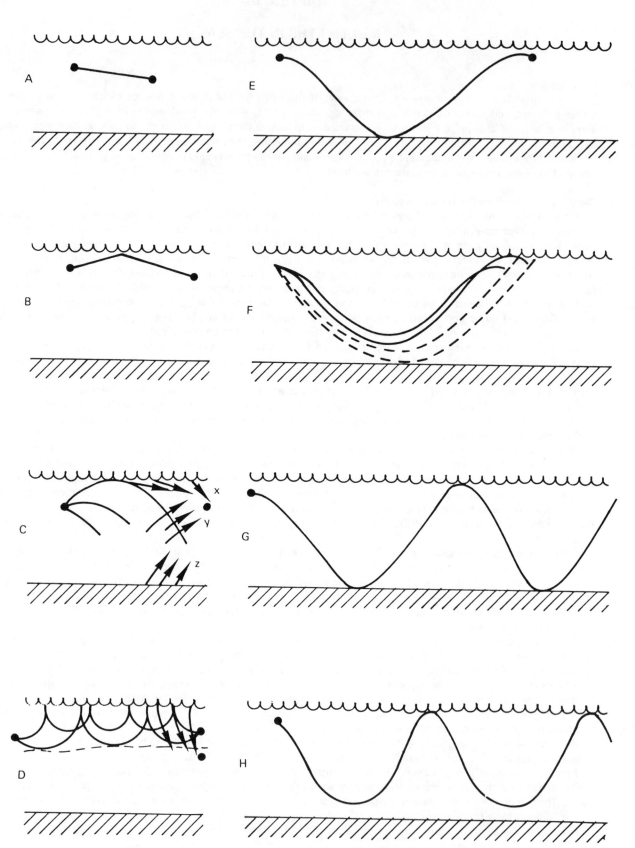

Fig. 1.   Diagrammatic ray paths from a shallow source in deep water.

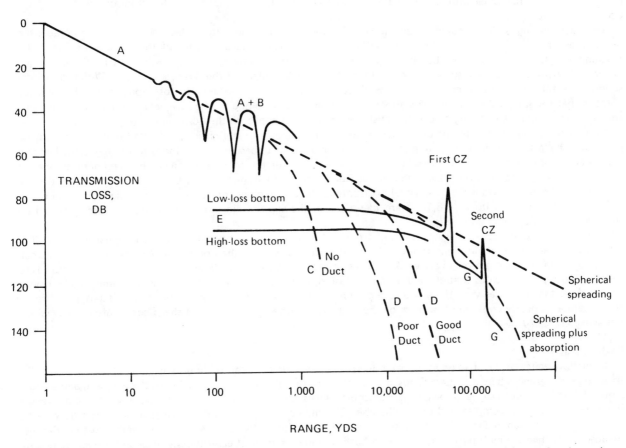

Fig. 2. Diagrammatic transmission loss for the various paths identified in Fig. 1. The actual losses for the various paths will depend upon the many factors affecting propagation in the ocean, such as frequency and source/ receiver depths.

Deep Water — Deep Source and Receiver

For a deep source, the distance over which direct path transmission is effective is much greater than for a shallow source. The reason is that a source in the body of the deep sea often lies well within the Deep Sound Channel. When it happens to lie on the axis of this channel, excellent transmission to an axial receiver takes place out to extremely long ranges. The horizontal ray from a source anywhere within the channel is itself a caustic and is accompanied by pairs of caustics that diverge from its vertices. When the source is off-axis the ray diagram is characterized by "holidays", or shadow-zones, which are not penetrated by purely refracted paths. These shadow zones fill up or expand with changing source depth. In *Fig. 3*, the near-surface shadow zone A fills up with increasing source depth, while shadow zone B expands. In addition, there are shadows deep in the sea, such as A' and B', which behave in the opposite way. The locations and depths of such shadows, cast by the surface or bottom, have to be found from the ray diagram for a particular profile. All of the shadows are insonified by paths reflected from one or both of the ocean boundaries.

The rays leaving a deep source in an upward direction and reaching the surface are called *reliable acoustic paths*; they are so called because they are unaffected by the near-surface vagaries of the velocity profile. After reaching the surface, these paths become surface-reflected. The limiting reliable acoustic path is the one which becomes horizontal at the sea surface so as to form the outer boundary of the direct sound field. Within the direct sound field, there is a convergence gain of a few db before the shadow is reached. The loss along the reliable acoustic paths is that for spherical spreading plus attenuation, minus a small amount of convergence gain, as determined by the particlar profile used, at ranges near the caustic where the rays approach the horizontal.

From a deep source to a distant deep receiver there are normally several entirely refracted paths. These may be designated by a pair of digits (m, n) that denote the number of upper and lower loops in the ray path. For any ray, m and n are either equal, or differ by one. From a given source to a given receiver, the maximum number of loops (m, n) occur for the ray leaving the source horizontally; the minimum number of loops occurs for the ray skimming the top or bottom of the channel horizontally. In one experiment (2), ray paths designated by (11, 12), (12,12), 13,12), (12,13) up to (16,16) were identified in the signal from a shallow explosive source received on the channel axis 600 miles away *(Fig. 4a)*.

These various paths cause a signal received from a distant source to have a complex, irregular envelope. The different arrivals arrive at different times and at different angles from the horizontal. Arrivals via paths of small (m, n) come in first and are relatively weak; arrivals of high (m, n) come in later and are stronger. The result is to cause a short pulse, such as that created by an explosion, to be received as a long, irregular, bumpy signal having an envelope that increases with time, with a short tail of scattered and reflected sound. For axis-axis transmission the envelope is nearly continuous because of the multiplicity of arrivals and has a sharp cutoff after the axial ray has arrived *(Fig 4b)*.

Shallow Water

In shallow water many of these same paths tend to occur, but they can seldom be isolated because of the small travel-time differences between them. Thus, even at short ranges, the direct path, surface-reflected path, and bottom path all interfere, and can be resolved only at short ranges by using very short pulses. At even moderate ranges the arrival structure is complex and undecipherable. The mixed-layer path is still an effective path in shallow water, and even more so than in deep water, because it tends to be reinforced by sound scattered from the bottom. Because shallow water involves multiple encounters with both boundaries, in most cases the ray diagram is useless to quantitatively describe the sound field. The reason is that the reflection loss at the shallow sea bed, as well as the redistribution of sound by scattering, in general are all but unknown.

Figure 5 shows diagrammatic ray paths in shallow water. There are paths through the bottom as well as through the water. When the source is within the mixed layer, the *mixed layer paths A* are important for high frequency transmission to a shallow source. In addition, *doubly-reflected paths B* occur, suffering reflection losses at both surface and bottom. With the source below the layer, *RBR paths C* occur that are in the form of arches repeatedly reflected from the bottom.

The bottom plays a dominant role in shallow water transmission at frequencies too low to be well trapped in the water layer. Various paths may exist in the bottom itself, as depicted in Fig. 5. Path A occurs as a *surface wave* traveling along the bottom interface. *Reflections from sedimentary layers* may exist (B). A *refracted path (C)* in the bottom may occur because of an increase of velocity with depth in a sedimentary bottom due to age and compaction. Finally, a *reflection from a crystalline basement (D)*, if one exists, may contribute to the sound at a distant receiver. These bottom paths are best known in connection with seismic prospecting for oil, but have not been much studied in connection with propagation in the thin overlying layer of water.

Normal mode theory is sometimes useful to describe shallow water propagation, but only when the situation can be modelled in simple terms, such as a velocity profile that can be represented by one or two layers and a non-layered bottom of uniform depth. Even in these cases the theory is complex and requires elaborate computer programming. The simplest case is that of iso-velocity water overlying a flat fluid bottom; here intensity summation of modes yields general curves that may be useful for prediction when the simple model is valid.

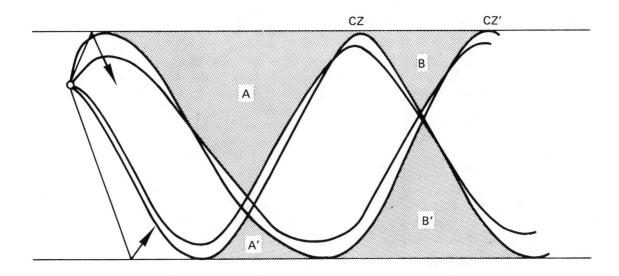

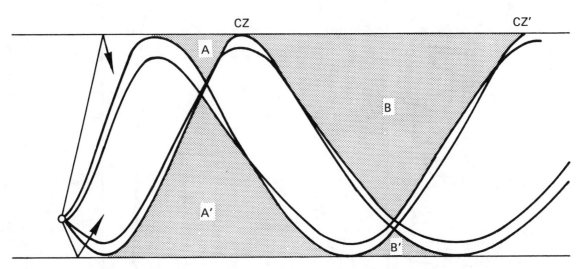

Fig. 3.   Limiting rays for a shallow and a deep source. The Regions A, A′, B, B′ are shadow zones into which no direct path rays penetrate, but which are insonified by reflected rays shown by the arrows. CZ and CZ′ are the first two convergence half-zones formed by up- and down-going rays from the source.

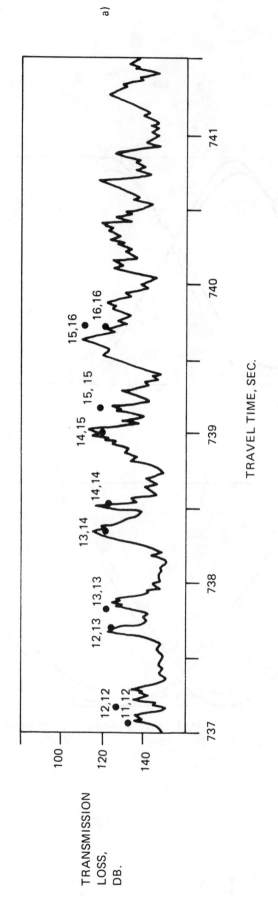

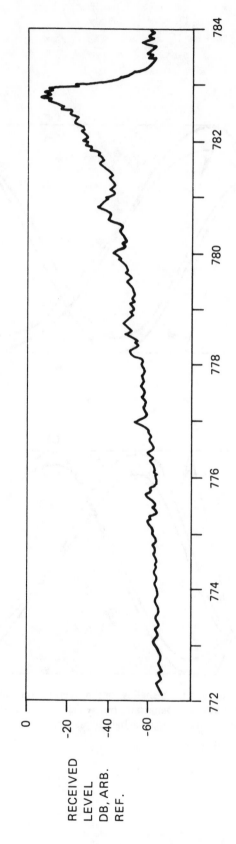

Fig. 4. Explosive shot envelopes received by an axial hydrophone at a distance of 600 miles. a) Shot depth 800 ft. The dots show computed levels and times of individual ray arrivals, where the number of upper loops (crests) and lower loops (troughs) in the ray paths. b) Shot depth, on axis, 3500 ft. The ray arrivals form a smooth envelope with a sudden cessation.

14-6

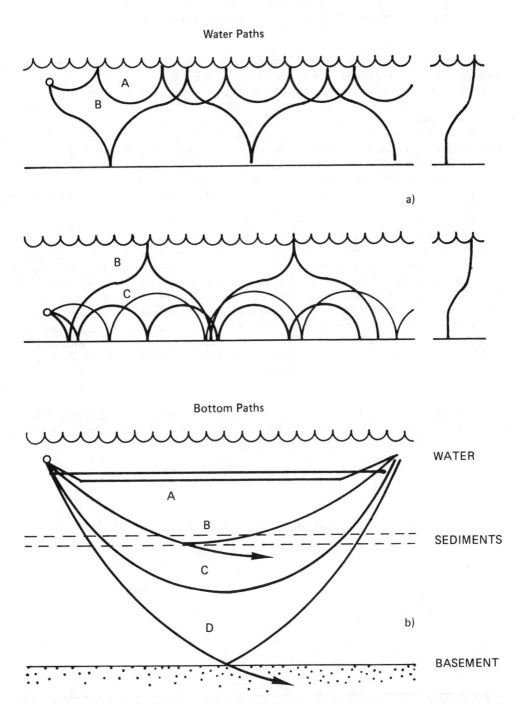

Water Paths

a)

Bottom Paths

WATER

SEDIMENTS

b)

BASEMENT

Fig. 5. Paths in shallow water. a) Paths within the water column for a source in and below a surface duct for the velocity profile at the right. Paths A and C repeatedly encounter one of the ocean boundaries, while B encounters both. In well-mixed shallow water the duct extends all the way to the bottom. b) Paths within the ocean floor. A is a refracted path through a well-defined upper layer; B is a reflection from a layer in the sedimentary column; C is refracted by the velocity gradient in the sediments, while D is the reflection from a crystalline basement. All these paths may contribute to the sound received from the source.

All in all, the propagation paths in shallow water are many and complex, with nearly the same travel time, and are not well known quantitatively due to lack of knowledge of the losses at the boundaries.

Multipath Effects

The transmission paths just described do not occur isolated from one another, but paths of different kinds (A-H), often with comparable losses, generally exist between two points in the sea. An obvious example is the sound field at short ranges caused by coherent interference between the direct path A and the surface reflection B; another example occurs at longer ranges when the transmission loss via the surface duct E is comparable to that via the bottom reflection F. Such multipaths can often be sorted out by directionality of source and receiver. But even a path of a single kind is usually multiple, as in the case of microstructure along the direct path A, or the various paths with different numbers of surface bounces to a receiver in the surface duct D. *Fig 6* illustrates the four paths between a source and a receiver that are reflected once from the bottom and have nearly the same transmission loss, since loss on surface reflection tends to be small, and nearly the same travel time when the source and receiver are shallow. Finally, the refracted paths within the Deep Sound Channel occur in multiples, as we have noted, so as to produce the highly distorted shot signals of Figs. 4a and 4b.

One result of multipath propagation is the fluctuation of transmitted signals. Signal fluctuations cause sonar targets to be detected during periods of signal surges at greater ranges than they would be in the absence of fluctuation, but cause targets to be lost during periods of signal fading. Thus, the probability of target detection becomes higher at long ranges and lower at short ranges, relative to what would be expected from the sonar equation if fluctuations were ignored. *Signal distortion* is another result of multipath propagation, where an initially short signal is stretched out in time and acquires an irregular envelope because of differences in travel time and transmission loss over the various multipaths. Signal distortion makes replica correlation and matched filtering useless for detection of a target at a long unknown range. *Decorrelation* of separated receivers is another effect of time-varying multipaths, causing the gain of an array to be less than it would be in the absence of multipaths. Finally, *frequency shifting and broadening* take place wherever the multipaths from a constant-frequency source encounter the moving sea surface, or when the motion of the source or receiver, or both, cause interferences among the transmission multipaths. Wider receiving filter bandwidths are necessary to accommodate the frequencies generated in propagation.

On balance it would appear that multipaths are generally deleterious to sonar operations since they degrade the predictability of sonar performance. They degrade to some extent the benefits of elaborate processing schemes and extended receiving arrays that would exist in an ideal, multipath-free ocean.

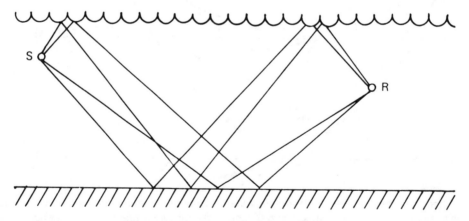

Fig. 6. The four paths between a source S and a receiver R making one bounce off the bottom. Four additional paths making two bounces occur, and four more making three bounces, etc. The four one-bounce paths have nearly the same transmission loss, since the differences in path length, bottom grazing angle, and the loss on surface reflection are small. The rays connecting a particular source and receiver are sometimes called "eigenrays" to distinguish them from all the other rays in a ray diagram.

REFERENCES

1. Physics of Sound in the Sea, National Defense Research Committee Division 6, Summary Tech. Rept. 8, 1946, pp. 120-123.
2. R. J. Urick, Ray Identification in Long Range Sound Transmission, Naval Ordnance Laboratory Tech. Rept. 65-104, 1965.

ABBREVIATIONS

AG	Array Gain
ARB REF	Arbitrary Reference
BB	Bottom Bounce
BT	Bathythermograph
CW	Continuous Wave
CZ	Convergence Zone
DARPA	Defense Advanced Research Projects Agency
DIMUS	Digital Multibeam Steering
DSC	Deep Sound Channel
FM	Fathom
G	Gradient (Velocity)
JASA	Journal of the Acoustical Society of America
KN	Knots
MILS	Missile Impact Location System
NAVOCEANO	Naval Oceanographic Office
NUSC	Naval Underwater Sound Center
RBR	Refracted-bottom reflected
RSR	Refracted-Surface-Reflected
S/N	Signal-To-Noise Ratio
SOFAR	Sound Fixing and Ranging
TA	Transmission Anomoly
TL	Transmission Loss
USNUSL	U. S. Navy Underwater Sound Laboratory
WKB	Wentzel-Kramers-Brillouin
XBT	Expendable Bathythermograph

AUTHOR INDEX

AUTHOR INDEX

Fortwin, 10-8
Fox, 5-2, 13-17
Frank, 11-10
Freund, 12-15
Fry, 9-3, 9-7, 11-4
Frye, 3-1

* * * * *

Garon, 3-3
Garrison, 3-1
Gaunaurd, 12-1
Geddes, 11-10, 11-15
Gerber, 12-8
Gershman, 13-13, 13-17
Gordon, 3-3, 6-3
Greene, 7-15
Greenspan, 4-3
Gulin, 12-8, 13-13, 13-17

* * * * *

Hale, 8-1
Hall, 3-3, 5-2, 3-1
Hamilton, E.L., 11-4, 11-7, 11-15, 11-16, 11-19,
    11-20, 11-21, 11-22, 11-23
Hamilton, L.D., 11-4
Harris, 3-1, 10-13
Hays, 4-1
Heaps, 10-1
Heck, 1-1, 4-1
Heezen, 11-7
Hess, 3-3, 3-4, 3-5
Hills, 13-5
Hoffman, 3-5
Holter, 12-7
Holton, 4-1
Hoover, 10-13
Hunkins, 7-16
Hurdle, 11-10

* * * * *

Ide, 9-3, 9-7
Igarashi, 10-8, 10-12
Ingenito, 3-3, 3-4, 3-5
Ishimari, 12-7
Ivanov, 6-4

* * * * *

Jennette, 3-4, 3-5
Jensen, 3-3

Johannssen, 12-7
Johnson, R., 4-6, 4-8
Jones, E.N., 5-6
Jones, J.L., 10-1
Jones, L.M., 4-6

* * * * *

Katz, 6-7
Kanabis, 3-3
Kaufman, 4-11
Keller, 3-1
Kennedy, 13-17
Kerr, 6-4
Kibblewhite, 4-9, 7-5, 7-9
Klein, 1-4
Knott, 11-23
Knopoff, 11-22
Knudsen, 9-5
Kornhauser, 9-3
Krol, 3-3
Kuperman, 3-3, 3-4, 3-5, 10-18
Kurtz, 5-2
Kutschale, 3-3, 7-16
Kuwahara, 4-1

* * * * *

Lacasce, 10-5
Lamb, 5-2
Lasky, 1-4
Lauer, 3-6
Lee, 3-2, 6-7
Leiss, 12-7
Leonard, 5-2
Leroy, 3-1, 7-19
Leslie, 10-1
Levenson, 1-6, 7-9
Lichte, 1-1
Lieberman, 5-2, 10-15, 12-7, 12-9
Longman, 9-3
Love, 3-1, 3-5
Lukas, 3-3, 3-4, 3-5
Lund, 8-9, 13-8
Lyons, 4-6
Lysanov, 11-1

* * * * *

Macelwane, 11-23
Mackenzie, 3-1, 4-1, 4-6, 10-8, 11-1, 12-11
Macpherson, 7-15, 9-9
Mahler, 3-4, 3-5

AUTHOR INDEX

AUTHOR INDEX

INDEX

INDEX

INDEX

Synopses of Reprint Classics
by Peninsula Publishing

Books can be ordered by mail or telephone.
See last page for instructions.

Acoustic Design — Michael Rettinger. Acoustic privacy and quiet living and working conditions essential to today's residential, industrial and business construction are highly dependent on effective isolation of undesirable airborne noise and vibrations. *Acoustic Design*, Volume 1 of a 2-book set, was revised and enlarged in 1977. It provides architects, builders, engineers, community planners and environmentalists with understandable principles and practices for effective acoustic design of homes, buildings, rooms, industrial spaces, theaters and stages, grandstands, churches, hi-fi and music rooms.
Hardcover. 288 pages. Order Book No. P127. $39.95 USA, $41.95 Int'l.

Ambient Noise in the Sea — Ambient noise, a subset of the ocean's total underwater noise, is defined as the residual, unwanted noise after all other noise sources have been identified. *Ambient Noise in the Sea* by Robert Urick encapsulates the body of knowledge on this subject. It discusses the sources of ambient noise, its variability, and its dependence on receiver depth, directionality, and coherence. This book is a *must* for engineers in the field of active and passive sonars, underwater sensor and weapons systems, and underwater signal processing.
Hardcover. 205 pages. Order Book No. P114. $29.95 USA, $31.95 Int'l.

An Introduction to Statistical Communication Theory — Written by David Middleton, pioneer in statistical communication theory. This classic established a unified approach to the basic theory and applications of random signals in communication systems. The book provides a detailed account of systems and their elements as operations and changes on signal and noise ensembles; it addresses the adaptation of statistical *decision theory* to communication problems. The book emphasizes system optimization and evaluation of threshold detection and extraction . . . system design . . . comparison between theoretical optimum and actual suboptimum systems . . . and structure of optimum systems in terms of existing elements.
Hardcover. 1100 pages. Order Book No. P107. $59.95 USA, $61.95 Int'l.

Applied Acoustics — G. Porges. This book develops the basic theory of sound from first principles and applies the theory to obtain practical formulae for the transmission and absorption of sound, sound levels in enclosures and the radiation of sound from common noise sources. The behavior of sound waves in enclosures is explained, leading to practical formulae for predicting sound levels in closed spaces. The transmission of waves through solids is discussed to show how real-life problems of noise and vibration isolation can be tackled. The final chapters introduce the radiation of sound from solids into fluids and describe the major sources of unwanted noise experienced today. In keeping with the practical orientation of the book, the mathematics used is relatively elementary.
Hardcover. 190 pages. Order Book No. P115. $24.95 USA, $26.95 Int'l.

Digital Communications with Space Applications — This book defined an entire new technology for space communications. It was known, irreverently, as "The Bible" at the Jet Propulsion Laboratory. Subjects addressed include: C^3, data telemetry, tracking and ranging, coding, sequences and synchronization techniques. The authors, Solomon W. Golomb, Andrew J. Viterbi, Leonard Baumert, Mahlon Easterling and Jack Stiffer are among the foremost experts in the communications field.
Hardcover. 210 pages. Order Book No. P109. $19.95 USA, $20.95 Int'l.

ECM and ECCM Techniques for Digital Communication Systems — Ray H. Pettit. This release presents an overview of contemporary concepts and techniques in the area of ECM and ECCM for digital communications. Focuses on applicable models and procedures, and gains and losses in systems performance, graphic illustrations and practical examples. Written in concise survey style for engineering and management professionals.
Hardcover. 178 pages. Order Book No. P105 $21.95 USA, $23.95 Int'l.

Electronic Countermeasures — Originally published as a secret reference in the 1960s by the U.S. Army Signal Corps, the book is now declassified. Its 1100 pages cover signal intercept, jamming and deception fundamentals that are as valid today as when first written. Other subjects include intercept probabilities, receiver parameters, detection and analysis, direction finding, jamming technique, IR and acoustic countermeasures. More than 600 references and a list of authors that reads like Who's Who in Electronic Warfare.
Hardcover. 1100 pages. Order Book No. P103. $40.00 USA, $42.00 Int'l.

Instruments of Darkness —The History of Electronic Warfare — This book is regarded as the standard reference work on World War II radar battle. It was Alfred Price's first book and the one on which his reputation as a historian was founded. The book was enlarged and updated to include air actions over North Vietnam and the Middle East. These air actions introduced a new term into the everyday language of armed conflict: electronic warfare. Previous accounts of

electronic warfare may have left the impression that the subject is completely shrouded in secrecy and too complex to be understood by the layman. These impressions are misleading. This book provides an excellent technical guide to electronic warfare from its beginnings until the present day and makes fascinating reading.
Hardcover. 284 pages. Order Book No. P101. $19.95 USA, $21.95 Int'l.

Introduction to the Theory and Design of Sonar Transducers — Oscar Bryan Wilson. Written in 1985 as a text at the Naval Postgraduate School, this book provides a complete treatment of the fundamentals of transducer theory and design using equivalent circuit techniques. The book contains ten chapters, each ending with a list of literature references and a set of problems for the student. Subjects addressed include: introductory baseline and definitions, equivalent circuits, properties of materials: piezoelectric and magnetorestrictive, hydrophone design and transducer arrays. *Introduction to the Theory and Design of Sonar Transducers* will be useful not only to the sonar transducer designer but also to underwater acousticians and sonar system engineers who would like to gain appreciation of the problems of transducer design.
Hardcover. 202 pages. Order Book No. P122. $31.95 USA, $33.95 Int'l.

Mechanics of Underwater Noise — Donald Ross. Originally published in 1976 this book continues to be the most authoritative work on the fundamentals of underwater noise radiated by ships, submarines and torpedoes. It features physical explanations of the basic mechanisms by which noise is generated, transmitted by structures and radiated into the sea. These complex phenomena are explained in a straightforward manner that stresses the dominant mechanisms.
Hardcover. 375 pages. Order Book No. P112. $47.95 USA, $49.95 Int'l.

Methods of Operation Research — One of the first books exclusively devoted to Operations Research (OR). Kimball and Morse examine the application of OR to decision-making problems in military operations. Topics include: probability; measures of effectiveness; tactical analyses; Lanchester equations; evaluation of equipment performance; mini-max; exchange rate; sweep rates; operations involving men and equipment; search theory. A highly articulate work that has special value to Systems Engineers and Operations Researchers.
Hardcover. 158 pages. Order Book No. P118. $21.95 USA, $23.95 Int'l.

Microwave Receivers and Related Components — One-volume reference on receivers. Author is James Tsui of the USAF Avionics Laboratory. Seven chapters are devoted to receiver technology: crystal video and superheterodyne receivers, IFM, channelized, compressive and Bragg cell receivers. Chapters discuss characteristics, receiver capabilities and limitations, basic design and principles of operation, mathematical analysis, probability of intercept, applications, and receiver evaluation. Another eight chapters provide a systems overview of the fundamental components of microwave receivers: transmission lines; delay lines; directional couplers; hybrid couplers and power dividers; attenuators, circulators and phase shifters; filters; linear and logarithmic amplifiers and limiters; mixers and detectors; oscillators and frequency synthesizers.
Hardcover. 530 pages. Order Book No. P106. $36.95 USA, $38.95 Int'l.

Microwave Scanning Antennas — R. C. Hansen. Three-volumes bound into a single hardcover book. This classic reference covers all types of narrow beam antennas with emphasis on those that scan the beam. Comprehensively treats phased arrays and quasi-optical antennas. Includes multiple-beam arrays, time domain and synthetic apertures and adaptive antennas. Concentrates on narrow beam antennas, both mechanically steered and electronically scanned. Constraining equations and design tradeoffs along with practical examples. Volume I reviews astronomy instruments and large radomes. Volumes II and III cover array theory; a variety of means for scanning phase shift and frequency; and the systems technology of time domain and adaptive antenna systems.
Hardcover. 1200 pages. Order Book No. P110. $53.95 USA, $55.95 Int'l.

Noise Control — Michael Rettinger. Companion to *Acoustic Design*. Contents cover the Physics of Sound and Noise Reduction. The book provides details of vibration control, absorptive treatment and barriers; noise effects and ratings; and basics of sound measurement. There is a multitude of easy-to-use formulas for estimation of noise from aircraft, helicopters, trains, cars, motorcycles, household appliances and for a wide variety of noise reduction techniques which provide the means to predict potential noise problems and solve them before they become actual problems.
Hardcover. 400 pages. Order Book No. P128. $47.95 USA, $49.95 Int'l.

Physics of Sound in the Sea — This is the classic work on underwater sound propagation resulting from the World War II program of studies organized by the National Defense Research Committee. The first two parts of this volume deal with propagation of sound in the absence of a target. Part I discusses the transmission loss of sound sent out from a projector while Part II deals with sound which has been scattered back. Part III deals with target strengths and echoes returned from submarines and surface ships. Part IV discusses the transmission of sound through wakes and echoes received from wakes.
Hardcover. 577 pages. Order Book No. P126. $46.95 USA, $48.95 Int'l.

Principles of Electronic Warfare — This book provides an overview of EW technology and tactics in the space age. Written by Robert J. Schlesinger from an overall systems viewpoint, the book focuses on EW's contribution in the accomplishment of a military aircraft mission. Some highlights: radar countermeasure techniques; electronic intelligence (ELINT); elements of space environment; payload optimization between weapons and ECM; and air combat analysis.

Softcover. 213 pages. Order Book No. P104. $16.95 USA, $18.95 Int'l.

Principles of High-Resolution Radar — This 500 page book written by August Rihaczek presents a step-by-step development of the theory of radar resolution beginning with basic measurements on single targets and proceeds through an analysis of the nature of the resolution problem. Capabilities and limits of radar, and the details of waveform design are discussed. Synthetic aperture radar is used to illustrate the practical application of principles, and derivations are carefully spelled out and supported by extensive reasoning and interpretation. Principles are stressed as the author clearly conveys the theory of target resolution without resorting to advanced mathematics. Topics covered include: measurements, ambiguities, and pulse compression for single targets; target resolution and the limits on resolution performance; target detection in various forms of clutter and the relation to resolution; waveform design; higher order range derivatives, Doppler distortions, wideband signals, and general types of target motion.

Hardcover. 500 pages. Order Book No. P111. $41.95 USA, $43.95 Int'l.

Propagation of Short Radio Waves — Donald E. Kerr. The best known classic of the prestigious MIT Radiation Laboratory Series. Still today's most authoritative reference despite being written more than forty years ago. The book characterizes the phenomena of radio propagation of radar, communication and navigation systems in the frequency range of 100 MHz to 300 GHz. The first chapter introduces the reader to basic definitions and concepts. Ensuing chapters address: Theory of Propagation in a Horizontally Stratified Atmosphere; Refraction and Its Meteorological Characterization; Reflections from the Earth's Surface; Diffraction; Scattering; Atmospheric Attenuation; Radar Cross Section Theory and Measurements; Radar Targets and Meteorological Echoes; and Clutter. The text in *Propagation* is logical and easy to understand. Its technical information, data and formulas constitute a bedrock of theory and measurements, making this book the most frequently quoted source in all of radio sciences literature.

Hardcover. 756 pages. Order Book No. P120. $45.95 USA, $47.95 Int'l.

Proposal Management Using the Modular Technique — The *Modular Technique* can help you achieve effective proposal results. It establishes a vehicle for the communication of complex ideas between manager and authors. It facilitates a large group of authors documenting ideas in a cohesive, easily-read proposal. The Modular Technique, based on storyboarding procedures as outlined in this book, provides the manager with the technique for planning the work, assigning design and writing tasks, implementing author-to-manager feedback and effecting document review in a timely manner.

Hardcover. 111 pages. Order Book No. P119. $23.95 USA, $25.95 Int'l.

Radar Signal Simulation — Richard L. Mitchell. Addresses modeling of radar signals: waveform modulation, interaction with the scattering environment, and receiver processing. This book presents radar environment model structures for simulation, mapping procedures, transformation techniques, sampled signals and generation techniques.

Hardcover. 200 pages. Order Book No. P116. $38.95 USA, $40.95 Int'l.

Side Scan Sonar Record Interpretation — Charles Mazel. Training manual produced by Klein Associates, Inc., manufacturer of side scan sonars. Applies to interpretation of all commercial side scan sonars. Covers basic interpretation. The 144 figures and photographs of actual sonar records depict mine and ship targets, shadows, clutter, noise, wakes and dolphins.

Softcover. 146 pages. Order Book No. P127. $42.95 USA, $44.95 Int'l.

Signal Detection and Recognition by Human Observers — Edited by John A. Swets in 1964, this book was the first to bring together into one volume a broad discussion coverage of modern signal detection theory applications to human performance, specifically in auditory and visual sensory tasks. Applications in the book address several substantive problems in psychology including the integration of sensory information, signal uncertainty, auditory frequency analysis, speech communication, vigilance and recognition memory. *Signal Detection and Recognition* outlines how decision factors are centrally involved in even the simplest detection task and how sensory capacity can by assessed. The bibliography has been updated to 1988.

Hardcover. 734 pages. Order Book No. P124. $47.95 USA, $49.95 Int'l.

Signal Detection Theory and Psychophysics — David M. Green and John A. Swets. Summarizes the application of signal detection theory to the analysis and measurement of the human observer's sensory system. The theory provides a way to analyze the threshold or sensory limen, the basic unit of all discrimination studies, whether human or animal. The book outlines the theory of statistical decision making and its application to a variety of common psychophysical activities. It shows how signal detection theory can be used to separate sensory and decision aspects of discrimination responses. The concepts of the ideal observer and energy detector are presented and compared with human auditory detection data. Signal detection theory is applied to a variety of other substantive problems in a sensory psychology. *Signal Detection Theory and Psychophysics* is an invaluable book for psychologists dealing with sensory perception, especially auditory, and for human factors engineers dealing with man/machine interfaces. The bibliography has been updated to 1988.

Hardcover. 521 pages. Order Book No. P125. $45.95 USA, $47.95 Int'l.

Sound Propagation in the Sea — Robert J. Urick. Subjects addressed: basic theory; speed of sound in the ocean; attenuation and absorption; surface ducts; the deep sound channel; caustics and convergence zones; computer models of sound propagation; shallow-water ducts; reflections and scattering by the sea surface; reflections and scattering by the sea bottom; temporal coherence; spatial coherence; and multipath in the sea.

Hardcover. 225 pages. Order Book No. P113. $30.95 USA, $32.95 Int'l.

Space-Time Information Processing — Charles Loda and A. Winder. Indispensable reference tool for audio signal processing and data analysis. Oriented to acoustics and sonar engineering. The book features Fourier transforms, statistical analyses, correlation and spectra. Especially valuable chapters address measurement of spatially and temporally-limited functions, optimal filtering procedures and interpretation of results.

Hardcover. 192 pages. Order Book No. P117. $27.95 USA, $29.95 Int'l.

The Strategy of Electromagnetic Conflict — Written by the Air Force Academy faculty. Contents include: electronic countermeasures and counter-countermeasures; electronic reconnaissance; tradeoffs in air defense; use of chaff for aircraft self-protection; communications intelligence, security and cryptoloty; vulnerability of space stations; countermeasures in the millimeter, IR, optical, laser and UV regions. Required reading for engineering and analysis personnel dealing with design and development of military electronic systems and the planning of air operations.

Hardcover. 300 pages. Order Book No. P102. $23.95 USA, $25.95 Int'l.

Topics in Communication Theory — David Middleton. Provides a concise treatment of basic problems in statistical communication theory. Concepts are discussed and illustrated with simple but important examples. Chapter headings are: Communication from the Viewpoint of Decision Theory; The Detection of Signals in Noise; The Extraction of Signals from Noise; The Structure of Optimum Systems; and Critique, Extensions and Future Problems.

Hardcover. 125 pages. Order Book No. P108. $15.95 USA, $17.95 Int'l.

Underwater Electroacoustic Measurements — Robert J. Bobber. This book addresses the current theory and practice of measuring electroacoustic parameters such as response, sensitivity, directivity, impedance, efficiency, linearity and noise limits of transducers used in sonars. Discussed in detail are wide band transducers used as measurement instruments, near field and far field methods, and measurements on auxiliary materials such as acoustic windows, reflectors, baffles and absorbers.

Hardcover. 341 pages. Order Book No. P123. $33.95 USA, $35.95 Int'l.

ORDERING INFORMATION

You can order by postcard, personal letter or telephone, (415)948-2511. For orders by letter, pay by check or money order. Book order numbers and prices for each book are listed in the synopses. Add $1.50 per copy for postage and handling. California residents add 7% sales tax. Make remittance payable to:

Peninsula Publishing, P.O. Box 867, Los Altos, CA 94023 USA.

Enter my order as follows:

Book No.	Quantity	Unit Price	Total Cost
————	————	————	————
————	————	————	————
————	————	————	————
————	————	————	————
————	————	————	————
————	————	————	————
————	————	————	————

Total of Book Purchases ————

Calif. Residents add 7% sales tax ————

Postage & handling @ $1.50 per book ————

GRAND TOTAL OF ORDER   US$ ————

Charge to: □ Mastercard   □ Visa

Account Number: ——————————

Expiration Date: ——————————

——————————
signature as it appears on charge card

——————————
name (please print)

——————————
organization (if required for shipment)

——————————
address

——————————
city   state   zip

——————————

Air Mail Service (surcharges per copy):
US priority mail, $3.00
Canada, $5.00
Europe, $12.50
Asia/Africa/Oceana, $15.00
South & Central America, $6.00

Peninsula Publishing
PO Box 867
Los Altos, CA 94023 USA

Enter my order as follows:

Book No.	Quantity	Unit Price	Total Cost
————	————	————	————
————	————	————	————
————	————	————	————
————	————	————	————
————	————	————	————
————	————	————	————
————	————	————	————

Total of Book Purchases ————

Calif. Residents add 7% sales tax ————

Postage & handling @ $1.50 per book ————

GRAND TOTAL OF ORDER   US$ ————

Charge to: □ Mastercard   □ Visa

Account Number: ——————————

Expiration Date: ——————————

——————————
signature as it appears on charge card

——————————
name (please print)

——————————
organization (if required for shipment)

——————————
address

——————————
city   state   zip

——————————

Air Mail Service (surcharges per copy):
US priority mail, $3.00
Canada, $5.00
Europe, $12.50
Asia/Africa/Oceana, $15.00
South & Central America, $6.00

Peninsula Publishing
PO Box 867
Los Altos, CA 94023 USA

BUSINESS REPLY MAIL

First Class   PERMIT No. 722   Los Altos, CA 94022

POSTAGE WILL BE PAID BY ADDRESSEE

PENINSULA PUBLISHING
PO Box 867
Los Altos, CA 94023 USA

BUSINESS REPLY MAIL

First Class   PERMIT No. 722   Los Altos, CA 94022

POSTAGE WILL BE PAID BY ADDRESSEE

PENINSULA PUBLISHING
PO Box 867
Los Altos, CA 94023 USA